MODERN
OPERATIONAL MATHEMATICS
IN ENGINEERING

*This book is produced in full compliance
with the government's regulations for con-
serving paper and other essential materials.*

Modern
Operational Mathematics
in Engineering

BY

RUEL V. CHURCHILL

Professor of Mathematics
University of Michigan

FIRST EDITION

McGRAW-HILL BOOK COMPANY, INC.

NEW YORK AND LONDON

1944

PREFACE

This is a textbook on applications of the Laplace transformation. The applications are chiefly to problems in engineering and physics that involve differential equations, with emphasis on boundary value problems in partial differential equations.

In partial differential equations the method of using the Laplace transformation, which is the operational method, and the more classical one of using Fourier series supplement one another. Thus this book is a companion volume to the author's earlier book entitled "Fourier Series and Boundary Value Problems."

No previous preparation in the subject of partial differential equations is required of the student; in fact very little previous experience with ordinary differential equations is actually needed here. A year of college physics would seem to furnish a sufficient background for the physical and engineering problems treated here, since these problems are kept on a fairly elementary level.

The first four chapters of this book are somewhat more elementary than the material in the earlier volume. These chapters include a treatment of problems in ordinary as well as partial differential equations. They have served as a textbook for a short basic course in operational mathematics given to juniors and seniors at the University of Michigan and to research engineers in Detroit. Chapter X, which represents the operational properties of finite Fourier transformations, can well be included in such a course.

The remaining chapters are more advanced. They make use of certain material, described in Chapter V, from the theory of functions of a complex variable. For several years the material in these chapters has been included in a graduate course on methods in partial differential equations.

Important results are stated as theorems. Thus the reader who is primarily interested in engineering or physics rather than in applied mathematics should find it possible to skip over details in mathematical derivations. An attempt has been made to keep the mathematical analysis on a level that is as elementary

v

as possible without impairing the usefulness of the results. Such a program tends to make some developments more tedious, however, than they need be if more advanced concepts in function theory had been used.

The selection of material has been influenced by a large number of authors and by many suggestions from students. The book by G. Doetsch was probably the greatest single influence. The dissertation of H. Kniess, one of Doetsch's students, furnished the incentive for Chapter X. The publications of H. S. Carslaw, J. C. Jaeger, N. W. McLachlan, and others have influenced the selection of problems.

The author is grateful to Professor E. D. Rainville for his generous assistance in the reading of proof and for valuable suggestions and wishes to express his thanks to Miss Myra E. Schwan for her skillful and untiring efforts in the preparation of the manuscript.

RUEL V. CHURCHILL.

ANN ARBOR, MICH.,
May, 1944.

CONTENTS

CONTENTS   ix

CHAPTER VIII
PROBLEMS IN MECHANICAL VIBRATIONS

CHAPTER IX
STURM-LIOUVILLE SYSTEMS

CHAPTER X
FOURIER TRANSFORMS

MODERN OPERATIONAL MATHEMATICS
IN ENGINEERING

CHAPTER I

THE LAPLACE TRANSFORMATION

1. Introduction. Since the time of its introduction the operational calculus of Oliver Heaviside (1850–1925) has held a prominent place in the treatment of problems in electric circuits. It was also put to other less prominent but even more interesting uses, including applications to many applied problems in partial differential equations and the evaluation of certain integrals. But in its original form this method rested on rules of procedure that had no satisfactory logical justification. Nor were the rules always reliable.

The modern form of this operational calculus consists of the use of the Laplace transformation. This is a mathematical procedure which not only yields the rules of the operational calculus in a straightforward manner, but which demonstrates at the same time conditions under which the rules are valid. In addition to this, the theory of the Laplace transformation introduces a large number of additional rules and methods that are important in the analysis of problems in engineering and physics.

In this chapter we shall present the most important one of these rules, one concerning the transformation of derivatives of functions into products. By means of it we shall be able to make remarkable simplifications in certain types of problems in differential equations.

In the following chapters, further properties of the Laplace transformation will be derived and applied to problems of engineering and physics. The applications of this method to the solution of applied problems in partial differential equations will form our major interest. We shall give considerable attention

1

to other applications, however, including the solution of problems in ordinary differential equations. A sufficient development of the theory of the transformation leads to the theory of expanding an arbitrary function in series of characteristic functions of Sturm-Liouville systems. Such expansions in series form the basis for the solution of boundary value problems by separation of variables, a classical method of great importance in partial differential equations.

In addition, we shall introduce certain Fourier transforms and show how they can be used in a similar way to solve important types of boundary value problems.

2. Definition of the Laplace Transformation. If a function $F(t)$, defined for all positive values of the variable t, is multiplied by e^{-st} and integrated with respect to t from zero to infinity a new function $f(s)$ of the variable s is obtained; that is,

$$\int_0^\infty e^{-st}F(t)\ dt = f(s).$$

This operation on a function $F(t)$ is called the *Laplace transformation* of $F(t)$. It will be abbreviated here by the symbol $L\{F\}$, or by $L\{F(t)\}$; thus

$$L\{F\} = \int_0^\infty e^{-st}F(t)\ dt.$$

The new function $f(s)$ is called the *Laplace transform* of $F(t)$. Wherever it is convenient to do so, we shall denote the original function by a capital letter and its transform by the same letter in lower case. At other times we shall use a bar to indicate the transform, for example,

$$\bar{F}(s) = L\{F(t)\}.$$

For the present, the variable s is assumed to be real. Later on, we shall let it assume complex values. The limitations on the character of the function $F(t)$ and on the range of the variable s will be discussed soon.

Let us note the transforms of a few functions. First, let $F(t) = 1$ when $t > 0$. Then

$$L\{F\} = \int_0^\infty e^{-st}\ dt = -\frac{1}{s}\ e^{-st}\bigg]_0^\infty;$$

hence, when $s > 0$,

$$L\{1\} = \frac{1}{s}.$$

Let $F(t) = e^{kt}$ when $t > 0$.   Then

$$L\{F\} = \int_0^\infty e^{kt} e^{-st}\, dt = \frac{1}{k-s}\, e^{-(s-k)t}\Big]_0^\infty ;$$

hence, when $s > k$,

$$L\{e^{kt}\} = \frac{1}{s-k}.$$

With the aid of elementary methods of integration, the transforms of many other functions can be written.   For instance,

$$L\{t\} = \frac{1}{s^2}, \qquad L\{t^2\} = \frac{2}{s^3},$$

and

$$L\{\sin kt\} = \frac{k}{s^2 + k^2};$$

but we shall soon have still simpler ways to obtain these transformations.

The transformation sets up a correspondence between the pairs of functions $F(t)$ and $f(s)$, called the *object* and *result* functions, respectively, of the transformation.   For instance, e^{kt} and $1/(s-k)$ are corresponding functions.   The reader is familiar with the transformations known as differentiation and integration, $d/dt\{F(t)\}$ and $\int_0^x F(t)\, dt$, which set up other correspondences between pairs of functions.   As in the case of these familiar transformations, the Laplace transformation is *linear;* that is, if A and B are constants then

$$L\{AF(t) + BG(t)\} = AL\{F(t)\} + BL\{G(t)\}.$$

This follows from the definition of the transformation.

We can illustrate this linearity by writing

$$L\left\{\frac{1}{2}\, e^{kt} - \frac{1}{2}\, e^{-kt}\right\} = \frac{1}{2}\frac{1}{s-k} - \frac{1}{2}\frac{1}{s+k};$$

that is,

$$L\{\sinh kt\} = \frac{k}{s^2 - k^2}.$$

PROBLEMS

Obtain the following transformations:

1. $L\{a + bt\} = \dfrac{as + b}{s^2}.$ **2.** $L\{t^3\} = \dfrac{3!}{s^4}.$

3. $L\{\cos kt\} = \dfrac{s}{s^2 + k^2}.$ **4.** $L\{\cosh kt\} = \dfrac{s}{s^2 - k^2}.$ *Refer*
page 8 3

3. Functions of Exponential Order.

A function $F(t)$ is *sectionally continuous* on a finite interval $a \leqq t \leqq b$ if it is possible to subdivide that interval into a finite number of subintervals in each of which $F(t)$ is continuous and has finite limits as t approaches either end point of the subinterval from the interior. Any discontinuities of such a function in the interval (a, b) are of the type known as *ordinary* points of discontinuity, where the value of the function makes a finite jump.   Of course, this class

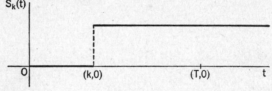

FIG. 1.

of functions includes continuous functions.   Also, the integral of every function of this class exists over the interval.

The step function

$$S_k(t) = 0 \qquad \text{when } 0 < t < k,$$
$$= 1 \qquad \text{when } t > k,$$

is an example of a function that is sectionally continuous in the interval $0 \leqq t \leqq T$ for every positive number T (Fig. 1).   The Laplace transform of this function is

$$\int_0^\infty S_k(t)e^{-st}\, dt = \int_k^\infty e^{-st}\, dt = -\frac{1}{s}\, e^{-st}\Big]_k^\infty\, ;$$

thus, assuming $s > 0$,

$$L\{S_k(t)\} = \frac{e^{-ks}}{s}.$$

A function $F(t)$ is of *exponential order* as t tends to infinity provided some constant α exists such that the product

$$e^{-\alpha t}|F(t)|$$

is bounded for all t greater than some finite number T. Thus $|F(t)|$ does not grow more rapidly than $Me^{\alpha t}$ as $t \to \infty$, where M is some constant. This is also expressed by saying that $F(t)$ is of the order of $e^{\alpha t}$, or that $F(t)$ is $O(e^{\alpha t})$.

The function $S_k(t)$ above, as well as the function $t^n (n \geqq 0)$, is of the order of $e^{\alpha t}$ as $t \to \infty$ for any $\alpha > 0$; in fact for the first function and, when $n = 0$, for the second, we may take $\alpha = 0$. The function e^{2t} is of exponential order with $\alpha \geqq 2$; but the function e^{t^2} is not of exponential order.

The Laplace transform of a function $F(t)$ exists if $F(t)$ is sectionally continuous in every finite interval in the range $t \geqq 0$ and if the function is of exponential order as $t \to \infty$. This follows from a well-known test for the convergence of infinite integrals. For under the conditions stated, the integrand of the Laplace integral is integrable over the finite interval $0 \leqq t \leqq T$ for every positive number T, and

$$|e^{-st}F(t)| < Me^{-(s-\alpha)t}$$

where M is some constant. But the integral from 0 to ∞ of the function on the right exists provided $s > \alpha$. These facts establish* not only the convergence, but also the absolute convergence, of the Laplace integral when $s > \alpha$.

The above conditions for the existence of the transform of a function are elementary and practical for most of our applications; but they are sufficient rather than necessary conditions. The function $F(t)$ may have an infinite discontinuity at $t = 0$, for instance, provided $|t^n F(t)|$ remains bounded there for some positive $n < 1$; then if $F(t)$ satisfies the above conditions when $t > 0$, its transform still exists. Let $F(t) = t^{-\frac{1}{2}}$, for example. Then its transform is

$$\int_0^\infty t^{-\frac{1}{2}}e^{-st}\,dt = \frac{2}{\sqrt{s}}\int_0^\infty e^{-x^2}\,dx \qquad (s > 0),$$

and hence

$$L\{t^{-\frac{1}{2}}\} = \left(\frac{\pi}{s}\right)^{\frac{1}{2}} \qquad (s > 0).$$

---

* See, for instance, Philip Franklin, "Treatise on Advanced Calculus," p. 271, 1940.

4. Transforms of Derivatives. By a formal integration by parts we have

$$L\{F'(t)\} = \int_0^\infty e^{-st}F'(t)\ dt$$

$$= e^{-st}F(t)\Big]_0^\infty + s\int_0^\infty e^{-st}F(t)\ dt.$$

Let $F(t)$ be of order $e^{\alpha t}$ as t approaches infinity. Then for every $s > \alpha$ the first term on the right becomes $-F(0)$ and it follows that

(1) $$L\{F'(t)\} = sf(s) - F(0),$$

where $f(s) = L\{F(t)\}$.

Therefore in our correspondence between functions, *differentiation* of the object function corresponds to the *multiplication* of the result function by its variable s and the addition of the constant $-F(0)$. Formula (1) thus gives the fundamental operational property of the Laplace transformation, the property that makes it possible to replace the operation of differentiation by a simple algebraic operation on the transform.

As noted above, formula (1) was obtained only in a formal manner. It is not even correct when $F(t)$ has discontinuities. The following theorem will show to what extent we can rely on our formula.

Theorem 1. *Let the function $F(t)$ be continuous with a sectionally continuous derivative $F'(t)$, in every finite interval $0 \leqq t \leqq T$. Also let $F(t)$ be of order $e^{\alpha t}$ as $t \to \infty$. Then when $s > \alpha$, the transform of $F'(t)$ exists and*

(2) $$L\{F'(t)\} = sL\{F(t)\} - F(+0).$$

The symbol $F(+0)$ denotes the limit of $F(t)$ as t approaches zero through positive values.

To prove this theorem we note first that

$$L\{F'(t)\} = \lim_{T \to \infty} \int_0^T e^{-st}F'(t)\ dt$$

and write the integral here as the sum of integrals in each of which the integrand is continuous. For any given T, let t_1, $t_2, \cdots, t_n$ denote those values of t between $t = 0$ and $t = T$ for which $F'(t)$ is discontinuous (Fig. 2). Then

$$\int_0^T e^{-st}F'(t)\,dt = \int_0^{t_1} e^{-st}F'(t)\,dt + \int_{t_1}^{t_2} e^{-st}F'(t)\,dt + \cdots$$
$$+ \int_{t_n}^T e^{-st}F'(t)\,dt.$$

After integrating each of these integrals by parts, we can write their sum as

$$e^{-st}F(t)\Big]_0^{t_1} + e^{-st}F(t)\Big]_{t_1}^{t_2} + \cdots + e^{-st}F(t)\Big]_{t_n}^T + s\int_0^T e^{-st}F(t)\,dt.$$

Now $F(t)$ is continuous so that $F(t_1 - 0) = F(t_1 + 0)$, etc., and hence

$$(3) \quad \int_0^T e^{-st}F'(t)\,dt = -F(+0) + e^{-sT}F(T) + s\int_0^T e^{-st}F(t)\,dt.$$

consul. again here

Since $|F(t)| < Me^{\alpha t}$ for large t for some constants α and M, it follows that

$$\left|e^{-sT}F(T)\right| < Me^{-(s-\alpha)T}$$

and since $s > \alpha$ this product vanishes as $T \to \infty$. Also the last

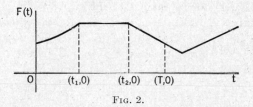

F(t)

O $(t_1,0)$ $(t_2,0)$ $(T,0)$ t

Fig. 2.

integral in equation (3) approaches $L\{F\}$ as T tends to infinity. Hence the left-hand member of (3) has a limit and Theorem 1 is established.

If $F(t)$ is continuous except for an ordinary discontinuity at $t = t_0$, the other conditions remaining as stated in the theorem, we can see from the above proof that our formula (2) must be replaced by the formula

$$(4) \quad L\{F'(t)\} = sf(s) - F(+0) - [F(t_0 + 0) - F(t_0 - 0)]e^{-t_0 s}.$$

important

The quantity in brackets is the jump of $F(t)$ at $t = t_0$.

The reader should note that we use the symbol $F'(t)$ here and in the sequel to denote the derivative of $F(t)$ wherever the derivative exists, even though $F(t)$ fails to have a derivative for certain values of t. In the case of our step function $S_k(t)$, for instance,

$$S_k'(t) = 0 \quad \text{when } 0 < t < k \text{ and when } t > k,$$

but $S_k'(k)$ has no value.

To obtain the transformation of the derivative of the second order $F''(t)$, we apply Theorem 1 to the function $F'(t)$. Let $F'(t)$ be continuous and $F''(t)$ sectionally continuous in each finite interval, and let $F(t)$ and $F'(t)$ be of exponential order. Since $F'(t)$ is continuous, it follows that $F(t)$ is continuous. Then

$$L\{F''(t)\} = sL\{F'(t)\} - F'(+0)$$
$$= s[sL\{F(t)\} - F(+0)] - F'(+0).$$

Hence we have the transformation

(5) $$L\{F''(t)\} = s^2 f(s) - sF(+0) - F'(+0).$$

By applying Theorem 1 in the same manner to the derivative of order n, the following theorem is obtained.

Theorem 2. *Let the function $F(t)$ have a continuous derivative $F^{(n-1)}(t)$ of order $n - 1$ and a sectionally continuous derivative $F^{(n)}(t)$, in every finite interval $0 \leqq t \leqq T$. Also let $F(t)$, $F'(t)$, $\cdots$, $F^{(n-1)}(t)$ be of order $e^{\alpha t}$ as t tends to infinity. Then the transform of $F^{(n)}(t)$ exists when $s > \alpha$ and it has the following algebraic expression in terms of the transform $f(s)$ of $F(t)$:*

(6) $$L\{F^{(n)}(t)\} = s^n f(s) - s^{n-1} F(+0) - s^{n-2} F'(+0)$$
$$- s^{n-3} F''(+0) - \cdots - F^{(n-1)}(+0).$$

5. Examples. The Gamma Function. In order to gain familiarity with the above fundamental operational property of the transformation, let us first use it to obtain a few transforms.

Example 1.   Find $L\{t\}$.

The functions $F(t) = t$ and $F'(t) = 1$ are continuous and of exponential order for any $\alpha > 0$.   Hence,

$$L\{F'(t)\} = sL\{F(t)\} - F(0) \qquad (s > 0),$$

or

$$L\{1\} = sL\{t\}.$$

Since $L\{1\} = 1/s$, it follows that

$$L\{t\} = \frac{1}{s^2} \qquad (s > 0).$$

Example 2.   Find $L\{\sin kt\}$.

The function $F(t) = \sin kt$ and its derivatives are all continuous and bounded, and therefore of exponential order with $\alpha = 0$.   Hence

$$L\{F''(t)\} = s^2 L\{F(t)\} - sF(0) - F'(0) \qquad (s > 0),$$

or

$$-k^2 L\{\sin kt\} = s^2 L\{\sin kt\} - k.$$

Solving for $L\{\sin kt\}$, we see that

$$L\{\sin kt\} = \frac{k}{s^2 + k^2} \qquad (s > 0).$$

Example 3.   Find $L\{t^m\}$ where m is any positive integer.

The function $F(t) = t^m$ satisfies all the conditions of Theorem 2 for any positive α.   Here

$$F(0) = F'(0) = \cdots = F^{(m-1)}(0) = 0,$$
$$F^{(m)}(t) = m!, \qquad F^{(m+1)}(t) = 0.$$

Applying formula (6) with $n = m + 1$, we find

$$L\{F^{(m+1)}(t)\} = 0 = s^{m+1} L\{t^m\} - m!,$$

and therefore

(1) $$\qquad\qquad L\{t^m\} = \frac{m!}{s^{m+1}} \qquad (s > 0).$$

This formula can be generalized to the case in which the exponent is not necessarily an integer.   To obtain $L\{t^k\}$ where $k > -1$, we make the substitution $x = st$ in the Laplace integral, giving

$$\int_0^\infty t^k e^{-st}\, dt = \frac{1}{s^{k+1}} \int_0^\infty x^k e^{-x}\, dx \qquad (s > 0).$$

The integral on the right represents the gamma function, or factorial function, with the argument $k + 1$.   Hence

(2) $$\qquad\qquad L\{t^k\} = \frac{\Gamma(k + 1)}{s^{k+1}} \qquad (k > -1, s > 0).$$

Formula (1) is a special case of (2) when k is a positive integer.

Example 4.   Find $L \left\{ \int_0^t F(\tau)\, d\tau \right\}$ when $F(\tau)$ is sectionally continuous and of exponential order.

Let

$$G(t) = \int_0^t F(\tau)\, d\tau.$$

Then $G(t)$ is continuous and of exponential order, and $G(0) = 0$. Also

$$G'(t) = F(t)$$

and therefore

$$sL\{G(t)\} = L\{F(t)\}.$$

That is,

(3) $$L\left\{\int_0^t F(\tau)\, d\tau\right\} = \frac{1}{s} f(s).$$

This operational property for integration will be derived in another way later on.

PROBLEMS

1. Obtain the following transforms with the aid of Theorem 2:

(a) $L\{\cos kt\} = \dfrac{s}{s^2 + k^2};$ (b) $L\{\sinh kt\} = \dfrac{k}{s^2 - k^2};$

(c) $L\{\cosh kt\} = \dfrac{s}{s^2 - k^2}.$

2. From the formula $L\{t^{-\frac{1}{2}}\} = (\pi/s)^{\frac{1}{2}}$ obtained in Sec. 3, show that

$$L\{t^{\frac{1}{2}}\} = \frac{\pi^{\frac{1}{2}}}{2s^{\frac{3}{2}}}.$$

Also show that this follows from the formula in Theorem 1, even though the derivative of the function $t^{\frac{1}{2}}$ is not sectionally continuous. This illustrates the fact that the conditions in our theorems are not the necessary conditions.

3. Using the result of Prob. 2 and Theorem 2, show that

$$L\{t^{n+\frac{1}{2}}\} = \frac{1 \cdot 3 \cdot 5 \cdots (2n + 1)}{s^{n+\frac{3}{2}}} \frac{\pi^{\frac{1}{2}}}{2^{n+1}} \quad (n = 0, 1, 2, \cdots).$$

4. Apply formula (4), Sec. 4, to the step function $S_k(t)$ to find $L\{S_k(t)\}$.

6. The Inverse Transform. Let the symbol $L^{-1}\{f(s)\}$ denote a function whose Laplace transform is $f(s)$. Thus if

$$L\{F(t)\} = f(s)$$

then

$$F(t) = L^{-1}\{f(s)\}.$$

Using two of the transforms obtained in the foregoing sections we can write, for instance,

$$L^{-1}\left\{\frac{1}{s-k}\right\} = e^{kt}, \qquad L^{-1}\left\{\frac{k}{s^2+k^2}\right\} = \sin kt.$$

This correspondence between functions $f(s)$ and $F(t)$ is called the *inverse Laplace transformation*, $F(t)$ being the *inverse transform* of $f(s)$.

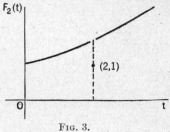

Fig. 3.

In the strict sense of the concept of uniqueness of functions, the inverse Laplace transform is not unique. The function $F_1(t) = e^{kt}$ is an inverse transform of $1/(s-k)$; but another, for instance, is the function (Fig. 3)

$$\begin{aligned}F_2(t) &= e^{kt} \quad \text{when } 0 < t < 2, \text{ or } t > 2,\\ &= 1 \quad \text{when } t = 2.\end{aligned}$$

For the transform of $F_2(t)$ is

$$\int_0^\infty e^{-st}F_2(t)\,dt = \int_0^2 e^{-st}e^{kt}\,dt + \int_2^\infty e^{-st}e^{kt}\,dt,$$

and this is the same as $L\{e^{kt}\}$. The function $F_2(t)$ could have been chosen equally well as one that differs from $F_1(t)$ at any finite set of values of t, or even at such an infinite set as $t = 1, 2, 3, \cdots$.

A theorem on the uniqueness of the inverse transform, due to Lerch, states that if two functions $F_1(t)$ and $F_2(t)$ have the same Laplace transform $f(s)$ then

$$F_2(t) = F_1(t) + N(t),$$

where $N(t)$ is a null function, that is, a function such that

$$\int_0^T N(t)\,dt = 0$$

for every positive T. In the above example, $N(t) = 0$, except when $t = 2$, and $N(2) = 1 - e^{2k}$. We shall take up the proof of Lerch's theorem later on.

In view of this theorem, we can say that the inverse transform is essentially unique, since a null function is usually of no importance in the applications.   As a consequence of the theorem, a given function $f(s)$ cannot have more than one inverse transform $F(t)$ that is continuous for each positive t.   But a function $f(s)$ may not have a continuous inverse transform.   This is illustrated by the function $\frac{1}{s} e^{-ks}$ whose inverse transform is the step function $S_k(t)$.   It is well to note here that not every function of s is a transform.   The class of functions $f(s)$ that are transforms is limited, as we shall see, by several conditions of continuity, among which are the requirements that $f(s)$ be continuous when $s > \alpha$ and that $f(s)$ vanish as s tends to infinity.

We have noted that

$$L\{AF(t) + BG(t)\} = Af(s) + Bg(s),$$

where A and B are constants.   This relation can be written

$$\begin{aligned} L^{-1}\{Af(s) + Bg(s)\} &= AF(t) + BG(t) \\ &= AL^{-1}\{f(s)\} + BL^{-1}\{g(s)\}. \end{aligned}$$

Therefore the inverse transformation is a linear transformation of functions.

The most obvious way of finding the inverse transform of a given function of s consists of reading the result from a table of transforms.   A fairly extensive table is given in Appendix III. But we shall take up methods of obtaining inverse transforms of certain combinations and modifications of functions of s, as well as methods of resolving such functions into those listed in the tables.   With the aid of such procedures, we shall be able to make much use of the transformation.   In addition, there are explicit formulas for $L^{-1}\{f(s)\}$.   The most useful of these formulas involves an integral in the complex plane.   To use this integral, we must let s be a complex variable and we must be prepared to employ a few important theorems in the theory of functions of a complex variable.

7. A Theorem on Substitution.   Let the function $F(t)$ be such that its Laplace integral converges when $s > \alpha$.   Then, replacing the argument of the transform $f(s)$ by $s - a$, where a is a constant, we have

$$f(s - a) = \int_0^\infty e^{-(s-a)t} F(t)\, dt = \int_0^\infty e^{-st} e^{at} F(t)\, dt,$$

when $s - a > \alpha$.   Therefore

(1) $$f(s - a) = L\{e^{at}F(t)\} \qquad (s > \alpha + a).$$

Let us state this simple but important property as a theorem.

Theorem 3.   *The substitution of $s - a$ for the variable s in the transform corresponds to the multiplication of the object function $F(t)$ by the function e^{at}, as shown in formula* (1).

To illustrate this property, let us recall that

$$\frac{m!}{s^{m+1}} = L\{t^m\} \qquad (m = 1, 2, \cdots ; s > 0).$$

Hence

$$\frac{m!}{(s - a)^{m+1}} = L\{t^m e^{at}\} \qquad (s > a).$$

As another illustration,

$$L\{\cos kt\} = \frac{s}{s^2 + k^2} \qquad (s > 0),$$

and therefore

$$L\{e^{-at} \cos kt\} = \frac{s + a}{(s + a)^2 + k^2}. \qquad (s > -a).$$

8. The Use of Partial Fractions.   A few examples will show how the theory of partial fractions can be used in finding inverse transforms of quotients of polynomials in s.   In the next chapter, a more systematic use of this procedure will be introduced.

Example 1.   Find $L^{-1}\left\{\dfrac{s + 1}{s^2 + 2s}\right\}$.

The denominator of the function of s here is of higher degree than the numerator and has factors that are linear and distinct. Therefore constants A and B can be found such that

$$\frac{s + 1}{s(s + 2)} = \frac{A}{s} + \frac{B}{s + 2}$$

for all values of s.   Clearing fractions, we have

$$s + 1 = (A + B)s + 2A,$$

and this is an identity if $A + B = 1$ and $2A = 1$.   Thus $A = B = \frac{1}{2}$ and hence

$$\frac{s + 1}{s^2 + 2s} = \frac{1}{2}\frac{1}{s} + \frac{1}{2}\frac{1}{s + 2}.$$

TABLE 1.—A SHORT TABLE OF TRANSFORMS

	$F(t)$	$f(s)$	$\alpha\ (s > \alpha)$
1	1	$\dfrac{1}{s}$	0
2	e^{at}	$\dfrac{1}{s-a}$	a
3	$t^n\ (n = 1, 2, \cdots)$	$\dfrac{n!}{s^{n+1}}$	0
4	$t^n e^{at}\ (n = 1, 2, \cdots)$	$\dfrac{n!}{(s-a)^{n+1}}$	a
5	$\sin kt$	$\dfrac{k}{s^2 + k^2}$	0
6	$\cos kt$	$\dfrac{s}{s^2 + k^2}$	0
7	$\sinh kt$	$\dfrac{k}{s^2 - k^2}$	$|k|$
8	$\cosh kt$	$\dfrac{s}{s^2 - k^2}$	$|k|$
9	$e^{-at} \sin kt$	$\dfrac{k}{(s+a)^2 + k^2}$	$-a$
10	$e^{-at} \cos kt$	$\dfrac{s+a}{(s+c)^2 + k^2}$	$-a$
11	$\sqrt{t}$	$\dfrac{\sqrt{\pi}}{2\sqrt{s^3}}$	0
12	$\dfrac{1}{\sqrt{t}}$	$\sqrt{\dfrac{\pi}{s}}$	0
13	$t^k\ (k > -1)$	$\dfrac{\Gamma(k+1)}{s^{k+1}}$	0
14	$t^k e^{at}\ (k > -1)$	$\dfrac{\Gamma(k+1)}{(s-a)^{k+1}}$	a
15	$S_k(t)$ (Sec. 3)	$\dfrac{e^{-ks}}{s}$	0
16	$e^{at} - e^{bt}\ (a > b)$	$\dfrac{a-b}{(s-a)(s-b)}$	a
17	$\dfrac{1}{a}\sin at - \dfrac{1}{b}\sin bt$	$\dfrac{b^2 - a^2}{(s^2 + a^2)(s^2 + b^2)}$	0
18	$\cos at - \cos bt$	$\dfrac{(b^2 - a^2)s}{(s^2 + a^2)(s^2 + b^2)}$	0

Since we know the inverse transforms of the two functions on the right, we have the result

$$L^{-1}\left\{\frac{s+1}{s^2 + 2s}\right\} = \frac{1}{2} + \frac{1}{2} e^{-2t}.$$

The procedure can be shortened for such a simple fraction by writing

$$s + 1 = \tfrac{1}{2}(s + 2) + \tfrac{1}{2}s,$$

and hence

$$\frac{s + 1}{s(s + 2)} = \frac{1}{2}\frac{1}{s} + \frac{1}{2}\frac{1}{s + 2}.$$

Example 2.   Find $L^{-1}\left\{\dfrac{a^2}{s(s + a)^2}\right\}$.

In view of the repeated linear factor, we write

$$\frac{a^2}{s(s + a)^2} = \frac{A}{s} + \frac{B}{s + a} + \frac{C}{(s + a)^2}.$$

Clearing fractions and identifying coefficients of like powers of s as before, or else by noting that

$$a^2 = (s + a)^2 - s(s + a) - as,$$

we find that

$$\frac{a^2}{s(s + a)^2} = \frac{1}{s} - \frac{1}{s + a} - \frac{a}{(s + a)^2}.$$

Referring to Table 1, we can now write the result

$$L^{-1}\left\{\frac{a^2}{s(s + a)^2}\right\} = 1 - e^{-at} - ate^{-at}.$$

Example 3.   Find $L^{-1}\left\{\dfrac{s}{(s^2 + a^2)(s^2 + b^2)}\right\}$ where $a^2 \neq b^2$.

Since

$$\frac{s}{(s^2 + a^2)(s^2 + b^2)} = \frac{s}{a^2 - b^2}\frac{(s^2 + a^2) - (s^2 + b^2)}{(s^2 + a^2)(s^2 + b^2)}$$

$$= \frac{1}{b^2 - a^2}\left(\frac{s}{s^2 + a^2} - \frac{s}{s^2 + b^2}\right),$$

when $a^2 \neq b^2$, it follows that

$$L^{-1}\left\{\frac{s}{(s^2 + a^2)(s^2 + b^2)}\right\} = \frac{1}{b^2 - a^2}(\cos at - \cos bt).$$

Example 4.   Find $F(t)$ if $f(s) = \dfrac{5s + 3}{(s - 1)(s^2 + 2s + 5)}$.

In view of the quadratic factor, we write

$$\frac{5s + 3}{(s - 1)(s^2 + 2s + 5)} = \frac{A}{s - 1} + \frac{Bs + C}{s^2 + 2s + 5}.$$

Proceeding as before, we find that $A = 1$, $B = -1$, and $C = 2$, so that

$$f(s) = \frac{1}{s - 1} - \frac{s - 2}{(s + 1)^2 + 4}$$

$$= \frac{1}{s - 1} - \frac{s + 1}{(s + 1)^2 + 4} + \frac{3}{(s + 1)^2 + 4}.$$

Referring to Table 1, or to Theorem 3, we see that

$$F(t) = e^t - e^{-t}(\cos 2t - \tfrac{3}{2} \sin 2t).$$

PROBLEMS

1. Obtain the following inverse transforms:

(a) $L^{-1}\left\{\dfrac{a}{s(s + a)}\right\} = 1 - e^{-at}.$

(b) $L^{-1}\left\{\dfrac{a^3}{s(s + a)^3}\right\} = 1 - (1 + at + \tfrac{1}{2}a^2t^2)e^{-at}.$

(c) $L^{-1}\left\{\dfrac{k^2}{s(s^2 + k^2)}\right\} = 1 - \cos kt.$

2. Derive the inverse transforms shown in entries 16 and 17 of Table 1.

9. The Solution of Simple Differential Equations. The use of the Laplace transformation to solve homogeneous and non-homogeneous linear ordinary differential equations, or systems of such equations, can now be made clear by means of examples. Such problems can of course be solved also by the methods studied in a first course in differential equations. Later on, when we have developed further properties of the transformation, we shall solve further problems of this sort with greater efficiency. We shall also be able to solve much more difficult problems in differential equations.

Example 1. Find the general solution of the differential equation

$$Y''(t) + k^2Y(t) = 0.$$

Let the value of the unknown function at $t = 0$ be denoted by the constant A and the value of its first derivative at $t = 0$ by

the constant B; that is,

$$Y(0) = A, \qquad Y'(0) = B.$$

In view of the differential equation, we can write

$$L\{Y''(t)\} + k^2 L\{Y(t)\} = 0.$$

If the unknown function satisfies the conditions of Theorem 2, then

$$L\{Y''(t)\} = s^2 y(s) - As - B,$$

where $y(s) = L\{Y(t)\}$. Hence $y(s)$ must satisfy the equation

$$s^2 y(s) - As - B + k^2 y(s) = 0,$$

which is a simple *algebraic equation.* Its solution is clearly

$$y(s) = A \frac{s}{s^2 + k^2} + \frac{B}{k} \frac{k}{s^2 + k^2}.$$

Now $Y(t) = L^{-1}\{y(s)\}$, and the inverse transforms of the functions on the right of the last equation are known. Hence

$$\begin{aligned} Y(t) &= A \cos kt + \frac{B}{k} \sin kt, \\ &= A \cos kt + B' \sin kt, \end{aligned}$$

where A and B' are arbitrary constants since the initial conditions were not prescribed.

It is easy to verify that the result is the solution of the differential equation so it is not necessary to justify the use of Theorem 2. However, the function $A \cos kt + B' \sin kt$ does satisfy the conditions of that theorem, and the order of the steps taken above can be reversed to show in another way that this. function does satisfy the differential equation. These remarks on the verification of the solution apply equally well to the other examples and problems to follow in this section.

Example 2. Find the solution of the differential equation

$$Y''(t) - Y'(t) - 6Y(t) = 2$$

satisfying the initial conditions

$$Y(0) = 1, \qquad Y'(0) = 0.$$

Applying the transformation to both members of the differential equation, and letting $y(s)$ denote the transform of $Y(t)$, we obtain the algebraic equation

$$s^2 y(s) - s - s y(s) + 1 - 6 y(s) = \frac{2}{s},$$

where we have used the initial conditions in writing the transforms of $Y''(t)$ and $Y'(t)$.   Hence

$$(s^2 - s - 6) y(s) = \frac{s^2 - s + 2}{s},$$

or

$$y(s) = \frac{s^2 - s + 2}{s(s - 3)(s + 2)} = \frac{A}{s} + \frac{B}{s - 3} + \frac{C}{s + 2}.$$

Evaluating the coefficients A, B, and C as in the last section, we find that

$$y(s) = -\frac{1}{3}\frac{1}{s} + \frac{8}{15}\frac{1}{s - 3} + \frac{4}{5}\frac{1}{s + 2}.$$

Hence

$$Y(t) = -\tfrac{1}{3} + \tfrac{8}{15} e^{3t} + \tfrac{4}{5} e^{-2t}.$$

This result is easily verified.

Example 3.   Find the functions $Y(t)$ and $Z(t)$ that satisfy the following system of differential equations:

$$Y''(t) - Z''(t) + Z'(t) - Y(t) = e^t - 2,$$
$$2Y''(t) - Z''(t) - 2Y'(t) + Z(t) = -t,$$
$$Y(0) = Y'(0) = Z(0) = Z'(0) = 0.$$

Let $y(s)$ and $z(s)$ denote the transforms of $Y(t)$ and $Z(t)$, respectively.   Then in view of the differential equations and the initial conditions, these transforms satisfy the following simultaneous algebraic equations:

$$s^2 y(s) - s^2 z(s) + s z(s) - y(s) = \frac{1}{s - 1} - \frac{2}{s},$$
$$2 s^2 y(s) - s^2 z(s) - 2 s y(s) + z(s) = -\frac{1}{s^2}.$$

These equations can be written

$$(s + 1) y(s) - s z(s) = -\frac{s - 2}{s(s - 1)^2},$$
$$2 s y(s) - (s + 1) z(s) = -\frac{1}{s^2(s - 1)}.$$

Eliminating $z(s)$, we find that

$$(s^2 - 2s - 1)y(s) = \frac{s^2 - 2s - 1}{s(s-1)^2}.$$

With the aid of partial fractions, we find

$$y(s) = \frac{1}{s(s-1)^2} = \frac{A}{s} + \frac{B}{s-1} + \frac{C}{(s-1)^2}$$

$$= \frac{1}{s} - \frac{1}{s-1} + \frac{1}{(s-1)^2}.$$

Therefore

$$Y(t) = 1 - e^t + te^t.$$

Likewise we find that

$$z(s) = \frac{2s-1}{s^2(s-1)^2} = -\frac{1}{s^2} + \frac{1}{(s-1)^2},$$

and therefore

$$Z(t) = -t + te^t.$$

Example 4.   Solve the problem

$$Y'''(t) - 2Y''(t) + 5Y'(t) = 0,$$
$$Y(0) = Y'(0) = 0,\ Y''(0) = 1.$$

Proceeding as before, we have the equation

$$s^3 y(s) - 1 - 2s^2 y(s) + 5s y(s) = 0,$$

whose solution is

$$y(s) = \frac{1}{s(s^2 - 2s + 5)} = \frac{1}{5}\left(\frac{1}{s} - \frac{s-2}{s^2 - 2s + 5}\right).$$

This can be written

$$y(s) = \frac{1}{5}\frac{1}{s} - \frac{1}{5}\frac{s-1}{(s-1)^2 + 4} + \frac{1}{10}\frac{2}{(s-1)^2 + 4},$$

and therefore the solution is

$$Y(t) = \tfrac{1}{5} - \tfrac{1}{5}e^t \cos 2t + \tfrac{1}{10}e^t \sin 2t.$$

PROBLEMS

Solve the following problems and verify your solution.

1. $Y''(t) - k^2 Y(t) = 0.$ *Ans.* $Y(t) = C_1 e^{kt} + C_2 e^{-kt}.$

2. $Y''(t) - (a + b)Y'(t) + abY(t) = 0.$

$$\text{\emph{Ans.}}\ Y(t) = C_1 e^{at} + C_2 e^{bt}.$$

$\mathcal{C}$ **3.** $Y''(t) + k^2 Y(t) = a.$ *Ans.* $Y(t) = C_1 \sin kt + C_2 \cos kt + \dfrac{a}{k^2}.$

$\mathcal{d}$ **4.** $Y''(t) + 2kY'(t) + k^2 Y(t) = 0.$ *Ans.* $Y(t) = e^{-kt}(C_1 + C_2 t).$

$\mathcal{e}$ **5.** $Y''(t) - 2aY'(t) + (a^2 + b^2)Y(t) = 0,\ Y(0) = 0,\ Y'(0) = 1.$

$$\textit{Ans. } Y(t) = \frac{1}{b}\, e^{at} \sin bt.$$

$\mathcal{f}$ **6.** $Y''(t) + 4Y(t) = \sin t,\ Y(0) = Y'(0) = 0.$

$$\textit{Ans. } Y(t) = \tfrac{1}{3}\sin t - \tfrac{1}{6}\sin 2t.$$

$\mathcal{g}$ **7.** $Y'''(t) + Y'(t) = e^{2t},\ Y(0) = Y'(0) = Y''(0) = 0.$

$$\textit{Ans. } Y(t) = -\tfrac{1}{2} + \tfrac{1}{10}e^{2t} - \tfrac{1}{5}\sin t + \tfrac{2}{5}\cos t.$$

$\mathcal{h}$ **8.** $Y''(t) + Y'(t) = t^2 + 2t,\ Y(0) = 4,\ Y'(0) = -2.$

$$\textit{Ans. } Y(t) = \tfrac{1}{3}t^3 + 2e^{-t} + 2.$$

$\mathcal{i}$ **9.** $Y^{(4)}(t) + Y'''(t) = \cos t,\ Y(0) = Y'(0) = Y'''(0) = 0,\ Y''(0)$ arbitrary.   *Ans.* $Y(t) = -1 + t + Ct^2 + \tfrac{1}{2}(e^{-t} + \cos t - \sin t).$

$\mathcal{j}$ **10.** $Y'(t) - Z'(t) - 2Y(t) + 2Z(t) = 1 - 2t,\ Y''(t) + 2Z'(t) + Y(t) = 0,$
$Y(0) = Z(0) = Y'(0) = 0.$ *Ans.* $Y(t) = 2 - 2e^{-t} - 2te^{-t},$

$$Z(t) = 2 - 2e^{-t} - 2te^{-t} - t.$$

CHAPTER II

FURTHER PROPERTIES OF THE TRANSFORMATION

10. Translation of F(t).   There are several further operational properties of the Laplace transformation that are important in the applications.   Those properties whose derivations and applications do not necessarily involve the use of complex variables will be taken up in this chapter.

We begin with an analogue of Theorem 3 of the first chapter. According to that theorem, the multiplication of the object function by an exponential function corresponds to a linear substitution for s in the transform.   Now let us note the correspondence arising from the multiplication of the transform by an exponential function.

Let $F(t)$ have a transform,

$$f(s) = \int_0^\infty e^{-st} F(t) \, dt.$$

Then

$$e^{-bs} f(s) = \int_0^\infty e^{-s(t+b)} F(t) \, dt,$$

where b is a constant, assumed to be positive.   Substituting $t + b = \tau$, we can write the last integral in the form

$$\int_b^\infty e^{-s\tau} F(\tau - b) \, d\tau = \int_0^b 0 + \int_b^\infty e^{-s\tau} F(\tau - b) \, d\tau.$$

Thus if we define a function $F_b(t)$ as follows,

(1) $$\begin{aligned} F_b(t) &= 0 &\text{when } 0 < t < b, \\ &= F(t - b) &\text{when } t > b, \end{aligned}$$

we see that

$$f(s)e^{-bs} = \int_0^\infty e^{-s\tau} F_b(\tau) \, d\tau.$$

The following property is therefore established.

Theorem 1.   *If $f(s) = L\{F(t)\}$ then for any positive constant b,*

(2) $$e^{-bs}f(s) = L\{F_b(t)\},$$

where $F_b(t)$ is the function defined by equation (1).

The function $F_b(t)$ is illustrated in Fig. 4.   Its graph is obtained by translating the graph of $F(t)$ to the right through a distance of b units and making $F_b(t)$ identically zero between $t = 0$ and $t = b$.   On some occasions, it is convenient to define $F(t)$ as zero for all negative values of t, and when this is done the graph of $F_b(t)$ is simply a translation of the graph of $F(t)$.   We can refer to $F_b(t)$ as the translated function.

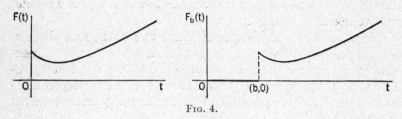

FIG. 4.

Our step function $S_k(t)$ is the translation of $F(t) = 1$ $(t > 0)$, and it serves as a familiar illustration of the above theorem.   Its transform is $e^{-ks}\dfrac{1}{s}$.   As another example, we know that

$$L^{-1}\left\{\frac{k}{s^2 + k^2}\right\} = \sin kt,$$

and consequently

$$L^{-1}\left\{\frac{ke^{-bs}}{s^2 + k^2}\right\} = 0 \qquad \text{when } 0 < t < b$$
$$= \sin k(t - b) \quad \text{when } t > b.$$

Similarly,

$$L^{-1}\left\{\frac{e^{-bs}}{s^2}\right\} = 0 \qquad \text{when } 0 < t < b,$$
$$= t - b \quad \text{when } t > b.$$

In Theorem 1 the substitution of $t - b$ for the variable t was involved.   Consider the simpler linear substitution of replacing t by at where a is a positive constant.   Since

$$L\{F(at)\} = \int_0^\infty e^{-st}F(at)\, dt$$
$$= \frac{1}{a}\int_0^\infty e^{-\frac{s}{a}\tau}F(\tau)\, d\tau = \frac{1}{a}f\left(\frac{s}{a}\right),$$

we have established the following theorem.

Theorem 2. *If $L\{F(t)\} = f(s)$ when $s > \alpha$, then*

$$(3) \qquad L\{F(at)\} = \frac{1}{a}f\left(\frac{s}{a}\right) \qquad (s > a\alpha,\ a > 0).$$

This correspondence can of course be written in the form

$$(4) \qquad L^{-1}\{f(cs)\} = \frac{1}{c}F\left(\frac{t}{c}\right) \qquad (c > 0).$$

Given, for example, that

$$\frac{s}{s^2 + 1} = L\{\cos t\},$$

it follows from formula (3) that

$$\frac{s}{s^2 + k^2} = \frac{1}{k}\frac{\dfrac{s}{k}}{\left(\dfrac{s}{k}\right)^2 + 1} = L\{\cos kt\}.$$

The effect of a general linear substitution for s can be seen from formula (4) and Theorem 3, Chap. I, since

$$(5) \qquad f(as - b) = f\left[a\left(s - \frac{b}{a}\right)\right] = L\left[\frac{1}{a}e^{\frac{b}{a}t}F\left(\frac{t}{a}\right)\right] \quad (a > 0).$$

11. Difference Equations. Some types of problems in difference and difference-differential equations can be solved with the aid of Theorem 1.

Example 1. Find the function $Y(t)$ that satisfies the first-order difference equation

$$(1) \qquad Y(t) - aY(t - h) = F(t)$$

and the boundary condition

$$(2) \qquad Y(t) = 0 \qquad \text{when } t < 0,$$

where a and h are prescribed constants, $h > 0$, and the given function $F(t)$ is zero when $t < 0$.

In view of the condition (2), the function $Y(t - h)$ is zero when $t < h$ and, according to Theorem 1, its transform is $e^{-hs}y(s)$. We are assuming that $Y(t)$ has a transform $y(s)$. Transforming both members of equation (1), we have

$$y(s) - ae^{-hs}y(s) = f(s),$$

or

$$y(s) = f(s) \frac{1}{1 - ae^{-hs}}.$$

By taking s sufficiently large, $|ae^{-hs}| < 1$ and hence

$$\frac{1}{1 - ae^{-hs}} = 1 + ae^{-hs} + a^2e^{-2hs} + a^3e^{-3hs} + \cdots$$

$$= 1 + \sum_{1}^{\infty} a^n e^{-nhs}.$$

Therefore

$$y(s) = f(s) + \sum_{1}^{\infty} a^n e^{-nhs} f(s).$$

According to Theorem 1,

$$L^{-1}\{e^{-nhs}f(s)\} = F(t - nh),$$

where it is to be recalled that the function on the right is zero when $t - nh < 0$. Assuming that it is permissible to apply the inverse transformation to the above infinite series term by term, that is, assuming that the order of the operators L^{-1} and $\sum_{1}^{\infty}$ can be interchanged, it would follow that

$$(3) \qquad Y(t) = F(t) + \sum_{1}^{\infty} a^n F(t - nh).$$

The series in (3) is finite for each fixed t, since $F(t - nh) = 0$ when $nh > t$. Let $mh < t < (m + 1)h$, where $m = 0, 1, 2, \cdots$; then our result can be written

$$(4) \quad Y(t) = F(t) + aF(t - h) + a^2F(t - 2h) + \cdots$$
$$+ a^m F(t - mh).$$

By writing our difference equation in the form

$$Y(t) = aY(t - h) + F(t)$$

and considering first those values of t between 0 and h, then between h and $2h$, etc., it is evident that the function (4) is the required solution.

When $F(t) = c$, $(t > 0)$, and $a = 1$, it follows from formula (4) that the solution is

(5) $Y(t) = c(m + 1)$ when $mh < t < (m + 1)h$ $(m = 0, 1, 2, \cdots)$.

This function, sometimes called the staircase function, is shown graphically in Fig. 5. If we denote it by $cS(h, t)$, our first formula for $y(s)$ indicates that

(6) $$L\{S(h, t)\} = \frac{1}{s(1 - e^{-hs})} = \frac{1}{2s}\left(1 + \coth\frac{hs}{2}\right).$$

This transformation can be verified, for $s > 0$, by evaluating the Laplace integral of the staircase function.

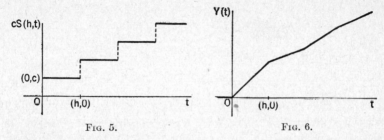

FIG. 5.　　　　　　　FIG. 6.

When $F(t) = t$, $t > 0$, and $a = -\frac{1}{2}$ in the above example, our solution becomes

$$Y(t) = t - \frac{1}{2}(t - h) + \frac{1}{2^2}(t - 2h) - \cdots + \frac{(-1)^m}{2^m}(t - mh),$$

when $mh < t < (m + 1)h$. The graph of this function is shown in Fig. 6.

Example 2. Find the function $Y(t)$ that satisfies the second-order difference equation

(7) $$Y(t) + 2Y(t - 1) - 3Y(t - 2) = F(t),$$

where the given function $F(t)$ is zero when $t < 0$, and the boundary condition

(8) $$Y(t) = 0 \qquad \text{when } t < 0.$$

Transforming both members of the equation we have, in view of the condition (8),

$$y(s) + 2e^{-s}y(s) - 3e^{-2s}y(s) = f(s),$$

and thus, with the aid of partial fractions,

$$y(s) = \frac{f(s)}{(1 - e^{-s})(1 + 3e^{-s})} = \frac{1}{4} f(s) \left(\frac{1}{1 - e^{-s}} + \frac{3}{1 + 3e^{-s}} \right)$$

$$= f(s) + \frac{1}{4} \sum_{1}^{\infty} [1 + (-1)^n 3^{n+1}] e^{-ns} f(s).$$

Then, formally,

$$(9) \qquad Y(t) = F(t) + \frac{1}{4} \sum_{1}^{\infty} [1 - (-3)^{n+1}] F(t - n).$$

This result can be written

$$Y(t) = F(t) + \frac{1}{4} \{ (1 - 3^2) F(t - 1) + (1 + 3^3) F(t - 2)$$
$$+ \cdots + [1 - (-3)^{m+1}] F(t - m) \}$$

where $m < t < m + 1$ $(m = 0, 1, 2, \cdots)$. Consequently,

$$2Y(t - 1) = 2F(t - 1) + \frac{1}{2} \{ (1 - 3^2) F(t - 2) + \cdots$$
$$+ [1 - (-3)^m] F(t - m) \},$$

since $F(t - m - 1) = 0$ when $t < m + 1$. Similarly,

$$-3Y(t - 2) = -3F(t - 2) - \frac{3}{4} \{ (1 - 3^2) F(t - 3) + \cdots$$
$$+ [1 - (-3)^{m-1}] F(t - m) \}.$$

Upon adding the corresponding members of the last three equations, we see that our function does satisfy the difference equation (7). It clearly satisfies the condition (8).

When $F(t) = 1$ for $t > 0$ in Example 2, it can be shown from formula (9) that, for $m < t < m + 1$,

$$Y(t) = \frac{1}{16} [7 + 4m + (-3)^{m+2}] \quad (m = 0, 1, 2, \cdots).$$

The above method can be used successfully in some problems involving derivatives as well as finite differences of the unknown function.

Example 3. Solve the difference-differential equation

$$Y'(t) - aY(t - 1) = b \qquad\qquad (t > 0),$$

under the condition that

$$Y(t) = 0 \qquad\qquad \text{when } t \leqq 0,$$

where the constant b is to be replaced by zero when $t < 0$.

Applying the transformation as before, we have

$$sy(s) - ae^{-s}y(s) = \frac{b}{s}.$$

Therefore

$$y(s) = \frac{b}{s^2}\left(1 - \frac{a}{s}e^{-s}\right)^{-1}$$

$$= b\left(\frac{1}{s^2} + \sum_1^\infty a^n \frac{1}{s^{n+2}} e^{-ns}\right),$$

and consequently

$$Y(t) = b\left[t + \sum_1^\infty \frac{a^n}{(n+1)!}(t-n)^{n+1}\right],$$

where $(t-n)^{n+1}$ is to be replaced by zero when $t - n < 0$ $(n = 0, 1, 2, \cdots)$. Thus when $m < t < m + 1$, we have

$$Y(t) = b\left[t + \frac{a}{2!}(t-1)^2 + \frac{a^2}{3!}(t-2)^3 + \cdots \right.$$

$$\left. + \frac{a^m}{(m+1)!}(t-m)^{m+1}\right],$$

$(m = 0, 1, 2, \cdots)$. This result can be verified directly.

It should be noted that the above method is limited to the solution of linear difference equations with constant coefficients, under the boundary condition

$$Y(t) = 0 \qquad \text{when } t < 0.$$

This boundary condition arises, or it can be used, in some applications of difference equations, but not in all.*

PROBLEMS

Solve for $Y(t)$, and verify your result.

1. $Y(t) - (a + b)Y(t - h) + abY(t - 2h) = F(t)$, $Y(t) = 0$ when $t < 0$, where $F(t) = 0$ when $t < 0$ and $a \neq b$.

$$Ans. \ Y(t) = F(t) + \frac{1}{a - b}\sum_1^\infty (a^{n+1} - b^{n+1})F(t - nh).$$

---

* For a further study of methods, and examples of physical applications, of difference equations see, for example, Gardner and Barnes, "Transients in Linear Systems," Chap. IX, 1942; and Kármán and Biot, "Mathematical Methods in Engineering," 1940, and the bibliography in those two books.

2. $Y(t) - 2aY(t - h) + a^2Y(t - 2h) = F(t)$, $Y(t) = 0$ when $t < 0$, where $F(t) = 0$ when $t < 0$.

$$\text{Ans. } Y(t) = F(t) + \sum_{1}^{\infty} (n + 1)a^nF(t - nh).$$

3. $Y''(t) - Y(t - 1) = b$, $Y(t) = 0$ when $t \leqq 0$, $Y'(+ 0) = 0$, where b is to be replaced by zero when $t < 0$.

$$\text{Ans. } Y(t) = \frac{1}{2} bt^2 + b \sum_{1}^{\infty} \frac{1}{(2n + 2)!} (t - n)^{2n+2}, \quad \text{where} \quad t^2 \text{ and}$$

$(t - n)^{2n+2}$ are to be replaced by zero when $t < 0$ and $n > t$, respectively.

12. Derivatives of Transforms. Let $F(t)$ be a function that is sectionally continuous in each finite interval $0 \leqq t \leqq T$ and of exponential order as t tends to infinity; that is,

$$|F(t)| < Me^{\alpha_0 t}$$

where M and α_0 are constants. Then if $s \geqq \alpha$ where α is any constant greater than α_0,

$$e^{-st}|F(t)| < Me^{\alpha_0 t}e^{-\alpha t} = Me^{-(\alpha - \alpha_0)t}.$$

The function $e^{-(\alpha - \alpha_0)t}$ is independent of s and its integral from zero to infinity converges. Therefore the integral

$$\int_0^{\infty} e^{-st}F(t)\, dt$$

is uniformly convergent with respect to s when $s \geqq \alpha$. Furthermore, since

$$\left| \int_0^{\infty} e^{-st}F(t)\, dt \right| \leqq \int_0^{\infty} e^{-st}|F(t)|\, dt$$

it follows that

$$(1) \qquad |L\{F(t)\}| < M \int_0^{\infty} e^{-(\alpha - \alpha_0)t}\, dt = \frac{M}{\alpha - \alpha_0} \qquad (s \geqq \alpha).$$

From this property of the transform of $(F)t$ we may obtain a useful result on the behavior of $f(s)$ as s tends to infinity. If we let $s = \alpha$, we have

$$(2) \qquad |f(s)| < \frac{M}{s - \alpha_0};$$

consequently $f(s)$ must vanish as s tends to infinity.

If n is any positive integer, then

$$t^n e^{-st}|F(t)| < Mt^n e^{-(\alpha-\alpha_0)t} = Mt^n e^{-\frac{1}{2}(\alpha-\alpha_0)t} e^{-\frac{1}{2}(\alpha-\alpha_0)t} \leqq MK_n e^{-\frac{1}{2}(\alpha-\alpha_0)t}$$

where K_n is the maximum value of the function

$$t^n e^{-\frac{1}{2}(\alpha-\alpha_0)t} \qquad\qquad (t \geqq 0).$$

Therefore it follows as before that the Laplace integral of the function $t^n F(t)$ converges uniformly with respect to s and vanishes as s tends to infinity. We have thus demonstrated the following theorem.

Theorem 3. *If $F(t)$ is sectionally continuous and of the order of $e^{\alpha_0 t}$ then each of the Laplace integrals $L\{F(t)\}$, $L\{tF(t)\}$, $L\{t^2F(t)\}$, $\cdots$, is uniformly convergent with respect to s when $s \geqq \alpha$ where $\alpha > \alpha_0$; moreover*

$$\lim_{s \,>\, \infty} f(s) = 0$$

and

$$\lim_{s \to \infty} L\{t^n F(t)\} = 0 \qquad (n = 1, 2, \cdots).$$

When $F(t)$ is sectionally continuous, the derivative, with respect to the parameter s, of the infinite integral

$$\int_0^\infty e^{-st}F(t)\ dt$$

is equal to the integral of the partial derivative of the integrand, provided the latter integral is uniformly convergent and that the first integral converges.* According to Theorem 3, these conditions are satisfied provided $F(t)$ is of exponential order, and hence

$$(3) \qquad f'(s) = \int_0^\infty e^{-st}(-t)F(t)\ dt = L\{-tF(t)\}.$$

Similarly, in view of Theorem 3,

$$f''(s) = \int_0^\infty e^{-st}(-t)^2 F(t)\ dt = L\{t^2 F(t)\},$$

and likewise for derivatives of higher order. The following theorem is now established.

---

* See, for instance, H. S. Carslaw, "Fourier's Series and Integrals," p. 200, 1930.

Theorem 4. *Differentiation of the transform of a function corresponds to the multiplication of the function by* $-t$:

$$(4) \qquad f^{(n)}(s) = L\{(-t)^n F(t)\} \qquad (n = 1, 2, \cdots);$$

moreover

$$\lim_{s \to \infty} f^{(n)}(s) = 0.$$

These properties hold true whenever $F(t)$ is sectionally continuous and of the order of $e^{\alpha t}$, if $s > \alpha$ in formula (4).

Since a function is continuous wherever its derivative exists, it is true that $f(s)$ and each of its derivatives are continuous when $s > \alpha$.

To illustrate the last theorem, we can note that since

$$\frac{k}{s^2 + k^2} = L\{\sin kt\} \qquad (s > 0),$$

it follows that

$$\frac{-2ks}{(s^2 + k^2)^2} = L\{-t \sin kt\}$$

or

$$(5) \qquad L\{t \sin kt\} = \frac{2ks}{(s^2 + k^2)^2} \qquad (s > 0).$$

The conditions in our theorem are satisfied here with $\alpha = 0$.

We noted in Sec. 5 that the division of a transform by s corresponds to an integration of the object function.   Since

$$\int_0^t \tau \sin k\tau \, d\tau = \frac{1}{k^2} (\sin kt - kt \cos kt),$$

it follows from the transformation (5) that

$$(6) \qquad L\{\sin kt - kt \cos kt\} = \frac{2k^3}{(s^2 + k^2)^2} \qquad (s > 0).$$

Formulas (5) and (6) are useful in finding inverse transforms with the aid of partial fractions.

13. Differential Equations with Variable Coefficients. We have seen that

$$L\{t^n Y(t)\} = (-1)^n \frac{d^n}{ds^n} L\{Y(t)\} = (-1)^n y^{(n)}(s),$$

and therefore we can write the transform of the product of t^n by any derivative of $Y(t)$ in terms of $y(s)$; for instance,

$$L\{t^2 Y'(t)\} = \frac{d^2}{ds^2}[sy(s) - Y(0)] = sy''(s) + 2y'(s),$$

$$L\{tY''(t)\} = -\frac{d}{ds}[s^2 y(s) - sY(0) - Y'(0)]$$

$$= -s^2 y'(s) - 2sy(s) + Y(0).$$

A linear differential equation in $Y(t)$ whose coefficients are polynomials in t transforms into a linear differential equation in $y(s)$ whose coefficients are polynomials in s. In case the transformed equation is simpler than the original, the transformation may enable us to find the solution of the original equation.

If the coefficients are polynomials of the first degree, the transformed equation is a linear equation of the first order, whose solution can be written in terms of an integral. To find the solution of the original equation, however, the inverse transform of the solution of the new equation must be obtained. This is frequently a difficult task.

Example 1. Find the solution of the problem

$$Y''(t) + tY'(t) - Y(t) = 0, \qquad Y(0) = 0, \qquad Y'(0) = 1.$$

The transformed equation is

$$s^2 y(s) - 1 - \frac{d}{ds}[sy(s)] - y(s) = 0,$$

or

$$y'(s) + \left(\frac{2}{s} - s\right) y(s) = -\frac{1}{s},$$

which is a linear equation of the first order. An integrating factor is

$$e^{\int \left(\frac{2}{s} - s\right) ds} = s^2 e^{-\frac{1}{2}s^2},$$

so the equation can be written

$$\frac{d}{ds}[s^2 e^{-\frac{1}{2}s^2} y(s)] = -s e^{-\frac{1}{2}s^2}.$$

Integrating, we have

$$y(s) = \frac{1}{s^2} + \frac{C}{s^2} e^{\frac{1}{2}s^2}$$

where C is a constant of integration. But C must vanish if $y(s)$

is a transform since $y(s)$ must vanish as s tends to infinity.   It follows that

$$Y(t) = t,$$

and this is readily verified as the solution.

   Example 2.   Solve Bessel's equation with index zero,

$$tY''(t) + Y'(t) + tY(t) = 0$$

under the condition that $Y(0) = 1$ and that $Y(t)$ has a transform.

   The point $t = 0$ is a singular point* of this differential equation such that every $Y(t)$ that satisfies this equation and is finite at $t = 0$ satisfies the condition $Y'(0) = 0$.

   The transformed equation is

$$-\frac{d}{ds}\left[s^2 y(s) - s - Y'(0)\right] + sy(s) - 1 - \frac{d}{ds}\,y(s) = 0,$$

or

$$(s^2 + 1)y'(s) + sy(s) = 0.$$

Separating variables, we have

$$\frac{dy}{y} = -\frac{s\,ds}{s^2 + 1},$$

and upon integrating and simplifying, we find that

$$y(s) = \frac{C}{\sqrt{s^2 + 1}}$$

where C is a constant of integration.

   Expanding the function for $y(s)$ by the binomial series we have, when $s > 1$,

$$y(s) = \frac{C}{s}\left(1 + \frac{1}{s^2}\right)^{-\frac{1}{2}} = \frac{C}{s}\left[1 - \frac{1}{2}\frac{1}{s^2} + \frac{1\cdot 3}{2^2 2!}\frac{1}{s^4} - \cdots\right]$$

$$= C\sum_0^\infty \frac{(-1)^n}{(2^n n!)^2}\frac{(2n)!}{s^{2n+1}}.$$

Applying the inverse transformation formally to the terms of this series, we find

$$Y(t) = C\sum_0^\infty \frac{(-1)^n}{(2^n n!)^2}\,t^{2n}.$$

---

* See E. D. Rainville, "Intermediate Differential Equations," 1943.

If this function is to satisfy the condition $Y(0) = 1$, it is necessary that $C = 1$, and our formal solution becomes

$$Y(t) = \sum_0^\infty \frac{(-1)^n}{(2^n n!)^2} t^{2n}.$$

This power series is easily seen to be convergent for all t, and it is not difficult to show that it satisfies the differential equation. The function defined by the series is Bessel's function $J_0(t)$; that is

$$J_0(t) = 1 - \frac{t^2}{2^2} + \frac{t^4}{2^2 \cdot 4^2} - \frac{t^6}{2^2 \cdot 4^2 \cdot 6^2} + \cdots.$$

Our first formula for $y(s)$ above indicates that

(1) $$L\{J_0(t)\} = \frac{1}{\sqrt{s^2 + 1}},$$

a transformation that can be established rigorously for $s > 0$.

Example 3. Find the solution of Bessel's equation of index n,

(2) $$t^2 Y''(t) + t Y'(t) + (t^2 - n^2) Y(t) = 0$$

that has a Laplace transform, where n is a positive integer.

Here again the point $t = 0$ is a singular point of the differential equation and, except for an arbitrary constant factor, there is only one solution that is finite at $t = 0$.

The reader can show that, regardless of the values of the constants $Y(0)$ and $Y'(0)$, the transformed equation reduces to

(3) $$(s^2 + 1)y''(s) + 3sy'(s) + (1 - n^2)y(s) = 0.$$

This seems to be no simpler than the original equation, unless $n = 1$.

However, if we substitute $t^{-n}Z(t)$ for $Y(t)$ in equation (2), so that

$$Z(t) = t^n Y(t),$$

we find that the equation in the new unknown function becomes one with linear coefficients, namely,

$$tZ''(t) + (1 - 2n)Z'(t) + tZ(t) = 0.$$

Observing that $Z(0) = 0$, we find that the transformed equation becomes

$$(s^2 + 1)z'(s) + (1 + 2n)sz(s) = 0.$$

After separating the variables here, we obtain the solution

$$z(s) = \frac{C}{(s^2 + 1)^{(n+\frac{1}{2})}} = \frac{C}{s^{2n+1}} \left(1 + \frac{1}{s^2}\right)^{-(n+\frac{1}{2})}$$

where C is a constant of integration. With the aid of the binomial expansion, this formula for $z(s)$ can be written

$$z(s) = \frac{n!C}{(2n)!} \sum_{k=0}^{\infty} \frac{(-1)^k}{2^{2k}k!(n+k)!} \frac{(2n+2k)!}{s^{2n+2k+1}}$$

when $s > 1$. Formally performing the inverse transformation term by term, we have then

$$Z(t) = \frac{n!C}{(2n)!} \sum_{k=0}^{\infty} \frac{(-1)^k}{2^{2k}k!(n+k)!} t^{2n+2k},$$

and our required function $Y(t)$ is obtained by dividing $Z(t)$ by t^n.
   If the constant C is taken so that

$$\frac{n!C}{(2n)!} = \frac{1}{2^n}$$

our solution becomes

$$(4) \qquad Y(t) = \sum_{k=0}^{\infty} \frac{(-1)^k}{k!(n+k)!} \left(\frac{t}{2}\right)^{n+2k} = J_n(t),$$

where $J_n(t)$ is Bessel's function of the first kind. The power series in equation (4) is convergent for all values of t and it satisfies Bessel's equation (2). Our formula for $z(s)$ above indicates that

$$(5) \qquad L\{t^n J_n(t)\} = \frac{(2n)!}{2^n n!(s^2 + 1)^{n+\frac{1}{2}}},$$

a transformation that is correct when $s > 0$.
   When $n = 1$, we noted that equation (3) in the transform of $Y(t)$ is a simple one even though coefficients of degree higher than the first occur in the original equation. In this case it will be left to the reader to show that the solution of equation (3) is

$$y(s) = \frac{C_1 s}{\sqrt{s^2 + 1}} + C_2$$

where C_1 and C_2 are constants of integration. As s tends to infinity, this function approaches $C_1 + C_2$, and so we must take $C_1 + C_2 = 0$. Therefore

$$y(s) = C_1\left(\frac{s}{\sqrt{s^2 + 1}} - 1\right).$$

Since $J_0(0) = 1$, we have, in view of equation (1),

$$L\{J_0'(t)\} = \frac{s}{\sqrt{s^2 + 1}} - 1,$$

and therefore

$$Y(t) = C_1 J_0'(t).$$

When $C_1 = -1$, this function is the same as $J_1(t)$. Thus a particular solution of Bessel's equation with $n = 1$ is

$$Y(t) = J_1(t) = -J_0'(t).$$

It also follows that

(6) $L\{J_1(t)\} = \dfrac{\sqrt{s^2 + 1} - s}{\sqrt{s^2 + 1}} = \dfrac{1}{\sqrt{s^2 + 1}\,(s + \sqrt{s^2 + 1})}.$

PROBLEMS

1. With the aid of Theorem 2 and the above transformations, show that

(a) $L\{J_0(ul)\} = \dfrac{1}{\sqrt{s^2 + a^2}};$

(b) $L\{J_1(at)\} = \dfrac{a}{\sqrt{s^2 + a^2}\,(s + \sqrt{s^2 + a^2})}.$

2. Find the solution, which has a transform, of

$$tY''(t) + (1 - n - t)Y'(t) + nY(t) = t - 1,$$

if $Y(0) = 0$, where n is a positive constant and $n \neq 1$.

Ans. $Y(t) = \dfrac{t}{n - 1} + Ct^n.$

3. Find the solution, which has a transform, of

$$tY''(t) + (2t + 3)Y'(t) + (t + 3)Y(t) = ae^{-t}.$$

Ans. $Y(t) = \left(C + \dfrac{a}{3}t\right)e^{-t}.$

4. Find the solution, which has a transform, of

$$tY''(t) - (2t + 1)Y'(t) + (t + 1)Y(t) = 0,$$

if $Y(0) = 0$.   *Ans.* $Y(t) = Ct^2e^t$.

14. Convolution.   Let $F_1(t)$ and $F_2(t)$ be two functions that are sectionally continuous and of the order of $e^{\alpha t}$, and let

$$f_1(s) = L\{F_1(t)\}, \qquad f_2(s) = L\{F_2(t)\}.$$

Then

$$f_1(s)f_2(s) = \int_0^\infty e^{-sx}F_1(x)\,dx \int_0^\infty e^{-sy}F_2(y)\,dy \quad (s > \alpha).$$

The product of the integrals on the right is the limit as $a \to \infty$ of $I(a)$, where

$$I(a) = \int_0^{\frac{1}{2}a} e^{-sx}F_1(x)\,dx \int_0^{\frac{1}{2}a} e^{-sy}F_2(y)\,dy$$

$$= \iint_A e^{-s(x+y)}F_1(x)F_2(y)\,dx\,dy,$$

where the region of integration of this double integral is the square bounded by the coordinate axes and the lines $x = \frac{1}{2}a$ and $y = \frac{1}{2}a$ (Fig. 7).

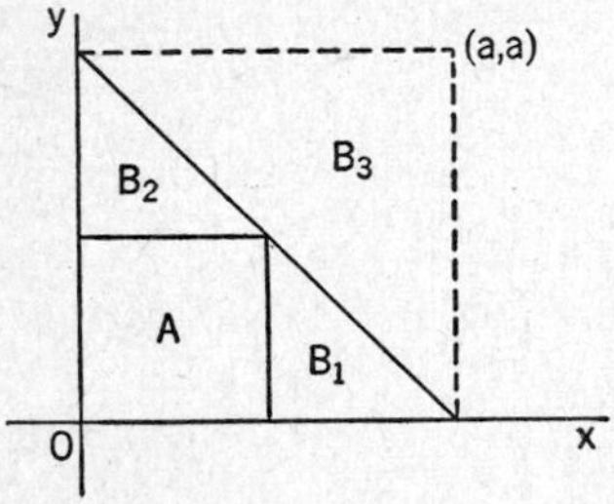

Since $I(a)$ has a limit as $a \to \infty$, the integral $I(2a)$ has the same limit, where $I(2a)$ is the integral over the square in Fig. 7 bounded by the dotted lines and the coordinate axes. Hence

$$\lim_{a \to \infty} [I(2a) - I(a)] = 0;$$

Fig. 7.

that is, the double integral over the region consisting of the triangles B_1, B_2, and B_3 has the limit zero. This is also true if $F_1(t)$ and $F_2(t)$ are replaced by their absolute values, since these functions are of exponential order. Hence the integrals over the triangles B_1 and B_2 must approach zero, and

$$f_1(s)f_2(s) = \lim_{a \to \infty} J(a)$$

where $J(a)$ is the double integral over the triangle made up of the square A and the triangles B_1 and B_2.

Introducing the new variables

$$t = x + y, \qquad \tau = y,$$

so that $x = t - \tau$, $y = \tau$, the region $x > 0$, $y > 0$, $x + y < a$ becomes the region $t > \tau$, $\tau > 0$, $t < a$ in the $t\tau$-plane (Fig. 8). The element of area $dx\,dy$ becomes, in the new plane,

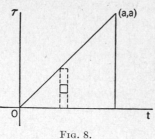

Fig. 8.

$$\begin{vmatrix} \dfrac{\partial x}{\partial t} & \dfrac{\partial y}{\partial t} \\[2mm] \dfrac{\partial x}{\partial \tau} & \dfrac{\partial y}{\partial \tau} \end{vmatrix} dt\,d\tau = \begin{vmatrix} 1 & 0 \\ -1 & 1 \end{vmatrix} dt\,d\tau = dt\,d\tau.$$

Hence

$$J(a) = \int_0^a \int_0^t e^{-st} F_1(t - \tau) F_2(\tau)\, d\tau\, dt,$$

and letting a tend to infinity, we have the result

$$(1) \qquad f_1(s) f_2(s) = \int_0^\infty e^{-st} \int_0^t F_1(t - \tau) F_2(\tau)\, d\tau\, dt.$$

The combination of the two functions $F_1(t)$ and $F_2(t)$ appearing inside the Laplace integral here is called the *convolution* of these functions. It is also known as the Faltung integral. We denote it by the symbol $F_1 * F_2$, so that

$$(2) \qquad F_1 * F_2 = \int_0^t F_1(t - \tau) F_2(\tau)\, d\tau.$$

Substituting $t - \tau = \lambda$, this becomes

$$\int_0^t F_2(t - \lambda) F_1(\lambda)\, d\lambda = F_2 * F_1;$$

therefore

$$(3) \qquad F_1 * F_2 = F_2 * F_1.$$

The result obtained in equation (1) can now be written as follows.

Theorem 5. *The multiplication of the transforms of two functions corresponds to the convolution of the functions:*

$$(4) \qquad f_1(s) f_2(s) = L\{F_1(t) * F_2(t)\}.$$

The transform on the right exists, and this formula is valid provided $F_1(t)$ and $F_2(t)$ are sectionally continuous and of the order of $e^{\alpha t}$, when $s > \alpha$.

We can now write the inverse transforms of products of transforms, since

$$L^{-1}\{f_1(s)f_2(s)\} = F_1(t) * F_2(t).$$

For example,

$$L^{-1}\left\{\frac{1}{s^2}\frac{1}{s-a}\right\} = t * e^{at}$$

$$= \int_0^t (t - \tau)e^{a\tau}\, d\tau = \frac{1}{a^2}(e^{at} - at - 1).$$

When $F_1(t) = F_2(t) = F(t)$, we have

$$[f(s)]^2 \equiv L\{F * F\}.$$

For example,

$$(5)\qquad L^{-1}\left\{\frac{s^2}{(s^2 + k^2)^2}\right\} = \cos kt * \cos kt$$

$$= \int_0^t \cos k(t - \tau)\cos k\tau\, d\tau$$

$$= \frac{1}{2k}(\sin kt + kt\cos kt).$$

If we have three functions $F_1(t)$, $F_2(t)$, and $F_3(t)$ that satisfy the conditions of our theorem, then

$$f_1(s)f_2(s)f_3(s) = L\{F_1(t) * L^{-1}\{f_2(s)f_3(s)\}\}.$$

Therefore

$$(6)\qquad f_1(s)f_2(s)f_3(s) = L\{F_1 * F_2 * F_3\}.$$

The same is true for the product of any number of transforms.

When $F_1(t) = 1$ and $F_2(t) = F(t)$, we have as a special case of formula (4)

$$\frac{1}{s}f(s) = L\{1 * F(t)\} = L\left\{\int_0^t F(\tau)\, d\tau\right\}.$$

When $F_1(t) = F_2(t) = 1$ in formula (6), we have the special case

$$\frac{1}{s^2}f(s) = L\left\{1 * \int_0^t F(\tau)\, d\tau\right\} = L\left\{\int_0^t \int_0^\tau F(\lambda)\, d\lambda\, d\tau\right\}.$$

The following property of the transformation, already noted in Sec. 5, is therefore a special case of the last theorem.

Theorem 6. *Division of the transform of a function by s corresponds to integration of the function between the limits 0 and t:*

$$(7) \qquad L^{-1}\left\{\frac{1}{s}f(s)\right\} = \int_0^t F(\tau)\,d\tau,$$

$$(8) \qquad L^{-1}\left\{\frac{1}{s^2}f(s)\right\} = \int_0^t \int_0^\tau F(\lambda)\,d\lambda\,d\tau,$$

etc., for division by s^n, provided $F(t)$ is sectionally continuous and of the order of $e^{\alpha t}$ ($\alpha > 0$), where $s > \alpha$.

As examples, we note that

$$L^{-1}\left\{\frac{k}{s(s^2+k^2)}\right\} = \int_0^t \sin k\tau\,d\tau = \frac{1}{k}\,(1 - \cos kt),$$

$$L^{-1}\left\{\frac{k}{s^2(s^2+k^2)}\right\} = \int_0^t \int_0^\tau \sin k\lambda\,d\lambda\,d\tau = \frac{1}{k^2}\,(kt - \sin kt).$$

Our formula (4) on the transformation of the convolution of two functions is sometimes called the Borel formula in operational calculus. The conditions for its validity stated in Theorem 5 are somewhat narrower than necessary. When $F_1(t) = t^{-\frac{1}{2}}$, for example, the formula is valid, because the Laplace integral of $F_1(t)$ is still absolutely convergent. Thus

$$L^{-1}\left\{\frac{1}{(s-1)\sqrt{s}}\right\} = e^t * \frac{1}{\sqrt{\pi t}} = e^t\,\frac{2}{\sqrt{\pi}}\int_0^t e^{-\tau}\,\frac{d\tau}{2\sqrt{\tau}},$$

and if we make the substitution $\lambda = \sqrt{\tau}$ here we have the result

$$(9) \qquad L^{-1}\left\{\frac{1}{\sqrt{s}\,(s-1)}\right\} = e^t\,\mathrm{erf}\,(\sqrt{t}),$$

where erf(x) is the *error function,*[*] defined as

$$\mathrm{erf}\,(x) = \frac{2}{\sqrt{\pi}}\int_0^x e^{-\lambda^2}\,d\lambda.$$

Other transformations follow readily from (9). For instance,

$$\frac{1}{\sqrt{s}-1} = \frac{\sqrt{s}+1}{s-1} = \frac{1}{s-1} + \frac{1}{\sqrt{s}}\left(1 + \frac{1}{s-1}\right),$$

---

[*] This function is also called the probability integral. See, for instance, B. O. Peirce, "Short Table of Integrals," 1929; H. B. Dwight, "Mathematical Tables," 1941.

and therefore

(10) $$L^{-1}\left\{\frac{1}{\sqrt{s}-1}\right\} = \frac{1}{\sqrt{\pi t}} + e^t[1 + \text{erf }(\sqrt{t})].$$

Since substitution of $s + 1$ for s corresponds to multiplication by e^{-t}, we obtain, directly from (9), the transformation

(11) $$L^{-1}\left\{\frac{1}{s\sqrt{s+1}}\right\} = \text{erf }(\sqrt{t}).$$

15. Differential and Integral Equations. The operational methods that we have developed at this point can be applied to the solution of nonhomogeneous linear differential equations in which the given function is an arbitrary one.

Example 1.   Find the solution of the differential equation

(1) $$Y''(t) + k^2 Y(t) = F(t),$$

where $F(t)$ is a given function.

Assuming for the present that $F(t)$, as well as the unknown function $Y(t)$, satisfies the conditions in our theorems, the equation in the transform $y(s)$ becomes

$$s^2 y(s) - sY(0) - Y'(0) + k^2 y(s) = f(s),$$

or

$$y(s) = \frac{1}{k}\frac{k}{s^2 + k^2}f(s) + Y(0)\frac{s}{s^2 + k^2} + \frac{Y'(0)}{k}\frac{k}{s^2 + k^2}.$$

The first term on the right is the product of the transforms of $(1/k)$ sin kt and $F(t)$, so its inverse transform is the convolution of those functions.   Thus

$$Y(t) = \frac{1}{k}\sin kt * F(t) + Y(0)\cos kt + \frac{Y'(0)}{k}\sin kt;$$

hence the formal solution of our differential equation can be written

(2) $$Y(t) = \frac{1}{k}\int_0^t \sin k(t - \tau)F(\tau)\,d\tau + C_1\cos kt + C_2\sin kt,$$

where C_1 and C_2 are arbitrary constants.   Using the rule, derived in advanced calculus, for differentiating a definite integral with respect to a parameter, we find that the derivative of the integral on the right, with respect to t, is

$$k \int_0^t \cos k(t - \tau)F(\tau) \, d\tau,$$

and the derivative of this function is

$$-k^2 \int_0^t \sin k(t - \tau)F(\tau) \, d\tau + kF(t).$$

We have assumed only that $F(t)$ is a continuous function. It follows easily that our function $Y(t)$ does satisfy the differential equation.

We may note, however, that even when

$$F(t) = \sec^2 kt,$$

a function that has discontinuities, our result (2) reduces to

$$Y(t) = \frac{1}{k^2} [\cos kt - 1 + \sin kt \log (\sec kt + \tan kt)],$$

when $C_1 = C_2 = 0$. This satisfies the differential equation except at the points of discontinuity of $Y(t)$.

An equation in which the unknown function occurs inside an integral is called an integral equation. In certain applied problems, which we shall illustrate in the following chapter, the integral in the equation is the convolution integral. Such integral equations of the convolution or Faltung type transform into algebraic equations.

Example 2. Find the function $Y(t)$ that satisfies the integral equation

$$Y(t) = at + \int_0^t \sin (t - \tau)Y(\tau) \, d\tau.$$

We can write this equation in the form

$$Y(t) = at + \sin t * Y(t).$$

Applying the transform to both members, we have the algebraic equation

$$y(s) = \frac{a}{s^2} + \frac{1}{s^2 + 1} \, y(s),$$

whose solution is

$$y(s) = a\left(\frac{1}{s^2} + \frac{1}{s^4}\right).$$

Therefore

$$Y(t) = a(t + \tfrac{1}{6}t^3),$$

which can be verified directly as the solution of the above integral equation.

The general integral equation of the convolution type has the form

$$(3) \qquad Y(t) = F(t) + \int_0^t G(t - \tau)Y(\tau)\,d\tau,$$

where the functions $F(t)$ and $G(t)$ are given and $Y(t)$ is to be found.   Since the transformed equation is

$$y(s) = f(s) + g(s)y(s),$$

the transform of the unknown function is

$$(4) \qquad y(s) = \frac{f(s)}{1 - g(s)}.$$

Even if equation (3) is modified by replacing $Y(t)$ by linear combinations of $Y(t)$ and its derivatives, where the coefficients in these combinations are constants, the transform of the modified equation is an algebraic equation in $y(s)$.   For instance, the integrodifferential equation

$$(5) \qquad aY(t) + bY'(t) = F(t) + \int_0^t G(t - \tau)Y(\tau)\,d\tau,$$

where a and b are constants, gives rise to the transformed equation

$$(a + bs)y(s) - bY(0) = f(s) + g(s)y(s),$$

which is easily solved for $y(s)$.

The equation

$$(6) \qquad F(t) = \int_0^t (t - \tau)^{-b}Y'(\tau)\,d\tau \qquad (0 < b < 1),$$

is known as Abel's integral equation.   The unknown function could of course be considered here as $Y'(t)$ instead of $Y(t)$; but no advantage is gained in this way.   The solution of this equation is

$$(7) \qquad Y(t) = Y(0) + \frac{1}{\Gamma(b)\Gamma(1 - b)}\,t^{b-1} * F(t),$$

valid when $F(t)$ satisfies certain conditions of continuity.* The formal derivation of this solution can be left to the reader.

PROBLEMS

Solve the following differential equations:

1. $Y''(t) - k^2 Y(t) = F(t)$, if $Y(0) = Y'(0) = 0$.

$$Ans. \quad Y(t) = \frac{1}{2k}\left[e^{kt} \int_0^t e^{-k\tau} F(\tau)\, d\tau - e^{-kt} \int_0^t e^{k\tau} F(\tau)\, d\tau \right].$$

2. $Y''(t) - 2kY'(t) + k^2 Y(t) = F(t)$.

$$Ans. \quad Y(t) = e^{kt}\left[C_1 + C_2 t + \int_0^t (t - \tau)e^{-k\tau} F(\tau)\, d\tau \right].$$

3. $Y''(t) + 4Y'(t) + 5Y(t) = F(t)$.

$$Ans. \quad Y(t) = e^{-2t}(C_1 \cos t + C_2 \sin t) + F(t) * (e^{-2t} \sin t).$$

4. $Y'''(t) - Y'(t) = F(t)$, if $Y(0) = Y'(0) = Y''(0) = 0$.

$$Ans. \quad Y(t) = \sinh t * \int_0^t F(\tau)\, d\tau.$$

5. $Y'''(t) + Y'(t) = F(t)$. Let $F(t) = \tan t$, finally.

Ans. $Y(t) = C_1 + C_2 \sin t + C_3 \cos t - \log \cos t - \sin t \log (\sec t + \tan t)$.

6. Show that the solution of the system of differential equations

$$Y'(t) - 2Z'(t) = F(t),$$
$$Y''(t) - Z''(t) + Z(t) = 0,$$

under the conditions $Y(0) = Y'(0) = Z(0) = Z'(0) = 0$, is

$$Y(t) = \int_0^t F(\tau)\, d\tau - 2 \cos t * F(t), \qquad Z(t) = - \cos t * F(t).$$

7. Solve the integral equation

$$Y(t) = a \sin t + \int_0^t \sin (t - \tau) Y(\tau)\, d\tau.$$

$$Ans. \quad Y(t) = at.$$

8. Solve the integral equation

$$Y(t) = a \sin bt + c \int_0^t \sin b(t - \tau) Y(\tau)\, d\tau, \quad (b > c > 0).$$

$$Ans. \quad Y(t) = \frac{ab}{\sqrt{b^2 - bc}} \sin t \sqrt{b^2 - bc}.$$

* For a fuller discussion of Abel's integral equation, see G. Doetsch, "Theorie und Anwendung der Laplace-Transformation," p. 293, 1937, and the references given there.

9. Show that the formal solution of the integrodifferential equation

$$Y(t) = \frac{2}{\sqrt{\pi}} \left[\sqrt{t} + \int_0^t \sqrt{t - \tau}\, Y'(\tau)\, d\tau \right],$$

when $Y(0) = 0$, is

$$Y(t) = e^t[\text{erf}\,(\sqrt{t}) + 1] - 1.$$

10. Show that the transform of the nonlinear integral equation

$$2Y(t) = F(t) + \int_0^t Y(t - \tau)Y(\tau)\, d\tau$$

has the solution

$$y(s) = \frac{f(s)}{1 + \sqrt{1 - f(s)}}.$$

When $F(t) = \sin t$, show that $Y(t) = J_1(t)$.

16. Heaviside's Partial Fractions Expansion. Let us now obtain a more efficient method of finding the inverse transform of the quotient of two polynomials in s. Let

$$f(s) = \frac{p(s)}{q(s)}$$

where $p(s)$ and $q(s)$ are polynomials with no common factors and the degree of $p(s)$ is lower than that of $q(s)$.

Suppose first that the factors of $q(s)$ are all linear and distinct, that is,

$$q(s) = (s - a_1)(s - a_2) \cdots (s - a_m),$$

where the a's are distinct constants. Then according to the theory of partial fractions, constants $C_1, C_2, \cdots, C_m$ exist such that

$$(1) \quad \frac{p(s)}{q(s)} = \frac{C_1}{s - a_1} + \frac{C_2}{s - a_2} + \cdots + \frac{C_n}{s - a_n}$$
$$+ \cdots + \frac{C_m}{s - a_m}.$$

In order to determine C_n, we multiply both members of this equation by $(s - a_n)$ and let s approach a_n. Thus we find that

$$\lim_{s \to a_n} \left[\frac{s - a_n}{q(s)}\, p(s) \right] = C_n.$$

Since the limit of $p(s)$ is $p(a_n)$, and since

$$\lim_{s \to a_n} \frac{s - a_n}{q(s)} = \lim_{s \to a_n} \frac{1}{q'(s)} = \frac{1}{q'(a_n)},$$

where we have differentiated the numerator and denominator of the first fraction, it follows that

$$C_n = \frac{p(a_n)}{q'(a_n)}.$$

Therefore

(2)
$$\frac{p(s)}{q(s)} = \sum_{n=1}^{m} \frac{p(a_n)}{q'(a_n)} \frac{1}{s - a_n}.$$

Carrying out the inverse transformation of the terms on the right, we have the formula

(3)
$$L^{-1} \left\{ \frac{p(s)}{q(s)} \right\} = \sum_{n=1}^{m} \frac{p(a_n)}{q'(a_n)} e^{a_n t},$$

which is known in operational calculus as one of Heaviside's expansions for $F(t)$.

It is true that the transform of e^{at} is $1/(s - a)$ even when the constant a is an imaginary number, although we have considered only real constants and variables up to the present time. Moreover our derivation of formula (2) is valid whether the factors of $q(s)$ are real or imaginary. Consequently, the expansion formula (3) is equally true when any of the numbers a_n are imaginary.

As an illustration of the use of this formula, let

$$f(s) = \frac{s^2 + 1}{s(s + 1)(s - 2)}.$$

Since we can write the derivative of the denominator in the form

$$q'(s) = s \frac{d}{ds} [(s + 1)(s - 2)] + (s + 1)(s - 2),$$

it follows that $q'(0) = -2$. Similarly, considering $q(s)$ as the product of $s + 1$ and $s(s - 2)$, it is seen that $q'(-1) = (-1)(-3)$. Likewise $q'(2) = 6$, and therefore

$$F(t) = -\tfrac{1}{2} + \tfrac{2}{3} e^{-t} + \tfrac{5}{6} e^{2t}.$$

As another illustration we can write the inverse transform of $s/(s^2 + k^2)$ with the aid of formula (3). Here

$$\frac{p(s)}{q'(s)} = \frac{s}{2s} = \frac{1}{2}$$

and $a_1 = ik$, $a_2 = -ik$, where $i = \sqrt{-1}$. Therefore

$$L^{-1}\left\{\frac{s}{s^2 + k^2}\right\} = \frac{1}{2}\left(e^{ikt} + e^{-ikt}\right) = \cos kt,$$

since this combination of imaginary exponential functions is $\cos kt$, by definition.

The first of the above illustrations suggests a somewhat simpler way of determining the coefficients in the expansion. Let $s - a$ represent any linear factor, not repeated, of $q(s)$, and let $\phi(s)$ denote the function left after removing that factor from the denominator of $f(s)$; that is

$$f(s) = \frac{p(s)}{q(s)} = \frac{\phi(s)}{s - a}.$$

According to the theory of partial fractions then,

$$\frac{\phi(s)}{s - a} = \frac{C}{s - a} + h(s),$$

where $h(s)$ represents the sum of the partial fractions corresponding to the other factors of $q(s)$, regardless of the type of those factors. Multiplying by $s - a$ and letting $s \to a$, we have

$$C = \phi(a).$$

Hence the term in $F(t)$ corresponding to this factor $s - a$ in $q(s)$ is

(4) $$\phi(a)e^{at}.$$

When all the factors of $q(s)$ are of this type, that is, when

$$q(s) = (s - a_1)(s - a_2) \cdots (s - a_m),$$

then if $q_n(s)$ denotes the product of all these factors except the factor $s - a_n$, it follows that

(5) $$L^{-1}\left\{\frac{p(s)}{q(s)}\right\} = \sum_{n=1}^{m} \frac{p(a_n)}{q_n(a_n)}\, e^{a_n t}.$$

The essential results can be given as follows.

Theorem 7. *If $f(s)$ is the quotient $p(s)/q(s)$ of two polynomials in s such that $q(s)$ has the higher degree and contains the factor $s - a$ which is not repeated, then the term in $F(t)$ corresponding to this factor can be written in either of these two forms:*

(6) $$\frac{p(a)}{q'(a)}\, e^{at}, \quad\text{or}\quad \phi(a)e^{at},$$

where $\phi(s)$ is the quotient of $p(s)$ and all factors of $q(s)$ except $s - a$.

Example. Find the function $Y(t)$ such that

$$\frac{d^4Y}{dt^4} - 2\frac{d^3Y}{dt^3} - \frac{d^2Y}{dt^2} + 2\frac{dY}{dt} = 6F(t)$$

if Y and its first three derivatives are zero when $t = 0$.

The equation in the transform $y(s)$ is

$$(s^4 - 2s^3 - s^2 + 2s)y(s) = 6f(s).$$

After factoring the polynomial in s here, we can write

$$y(s) = f(s)\,\frac{6}{s(s - 1)(s + 1)(s - 2)}.$$

With the aid of Theorem 7, or formula (5), we can write the inverse transform of the fraction on the right at once. Note for instance that $\phi(s)$ corresponding to the factor $s - 1$ is $6/[s(s + 1)(s - 2)]$. Using the convolution to express the inverse transform of the product of $f(s)$ by that fraction, we have the result

$$Y(t) = F(t) * (3 - 3e^t - e^{-t} + e^{2t}).$$

PROBLEMS

1. Find the inverse transforms tabulated below, where a, b, and c are distinct constants.

$f(s)$	$F(t)$
(a) $\dfrac{1}{(s - a)(s - b)}$	$\dfrac{e^{at} - e^{bt}}{a - b}$
(b) $\dfrac{s}{(s - a)(s - b)}$	$\dfrac{ae^{at} - be^{bt}}{a - b}$
(c) $\dfrac{-1}{(s - a)(s - b)(s - c)}$	$\dfrac{(b - c)e^{at} + (c - a)e^{bt} + (a - b)e^{ct}}{(a - b)(b - c)(c - a)}$

Note also that $F(t)$ in part (b) arises by differentiating $F(t)$ in part (a), and similarly that, in part (c), if the numerator of $f(s)$ is changed to either s or s^2 the inverse transform of the resulting function can be written at once.

2. Solve the differential equation

$$Y''(t) - Y(t) = 1 + e^{3t}.$$

Ans. $Y(t) = C_1 e^t + C_2 e^{-t} - 1 + \frac{1}{8} e^{3t}.$

3. Solve

$$Y''''(t) + Y''(t) - 4Y'(t) - 4Y(t) = F(t)$$

under the conditions that $Y(0) = 0$, $Y'(0) = 2$, $Y''(0) = 0$.

Ans. $Y(t) = \sinh 2t + \frac{1}{12} F(t) * (e^{2t} + 3e^{-2t} - 4e^{-t}).$

17. Repeated Linear Factors. Quadratic Factors. We now consider the case in which the denominator of $f(s)$ contains a linear factor to the power r. We write

$$(1) \qquad f(s) = \frac{p(s)}{q(s)} = \frac{\phi(s)}{(s - a)^r},$$

where $p(s)$ and $q(s)$ are polynomials, $p(s)$ being of lower degree than $q(s)$, and where $\phi(s)$ is the quotient obtained by removing the factor $(s - a)^r$ from the denominator.

In this case the sum of the partial fractions representing $f(s)$ has the form

$$(2) \qquad \frac{\phi(s)}{(s - a)^r} = \frac{A_1}{s - a} + \frac{A_2}{(s - a)^2} + \cdots + \frac{A_n}{(s - a)^n}$$
$$+ \cdots + \frac{A_r}{(s - a)^r} + h(s),$$

where the A's are constants and $h(s)$ is the sum of the partial fractions corresponding to those factors in $q(s)$ other than $(s - a)^r$. Multiplying by $(s - a)^r$, we have

$$\phi(s) = A_1(s - a)^{r-1} + \cdots + A_n(s - a)^{r-n} + \cdots$$
$$+ A_r + (s - a)^r h(s).$$

Letting $s \to a$, it follows that

$$A_r = \phi(a).$$

Differentiating both members $r - n$ times and letting $s \to a$, we find that

$$\phi^{(r-n)}(a) = (r - n)! A_n.$$

Thus the constants A_n are determined and it follows from (2) that

$$(3) \quad F(t) = e^{at}\left[\frac{\phi^{(r-1)}(a)}{(r-1)!} + \frac{\phi^{(r-2)}(a)}{(r-2)!}t + \cdots \right.$$
$$\left. + \phi(a)\frac{t^{r-1}}{(r-1)!}\right] + L^{-1}\{h(s)\}.$$

This result can be stated as follows.

Theorem 8. *The terms in $F(t)$ corresponding to a factor $(s-a)^r$ in the denominator of $f(s)$ are*

$$(4) \qquad e^{at}\sum_{n=1}^{r}\frac{\phi^{(r-n)}(a)}{(r-n)!}\frac{t^{n-1}}{(n-1)!},$$

where $\phi(s)$ is defined by equation (1).

In case $r = 2$, for instance, the terms corresponding to the factor $(s-a)^2$ are

$$e^{at}[\phi'(a) + \phi(a)t].$$

As an example, let

$$f(s) = \frac{1}{(s-1)(s-2)^2}.$$

Here the term in $F(t)$ corresponding to the factor $s-1$ is e^t. Corresponding to the factor $(s-2)^2$, we have

$$\phi(s) = \frac{1}{s-1}, \qquad \phi'(s) = -\frac{1}{(s-1)^2}$$

so that $\phi(2) = 1$ and $\phi'(2) = -1$ and the terms in $F(t)$ are

$$e^{2t}(-1 + t).$$

Consequently,

$$F(t) = e^t + e^{2t}(t-1).$$

Since the number a may be imaginary and since a factorization of every polynomial into linear factors, real or imaginary, exists, our last two theorems give a systematic way of finding the inverse transform of $p(s)/q(s)$ in all cases. If imaginary factors are present, however, the result is given in terms of imaginary exponential functions. The reduction of the latter to real functions is sometimes awkward.

When the coefficients in $q(s)$ are real, the imaginary linear factors arise from quadratic factors of the type

$$s^2 + \alpha s + \beta,$$

where $\alpha^2 - 4\beta < 0$. By completing the square in s, we can write such factors in the form

$$(s + b)^2 + a^2.$$

Proceeding as before, we write

(5) $$f(s) = \frac{\phi(s)}{(s + b)^2 + a^2} = \frac{As + B}{(s + b)^2 + a^2} + h(s),$$

and after multiplying through by the quadratic factor and letting s approach $-b + ai$ we find that

$$\phi(-b + ai) = A(-b + ai) + B = \phi_1 + i\phi_2,$$

where ϕ_1 and ϕ_2 are the real and imaginary parts of the complex number $\phi(-b + ai)$. Equating real and imaginary parts, we get

$$aA = \phi_2, \qquad B = \phi_1 + bA;$$

hence the partial fraction corresponding to the quadratic factor is

$$\frac{1}{a} \frac{(s + b)\phi_2 + a\phi_1}{(s + b)^2 + a^2}.$$

Consequently the corresponding terms in $F(t)$ are

(6) $$\frac{1}{a} e^{-bt}(\phi_2 \cos at + \phi_1 \sin at),$$

which can be written in the form

(7) $$\frac{1}{a} \sqrt{\phi_1^2 + \phi_2^2}\, e^{-bt} \sin (at + \epsilon)$$

where $\tan \epsilon = \phi_2/\phi_1$.

As an illustration, let

$$f(s) = \frac{s}{(s + k)(s^2 + a^2)}.$$

Corresponding to the quadratic factor here, $\phi(s) = s/(s + k)$ and

$$\phi(ai) = \frac{ai}{k + ai} = \frac{a^2 + aki}{k^2 + a^2};$$

hence $\phi_1 = a^2/(a^2 + k^2)$ and $\phi_2 = ak/(a^2 + k^2)$. Accounting for the linear factor $s + k$ in the usual way and including the terms (6), we find that

$$F(t) = \frac{1}{a^2 + k^2} (k \cos at + a \sin at - ke^{-kt}).$$

When $q(s)$ contains a repeated quadratic factor, a similar procedure can be used to obtain $F(t)$ directly in terms of real functions. We confine our attention here to the important case in which the square of the factor is present, so that $p(s)/q(s)$ can be written

$$\frac{\phi(s)}{[(s + b)^2 + a^2]^2} = \frac{As + B}{(s + b)^2 + a^2} + \frac{Cs + D}{[(s + b)^2 + a^2]^2} + h(s).$$

Multiplying through by the square of the quadratic factor and differentiating once with respect to s, then substituting $-b + ai$ for s in the two resulting equations, we can solve for A, B, C, and D in terms of the numbers ϕ_1, ϕ_2, ϕ_3, and ϕ_4, where

$$\phi(-b + ai) = \phi_1 + i\phi_2, \qquad \phi'(-b + ai) = \phi_3 + i\phi_4.$$

With the aid of transforms found in Sec. 12, we can then write the terms in $F(t)$ corresponding to the repeated factor as follows:

$$(8) \quad \frac{1}{2a^3} e^{-bt}[(\phi_2 - a\phi_3) \cos at + (\phi_1 + a\phi_4) \sin at$$
$$+ at(\phi_2 \sin at - \phi_1 \cos at)].$$

The presence of the cube of the quadratic factor will introduce terms of the above type and additional terms of the type $t^2 e^{-bt} \sin at$ and $t^2 e^{-bt} \cos at$. Our principal results can be stated as follows.

Theorem 9. *When $f(s) = p(s)/q(s)$ where $p(s)$ and $q(s)$ are polynomials, the terms in $F(t)$ corresponding to a distinct quadratic factor $(s + b)^2 + a^2$ in $q(s)$ are the terms (6), and those corresponding to such a factor to the second degree are the terms (8).*

PROBLEMS

1. Find the inverse transforms tabulated below.

$f(s)$	$F(t)$
(a) $\dfrac{s + c}{(s + a)(s + b)^2}$	$\dfrac{c - a}{(b - a)^2} e^{-at} + \left(\dfrac{c - b}{a - b} t + \dfrac{a - c}{(a - b)^2} \right) e^{-bt}$

(b) $\dfrac{1}{(s^2 + a^2)s^3}$ $\qquad$ $\dfrac{1}{a^4}(\cos at - 1) + \dfrac{1}{2a^2}t^2$

(c) $\dfrac{s^2 - a^2}{(s^2 + a^2)^2}$ $\qquad$ $t \cos at$

2. Solve the differential equation

$$Y''(t) - 2Y'(t) + Y(t) = 1.$$
$$Ans. \ Y(t) = (C_1 + C_2 t)e^t + 1.$$

3. Solve the equation

$$Y''(t) + Y(t) = 3 \sin t$$

if $Y(0) = 1$, $Y'(0) = -\frac{3}{2}$.

$$Ans. \ Y(t) = (1 - \tfrac{3}{2}t)\cos t.$$

4. Solve the equation

$$Y^{(4)}(t) + 2Y''(t) + Y(t) = 0$$

if $Y(0) = 0$, $Y'(0) = 1$, $Y''(0) = 2$, $Y'''(0) = -3$.
$$Ans. \ Y(t) = t(\sin t + \cos t).$$

18. Integration of Transforms. Let $F(t)$ be sectionally continuous in each finite interval and of the order of $e^{\alpha t}$ as t tends to infinity. Then when $x > \alpha$,

$$f(x) = \int_0^\infty e^{-xt}F(t)\ dt,$$

and this integral is uniformly convergent with respect to x. Consequently we can write,* for any $s > \alpha$ and any $b > \alpha$,

$$\int_s^b f(x)\ dx = \int_s^b \int_0^\infty e^{-xt}F(t)\ dt\ dx$$
$$= \int_0^\infty F(t) \int_s^b e^{-xt}\ dx\ dt$$
$$= \int_0^\infty \frac{F(t)}{t}(e^{-st} - e^{-bt})\ dt.$$

Now if the function $F(t)$ is such that $F(t)/t$ has a limit as t tends to zero, then the latter function is also sectionally continuous and of exponential order. It follows that the last integral is uniformly convergent with respect to b and that the

* See, for instance, Carslaw, *op. cit.*, p. 199, for a discussion of the integration of infinite integrals.

limit of this integral as b tends to infinity is the same as the integral of the limit of its integrand, that is,

$$\int_s^\infty f(x)\, dx = \int_0^\infty \frac{F(t)}{t}\, e^{-st}\, dt.$$

Thus we have established the following theorem.

Theorem 10. *Division of the function $F(t)$ by t corresponds to integration of the transform of the function, in this manner:*

$$(1) \qquad L\left\{\frac{F(t)}{t}\right\} = \int_s^\infty f(x)\, dx.$$

This formula is valid provided $F(t)$ is sectionally continuous and of the order $e^{\alpha t}$, if $s > \alpha$, and provided that the limit of $F(t)/t$ exists as $t \to +0$.

As an example,

$$L\left\{\frac{\sin kt}{t}\right\} = \int_s^\infty \frac{k\, dx}{x^2 + k^2} = \frac{\pi}{2} - \arctan \frac{s}{k},$$

where $s > 0$. Hence

$$(2) \qquad L\left\{\frac{\sin kt}{t}\right\} = \operatorname{arccot} \frac{s}{k}.$$

Recalling that integration with respect to t corresponds to division by s, we can now write the transform of the *sine-integral* function

$$\operatorname{Si}(t) = \int_0^t \frac{\sin \tau}{\tau}\, d\tau.$$

This is a function of considerable importance in applied mathematics. Its values have been tabulated in the more extensive mathematical tables. It follows from (2) with $k = 1$ that

$$(3) \qquad L\{\operatorname{Si}(t)\} = \frac{1}{s} \operatorname{arccot} s \qquad (s > 0).$$

As another example,

$$L\left\{\frac{e^{-at} - e^{-bt}}{t}\right\} = \int_s^\infty \left(\frac{1}{x+a} - \frac{1}{x+b}\right) dx$$

$$= \log \frac{x+a}{x+b}\Big]_s^\infty .$$

where $s > -a$ and $s > -b$.   Hence

$$(4) \qquad L\left\{\frac{e^{-at} - e^{-bt}}{t}\right\} = \log\frac{s+b}{s+a}.$$

Note that when $a = 0$ and $b = 1$ we have the transformation

$$(5) \qquad L\left\{\frac{1 - e^{-t}}{t}\right\} = \log\left(1 + \frac{1}{s}\right) \qquad\qquad (s > 0).$$

19. Periodic Functions.   Let $F(t)$ be a periodic function with period a; that is,

$$F(t + a) = F(t). \qquad\qquad (t > 0).$$

If it is sectionally continuous over a period $0 \leqq t \leqq a$, then its transform exists and we can write it as the sum of integrals over successive periods:

$$f(s) = \int_0^\infty e^{-st}F(t)\, dt = \sum_{n=0}^\infty \int_{na}^{(n+1)a} e^{-st}F(t)\, dt.$$

If we substitute $\tau = t - na$ and note that $F(\tau + na) = F(\tau)$ because of the periodicity of the function, we get

$$f(s) = \sum_0^\infty e^{-nas} \int_0^a e^{-s\tau}F(\tau)\, d\tau.$$

The integral on the right is a factor of the series, and the sum of the geometric series with terms e^{-nas} is $(1 - e^{-as})^{-1}$.   The following result is therefore derived.

Theorem 11.   *If $F(t)$ is periodic with the period a, then*

$$(1) \qquad f(s) = \frac{\int_0^a e^{-st}F(t)\, dt}{1 - e^{-as}}.$$

Let us apply this formula to the function

$$
\begin{aligned}
M(c, t) &= 1 &&\text{when } 0 < t < c, \\
&= -1 &&\text{when } c < t < 2c, \\
M(c, t + 2c) &= M(c, t).
\end{aligned}
$$

This is sometimes called the square wave or the meander function (Fig. 9).   Since

$$\int_0^{2c} e^{-st}M(c, t)\, dt = \int_0^c e^{-st}\, dt - \int_c^{2c} e^{-st}\, dt = \frac{1}{s}\left(1 - e^{-cs}\right)^2,$$

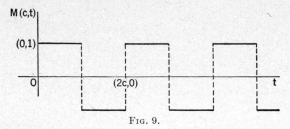

Fig. 9.

the transform of $M(c, t)$ is

$$\frac{(1 - e^{-cs})^2}{s(1 - e^{-2cs})} = \frac{1 - e^{-cs}}{s(1 + e^{-cs})}.$$

Hence

(2) $$L\{M(c, t)\} = \frac{1}{s} \tanh \frac{cs}{2} \qquad (s > 0).$$

The integral of the function $M(c, t)$ from 0 to t is the function $H(c, t)$ defined as follows:

$$H(c, t) = t \qquad \text{when } 0 < t < c,$$
$$= 2c - t \qquad \text{when } c < t < 2c,$$
$$H(c, t + 2c) = H(c, t).$$

This function, whose graph is the triangular wave shown in Fig.

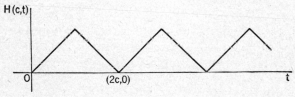

Fig. 10.

10, has the transform

(3) $$L\{H(c, t)\} = \frac{1}{s^2} \tanh \frac{cs}{2}.$$

Since

$$\frac{1}{s}\left(1 + \tanh \frac{cs}{2}\right) = \frac{2}{s(1 + e^{-cs})},$$

it follows from the transformation (2) that

(4) $$L\{\tfrac{1}{2} + \tfrac{1}{2}M(c, t)\} = \frac{1}{s(1 + e^{-cs})}.$$

Note that the function $\frac{1}{2} + \frac{1}{2}M(c, t)$ has the value 1 when $0 < t < c$ and 0 when $c < t < 2c$ and that it is periodic with the period $2c$; thus in the terminology of electrical engineering this function represents the half-wave rectification of the function $M(c, t)$.

Consider the half-wave rectification $F(t)$ of the function $\sin t$,

$$
(5) \qquad\qquad\qquad F(t) = \sin t \qquad \text{when } 0 < t < \pi, \\
= 0 \qquad \text{when } \pi < t < 2\pi,
$$

where $F(t + 2\pi) = F(t)$, (Fig. 11). By applying formula (1), the reader can verify that

$$
(6) \qquad\qquad\qquad f(s) = \frac{1}{(s^2 + 1)(1 - e^{-\pi s})}.
$$

By translating the graph of $F(t)$ through a distance π along the t-axis, which corresponds to multiplying the transform (6) by

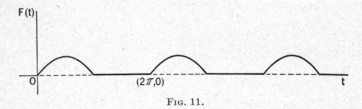

Fig. 11.

$e^{-\pi s}$, and then adding the ordinates from this graph to those in Fig. 11, we obtain at once the transform of the full-wave rectification $|\sin t|$ of the sine function:

$$
(7) \qquad L\{|\sin t|\} = \frac{1}{s^2 + 1} \frac{1 + e^{-\pi s}}{1 - e^{-\pi s}} = \frac{1}{s^2 + 1} \coth \frac{\pi s}{2}.
$$

The above observations are easily generalized. If $F(t)$ is any antiperiodic function, that is, if

$$
(8) \qquad\qquad\qquad F(t + c) = -F(t) \qquad\qquad\qquad (t > 0),
$$

then $F(t + 2c) = F(t)$ and it can be seen from formula (1) that

$$
(9) \qquad\qquad f(s) = \frac{1 - e^{-cs}}{1 - e^{-2cs}} \int_0^c e^{-st}F(t)\, dt \\
= \frac{1}{1 + e^{-cs}} \int_0^c e^{-st}F(t)\, dt.
$$

Let $F_1(t)$ denote the half-wave rectification of this function $F(t)$. Then, according to formula (1),

$$f_1(s) = \frac{1}{1 - e^{-2cs}} \int_0^c e^{-st} F(t) \, dt.$$

In view of formula (9), it follows that

(10) $$f_1(s) = \frac{f(s)}{1 - e^{-cs}};$$

hence the transform of the half-wave rectification of any antiperiodic function is simply the transform of the function divided by $1 - e^{-cs}$. The half-wave rectification of $\sin kt$, for example, has the transform

(11) $$\frac{k}{s^2 + k^2} \frac{1}{1 - e^{-\frac{\pi s}{k}}}.$$

By translating the graph of $F_1(t)$ to the right to a distance of c units and adding the ordinates in this graph to those in the graph of $F_1(t)$, we obtain at once for the transform of the full-wave rectification of the antiperiodic function described by (8),

(12) $$L\{|F(t)|\} = f(s) \coth \frac{cs}{2},$$

provided that $F(t) \geqq 0$ when $0 < t < c$. If $F(t)$ is negative at some points of that interval, our formula (12) should be written

(13) $$L\{F_2(t)\} = f(s) \coth \frac{cs}{2},$$

where $F_2(t)$ is the full-wave rectification of the antiperiodic function $F(t)$; that is, $F_2(t + c) = F_2(t)$ and

$$F_2(t) = F(t) \qquad \text{when } 0 < t < c.$$

20. Tables of Transforms and Operations. A list of the operations on the function $F(t)$ and the corresponding operations on the transform $f(s)$ will be found in the Table of Operations in Appendix II. This list will serve as a summary of our results to date on the theory of the Laplace transformation.

The Table of Transforms in Appendix III contains a fairly extensive list of transforms of particular functions. The derivations of a number of these have been indicated in the preceding pages. The following transformation, whose derivation has not yet been given, is of considerable importance.

Let

$$(1) \qquad\qquad F(t) = t^{-\frac{3}{2}} e^{-\frac{k^2}{4t}} \qquad\qquad (k > 0),$$

a function that arises in certain problems in heat conduction and diffusion. Then

$$f(s) = \int_0^\infty e^{-\frac{k^2}{4t}} e^{-st} t^{-\frac{3}{2}} \, dt$$

$$= \frac{4}{k} \int_0^\infty \exp\left(-\tau^2\right) \exp\left(-\frac{k^2 s}{4\tau^2}\right) d\tau,$$

where we have made the substitution $\tau = k/(2\sqrt{t})$, and where

$$\exp\,(x) = e^x.$$

Combining the exponents in the last integral and completing the square in the exponent, we have

$$(2) \qquad f(s) = \frac{4}{k} e^{-k\sqrt{s}} \int_0^\infty \exp\left[-\left(\tau - \frac{k\sqrt{s}}{2\tau}\right)^2\right] d\tau.$$

We now let $k\sqrt{s}/2 = b$ and $b/\tau = \lambda$. Then

$$\int_0^\infty \exp\left[-\left(\tau - \frac{b}{\tau}\right)^2\right] d\tau = \int_0^\infty \frac{b}{\lambda^2} \exp\left[-\left(\lambda - \frac{b}{\lambda}\right)^2\right] d\lambda,$$

and upon adding the integral on the left to each member of this equation, we have the equation

$$2 \int_0^\infty \exp\left[-\left(\tau - \frac{b}{\tau}\right)^2\right] d\tau = \int_0^\infty \left(1 + \frac{b}{\lambda^2}\right)$$

$$\exp\left[-\left(\lambda - \frac{b}{\lambda}\right)^2\right] d\lambda.$$

Finally we substitute $x = \lambda - b/\lambda$ in the last integral to get the formula

$$\int_0^\infty \exp\left[-\left(\tau - \frac{b}{\tau}\right)^2\right] d\tau = \frac{1}{2} \int_{-\infty}^\infty e^{-x^2} \, dx = \frac{1}{2}\sqrt{\pi}.$$

Therefore, in view of equation (2), our result becomes

(3)
$$f(s) = \frac{2\sqrt{\pi}}{k} e^{-k\sqrt{s}};$$

that is,

(4)
$$L\left\{\frac{k}{2\sqrt{\pi t^3}} e^{-\frac{k^2}{4t}}\right\} = e^{-k\sqrt{s}} \qquad (k > 0, s > 0).$$

Since multiplying by t corresponds to differentiating with respect to s and changing sign, it follows from Theorem 4 and formula (4) that

(5)
$$L\left\{\frac{1}{\sqrt{\pi t}} e^{-\frac{k^2}{4t}}\right\} = \frac{1}{\sqrt{s}} e^{-k\sqrt{s}} \qquad (k \geqq 0, s > 0).$$

Note that when $k = 0$ this reduces to the known transformation of $(\pi t)^{-\frac{1}{2}}$.

Finally, in view of the transformation (4), we note that

$$L^{-1}\left\{\frac{1}{s} e^{-k\sqrt{s}}\right\} = \frac{k}{2\sqrt{\pi}} \int_0^t e^{-\frac{k^2}{4\tau}} \tau^{-\frac{3}{2}} d\tau = \frac{2}{\sqrt{\pi}} \int_{\frac{k}{2\sqrt{t}}}^{\infty} e^{-\lambda^2} d\lambda$$

$$= \frac{2}{\sqrt{\pi}} \int_0^{\infty} e^{-\lambda^2} d\lambda - \frac{2}{\sqrt{\pi}} \int_0^{\frac{k}{2\sqrt{t}}} e^{-\lambda^2} d\lambda.$$

Therefore

(6)
$$L^{-1}\left\{\frac{1}{s} e^{-k\sqrt{s}}\right\} = 1 - \mathrm{erf}\left(\frac{k}{2\sqrt{t}}\right) \qquad (k \geqq 0, s > 0),$$

where erf (x) is the error function defined in Sec. 14. This formula can be written

(7)
$$L\left\{\mathrm{erfc}\left(\frac{k}{2\sqrt{t}}\right)\right\} = \frac{1}{s} e^{-k\sqrt{s}} \qquad (k \geqq 0, s > 0),$$

where the *complementary error function* erfc (x) is defined as

$$\mathrm{erfc}\ (x) = 1 - \mathrm{erf}\ (x) = \frac{2}{\sqrt{\pi}} \int_x^{\infty} e^{-\lambda^2} d\lambda.$$

CHAPTER III

ELEMENTARY APPLICATIONS

The properties of the Laplace transformation that we have derived up to this point enable us to solve many problems in engineering and physics involving ordinary and partial differential equations. In this chapter we shall solve a number of problems in elastic vibrations involving ordinary differential equations. These are problems in which our method is very convenient, although not at all essential. We shall also treat one or two simple applications of integral equations.

The next chapter contains applications that involve partial differential equations. The solution of problems of this type is the primary objective of this book. In later chapters we shall extend our treatment of such problems.

21. Free Vibrations of a Mass on a Spring. Let a body of mass m attached to the end of a coil spring (Fig. 12) be given an initial displacement and an initial velocity and allowed to vibrate. The other end of the spring is assumed to be kept fixed, and the spring is assumed to obey Hooke's law, so that the force exerted by the free end is proportional to the displacement of that end. The factor k of proportionality is called the spring constant. We also assume that the mass of the spring can be neglected in comparison with the mass m and that no frictional forces or other external forces act on m.

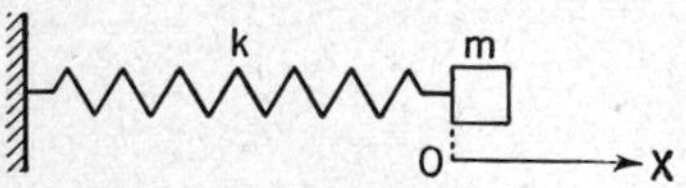

Fig. 12.

Let X denote the displacement of m from the position of equilibrium, that is, let the origin O denote the position of m when the spring is not deformed. Then according to Newton's second law of motion,

$$(1) \qquad m\frac{d^2X}{dt^2} = -kX.$$

Let x_0 denote the initial displacement and v_0 the initial velocity, so that the function $X(t)$ satisfies the conditions

(2) $X(0) = x_0, \qquad X'(0) = v_0.$

We can determine the function $X(t)$ by applying the Laplace transformation to both members of equation (1) and using the conditions (2). Thus if $x(s)$ denotes the transform of $X(t)$, it follows that

$$m[s^2x(s) - sx_0 - v_0] = -kx(s),$$

and therefore

$$x(s) = x_0 \frac{s}{s^2 + \dfrac{k}{m}} + v_0 \frac{1}{s^2 + \dfrac{k}{m}}.$$

Hence

(3) $X(t) = x_0 \cos \omega_0 t + \dfrac{v_0}{\omega_0} \sin \omega_0 t$

$$= \sqrt{x_0^2 + \left(\frac{v_0}{\omega_0}\right)^2} \sin(\omega_0 t + \alpha),$$

where

$$\omega_0 = \sqrt{\frac{k}{m}}, \qquad \tan \alpha = \frac{x_0\omega_0}{v_0}.$$

The motion described by formula (3) is a simple vibration with angular frequency ω_0, called the natural frequency of this system, and phase angle α, and with the amplitude $[x_0^2 + (v_0/\omega_0)^2]^{\frac{1}{2}}$.

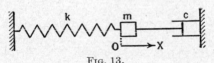

FIG. 13.

If a damping force proportional to the velocity also acts upon the mass m, as indicated by the presence of a dashpot c in Fig. 13, the equation of motion becomes

(4) $mX''(t) = -kX(t) - cX'(t).$

In this case let the mass start from O with the initial velocity v_0,

$$X(0) = 0, \qquad X'(0) = v_0.$$

The equation in the transform $x(s)$ becomes

$$ms^2x(s) - mv_0 = -kx(s) - csx(s)$$

or, if we let $2b = c/m$, and again write $\omega_0^2 = k/m$,

$$(5) \qquad x(s) = \frac{v_0}{s^2 + 2bs + \omega_0^2} = \frac{v_0}{(s + b)^2 + \omega_0^2 - b^2}.$$

If $b^2 < \omega_0^2$, that is, if the coefficient of damping is small enough that

$$c^2 < 4km,$$

then the formula for the displacement is

$$(6) \qquad X(t) = v_0(\omega_0^2 - b^2)^{-\frac{1}{2}} e^{-bt} \sin t \sqrt{\omega_0^2 - b^2}.$$

In the case of critical damping, that is, when $\omega_0 = b$ or

$$c^2 = 4km,$$

it follows from equation (5) that

$$(7) \qquad X(t) = v_0 t e^{-bt}.$$

It can be seen from this formula that the mass m moves in the direction of v_0 until the time $t = 1/b$, then reverses its direction and approaches O as t tends to infinity.

When $c^2 > 4km$, a similar motion of the mass takes place. The discussion of this case and the case of other initial conditions can be left to the problems.

The mathematical problem treated in this section can be interpreted also as a problem in electric circuits. This well-known analogy between problems in vibrations of mechanical systems and electric-circuit theory will be easy to see in other problems of this chapter. Naturally, the notation and terminology differ in the two types of problems.

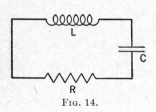

Fig. 14.

In the electric circuit shown in Fig. 14, let Q be the charge accumulated in the capacitor C at time t, and I the current in the circuit, so that

$$I = Q'(t).$$

If the circuit has a resistance R and a coil of inductance L, the differential equation in $Q(t)$ is

$$LQ''(t) + RQ'(t) + \frac{1}{C} Q(t) = 0.$$

Except for the notation used, this equation is the same as equation (4). When the resistance is negligible, $R = 0$, the equation reduces to our equation (1).

The initial conditions in the electrical problem can be made the same as those in the mechanical problem. For example, if the capacitor has an initial charge Q_0 and if the initial current is I_0, then

$$Q(0) = Q_0, \qquad Q'(0) = I_0,$$

which are the same as the initial conditions (2) in our first mechanical problem.

PROBLEMS

1. When $c^2 > 4km$ in the above problem of damped vibrations, show that the mass m moves in the direction of v_0 until the time

$$t = \frac{1}{2a} \log \frac{(b + a)}{(b - a)},$$

where $a = (b^2 - \omega_0^2)^{\frac{1}{2}}$, when it turns and approaches the origin.

2. When the mass m in the problem of damped vibrations is initially displaced to $X = x_0$ and released from that position with initial velocity zero, show that

$$X(t) = x_0 \frac{\omega_0}{\omega_1} e^{-bt} \sin (\omega_1 t + \alpha)$$

when $c^2 < 4km$, where $\omega_1 = \sqrt{\omega_0^2 - b^2}$ and $\tan \alpha = \omega_1/b$.

3. When $c^2 = 4km$ in Prob. 2, show that

$$X(t) = x_0 e^{-bt}(1 + bt),$$

and hence that the mass m never moves across the origin if $b \geq 0$. Also discuss the motion in case $c^2 > 4km$.

22. Forced Vibrations without Damping. Let an external force $F(t)$ act upon the mass in the mechanical system of the last

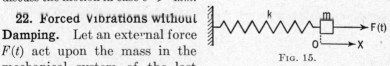

FIG. 15.

section, assuming there is no damping (Fig. 15). The displacement $X(t)$ of the mass m then satisfies the differential equation

$$(1) \qquad mX''(t) = -kX(t) + F(t).$$

If the initial conditions are

$$(2) \qquad X(0) = x_0, \qquad X'(0) = v_0,$$

the equation in the transform $x(s)$ becomes

$$m[s^2 x(s) - sx_0 - v_0] = -kx(s) + f(s)$$

where $f(s)$ is the transform of the force function $F(t)$. Let ω_0 again denote the natural frequency of the system

$$\omega_0 = \sqrt{\frac{k}{m}},$$

and we can write

(3) $$x(s) = \frac{x_0 s + v_0}{s^2 + \omega_0^2} + \frac{1}{m} f(s) \frac{1}{s^2 + \omega_0^2}.$$

Hence the displacement for any $F(t)$ can be written, with the aid of the convolution, as

(4) $$X(t) = x_0 \cos \omega_0 t + \frac{v_0}{\omega_0} \sin \omega_0 t + \frac{1}{m\omega_0} \int_0^t \sin \omega_0 (t - \tau) F(\tau)\, d\tau,$$

a result that can easily be shown to satisfy (1) and (2) above.

But the motion of the mass under particular external forces $F(t)$ is more interesting than this general formula (4). In these special cases it is often easier to refer to the transform (3) than to (4). When $F(t)$ is a constant F_0, as in the case when the X-axis is vertical and the force of gravity acts on m, equation (1) can be written

$$mX''(t) = -k\left[X(t) - \frac{F_0}{k} \right].$$

If $Y = X - F_0/k$, this becomes $mY'' = -kY$; so the motion is the same as free vibrations if displacements are measured from an origin F_0/k units from O.

Consider the following special case, taking $x_0 = v_0 = 0$ for convenience. Let

$$F(t) = F_0 \qquad \text{when } 0 < t < t_0,$$
$$= 0 \qquad \text{when } t > t_0.$$

In this case

$$f(s) = F_0 \left(\frac{1}{s} - \frac{e^{-t_0 s}}{s} \right),$$

and, since $x_0 = v_0 = 0$, it follows from equation (3) that

(5) $$x(s) = \frac{F_0}{m} \left[\frac{1}{s(s^2 + \omega_0^2)} - \frac{e^{-t_0 s}}{s(s^2 + \omega_0^2)} \right]$$

Now

$$L^{-1} \left\{ \frac{1}{s(s^2 + \omega_0^2)} \right\} = \frac{1}{\omega_0^2} (1 - \cos \omega_0 t) = \frac{2}{\omega_0^2} \sin^2 \frac{1}{2} \omega_0 t,$$

and if we write

$$\psi(t) = \sin^2 \tfrac{1}{2}\omega_0 t \qquad \text{when } t > 0,$$
$$= 0 \qquad \text{when } t < 0,$$

it follows from equation (5) that

(6) $$X(t) = \frac{2F_0}{k} [\psi(t) - \psi(t - t_0)].$$

The graph of this function can be drawn easily by composition of ordinates. When t_0 is approximately $\tfrac{1}{2}\pi/\omega_0$, the graph is the full-drawn curve in Fig. 16.

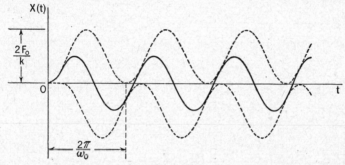

FIG. 16.

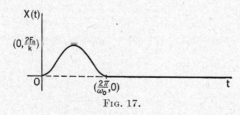

FIG. 17.

When $t_0 = 2\pi/\omega_0$, it follows from Fig. 16 that the mass m performs one oscillation and then remains at the origin (Fig. 17).

23. Resonance.   Let the external force in the problem of the last section be

$$F(t) = F_0 \sin \omega t,$$

where F_0 and ω are positive constants.   Then according to equation (3) of Sec. 22,

$$(1) \qquad x(s) = \frac{x_0 s + v_0}{s^2 + \omega_0^2} + \frac{F_0}{m} \frac{\omega}{(s^2 + \omega_0^2)(s^2 + \omega^2)}$$

and, if $\omega \neq \omega_0$,

$$(2) \quad X(t) = x_0 \cos \omega_0 t + \frac{1}{\omega_0}\left[v_0 + \frac{F_0 \omega}{m(\omega^2 - \omega_0^2)} \right] \sin \omega_0 t$$
$$- \frac{F_0}{m(\omega^2 - \omega_0^2)} \sin \omega t.$$

That is, the motion is the superposition of two simple harmonic motions, one with frequency ω_0 and known as the natural com-

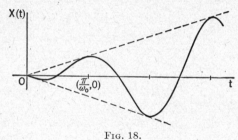

Fig. 18.

ponent of vibration, and the other with frequency ω which is called the forced component of the vibration.   Note that the natural vibrations are not present if we make

$$x_0 = 0, \qquad v_0 = \frac{F_0 \omega}{m(\omega_0^2 - \omega^2)}.$$

When $\omega = \omega_0$, however, we have

$$(3) \qquad x(s) = \frac{x_0 s + v_0}{s^2 + \omega_0^2} + \frac{F_0}{m} \frac{\omega_0}{(s^2 + \omega_0)^2}.$$

The presence of the repeated quadratic factor in the denominator here shows that $X(t)$ will contain a term having the form of the product of t by a sine or cosine function.   In fact,

$$(4) \quad X(t) = x_0 \cos \omega_0 t + \frac{1}{\omega_0^2}\left(v_0 \omega_0 + \frac{F_0}{2m} \right) \sin \omega_0 t - \frac{F_0}{2m\omega_0} t \cos \omega_0 t.$$

In view of the last term here, the amplitude of the oscillations of m increases indefinitely.

In this case the force $F(t)$ is said to be in resonance with the system. We note in particular that if $x_0 = 0$ and $v_0 = -F_0/(2m\omega_0)$ the resonance type of motion reduces to

$$X(t) = -\frac{F_0}{2m\omega_0} t \cos \omega_0 t,$$

shown in Fig. 18.

24. Forced Vibrations with Damping. When a force $F(t)$ acts on the mass of the damped system of Fig. 13, the equation of motion becomes

(1) $$mX''(t) = -kX(t) - cX'(t) + F(t).$$

Let

$$X(0) = 0, \qquad X'(0) = 0;$$

then the transformed equation has the solution

(2) $$x(s) = \frac{1}{m} f(s) \frac{1}{(s+b)^2 + \omega_0^2 - b^2}$$

where as before ω_0 is the natural frequency of the undamped system and $2b = c/m$.

Again let

$$F(t) = F_0 \sin \omega t.$$

If $b < \omega_0$, it follows from equation (2) and Theorem 9, Sec. 17, that $X(t)$ will consist of terms of type $e^{-bt} \sin (\omega_1 t + \alpha_1)$ and $\sin (\omega t + \alpha)$, where $\omega_1^2 - \omega_0^2 - b^2$, and where α_1 and α are constants. Consequently the component of the motion with frequency ω_1 is nearly damped out after a sufficiently long time and the steady-state motion

(3) $$X(t) = A \sin (\omega t + \alpha)$$

remains, where A is a constant.

The constant A in formula (3) depends on ω. The value of ω for which A takes on its maximum value is called the resonance frequency in the case of damped motion. Equation (2) shows that there is no value of the frequency ω of the exciting force which will induce terms of the type $t \sin (\omega t + \alpha)$ in the displacement $X(t)$, unless $b = 0$. For if $b \neq 0$ the formula for $x(s)$ shows that there can be no repeated factors of the type $(s^2 + \omega^2)^2$ in the denominator.

PROBLEMS

1. Find $X(t)$, and describe the motion for the system above when $F(t) = F_0 \sin \omega t$ and $b = \omega_0$.

2. Obtain the formula for A in equation (3) above, and show that the resonance frequency has the value $\sqrt{\omega_0^2 - 2b^2}$ when $2b^2 < \omega_0^2$.

3. In the solution of the problem of undamped vibrations of Sec. 22 with $x_0 = v_0 = 0$ and $F(t) = F_0$ when $t < t_0$, $F(t) = 0$ when $t > t_0$, let $F_0 t_0 = I$, a constant, and let $t_0 \to 0$ and show that the limiting value of $X(t)$ is

$$X(t) = \frac{I\omega_0}{k} \sin \omega_0 t.$$

Also note that $\lim_{t_0 \to 0} f(s) = I$ and that the above formula for $X(t)$ can be

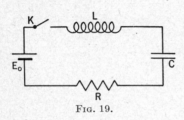

FIG. 19.

obtained formally by replacing $f(s)$ by the constant I in equation (3), Sec. 22. Here I is the impulse or increase in momentum given to the mass m at $t = 0$.

4. The electric current I and the charge Q on the capacitor C in the circuit shown in Fig. 19 are functions of t that satisfy the conditions

$$L\frac{dI}{dt} + RI + \frac{Q}{C} = E_0, \qquad Q = \int_0^t I(\tau)\, d\tau, \qquad I(0) = 0,$$

where t is the time after closing the switch K, and where Q and I are initially zero. The electromotive force E_0 is constant.

(*a*) Derive the formula

$$I = \frac{E_0}{\omega_1 L} e^{-bt} \sin \omega_1 t$$

where $b = \frac{R}{2L}$ and $\omega_1^2 = \frac{1}{LC} - \frac{R^2}{4L^2} > 0$.

(*b*) If $k^2 = \frac{R^2}{4L^2} - \frac{1}{LC} > 0$, show that

$$I = \frac{E_0}{kL} e^{-bt} \sinh kt.$$

25. A Vibration Absorber. We have seen that in the simple vibrating system with damping, with an exciting force $F_0 \sin \omega t$, the forced component of the vibration remains undamped. Let another spring and mass be connected in series with the original mass (Fig. 20), where the second system is undamped. Let us see whether it is possible to choose the spring constant and mass of the auxiliary system in such a way as to eliminate the forced vibrations of the first mass.

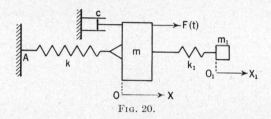

FIG. 20.

Let X and X_1 denote the displacements of the masses m and m_1, respectively, from the positions they have when neither spring is deformed.   If the exciting force is

$$F(t) = F_0 \sin \omega t,$$

and if m and m_1 are initially at rest at their respective origins, then the displacements $X(t)$ and $X_1(t)$ satisfy the following system of differential equations:

$$m \frac{d^2 X}{dt^2} = -kX + k_1(X_1 - X) - c \frac{dX}{dt} + F_0 \sin \omega t$$

$$m_1 \frac{d^2 X_1}{dt^2} = -k_1(X_1 - X),$$

$$X(0) = X'(0) = X_1(0) = X_1'(0) = 0.$$

The transforms $x(s)$ and $x_1(s)$ of $X(t)$ and $X_1(t)$ therefore satisfy the simultaneous algebraic equations

$$(ms^2 + cs + k + k_1)x(s) - k_1 x_1(s) = \frac{F_0 \omega}{s^2 + \omega^2},$$

$$k_1 x(s) - (m_1 s^2 + k_1)x_1(s) = 0.$$

Eliminating $x_1(s)$, we find that

(1) $$x(s) = F_0 \omega \frac{m_1 s^2 + k_1}{(s^2 + \omega^2)q(s)}$$

where

(2) $$q(s) = (m_1 s^2 + k_1)(ms^2 + cs + k + k_1) - k_1^2.$$

In view of the presence of the quadratic factor $s^2 + \omega^2$ in the denominator of the right-hand member of equation (1), it follows that $X(t)$ will contain a term of the type

$$(3) \qquad\qquad C \sin (\omega t + \alpha)$$

unless $k_1/m_1 = \omega^2$, in which case the numerator of the above fraction cancels with the factor in the denominator, leaving

$$(4) \qquad\qquad x(s) = F_0 \omega m_1 \frac{1}{q(s)}.$$

By substituting $s = ir$ in (2), where r is real, it is seen that $q(s)$ can have no pure imaginary zeros. Therefore it can have no quadratic factors of the type $s^2 + r^2$. In fact, if c is small, the real part of any zero of $q(s)$ can be shown to be negative, so the other terms in $X(t)$ represent damped oscillations, as one should expect. The component (3) of forced vibration is then the only undamped component of the motion of the mass m. But when $k_1/m_1 = \omega^2$, this latter component disappears and our conclusion is as follows.

The forced vibration of the mass m is eliminated by the system m_1, k_1, provided the natural frequency of that system is equal to the frequency ω of the exciting force. Thus all but the damped component of the vibration of m is absorbed, and the mass m approaches a fixed position as t increases.

This is the principle of the Frahm vibration absorber, which has been put to use in such practical appliances as electric hair clippers.*

By solving the above equations for $x_1(s)$, the reader will see that the mass m_1 has an undamped component of motion of the type (3).

PROBLEMS

1. Show that when the absorber system m_1, k_1 in Fig. 20 also has damping the forced vibrations cannot be completely absorbed as they are in the case above.

2. If there is no damping in the system discussed in this section, that is, if $c = 0$, show that resonance in the motion of the mass m cannot occur if $k_1/m_1 = \omega^2$. Also show that when $c = 0$ the quartic factor $q(s)$ has zeros of the type $\pm ir_1$, $\pm ir_2$ and, hence, that there are two resonance frequencies $\omega = r_1$, $\omega = r_2$ for the system m, k.

* Den Hartog, J. P., "Mechanical Vibrations," pp. 108*ff.*, 1940.

3. Show that the theory of the vibration absorber in this section is not affected by assuming initial conditions other than $X(0) = X'(0) = 0$, or $X_1(0) = X_1'(0) = 0$.

4. If in the system of this section the force is replaced by the force $F(t) = F_0 \sin (\omega t + \alpha)$, where α is any constant, show that the forced vibrations are absorbed as before when $k_1/m_1 = \omega^2$.

5. Show that the vibration absorber cannot be adjusted to absorb all forced vibrations when

$$F(t) = A_1 \sin \omega_1 t + A_2 \sin \omega_2 t$$

where the A's and ω's are constants and $\omega_1 \neq \omega_2$.

6. If the force $F(t)$ is removed from m in Fig. 20 and the point A of support of the spring k is forced to move so that its distance from the wall is $F(t)/k$, show that the differential equations of motion are the same as in the case of the fixed support with force $F(t)$ present. Thus the motion is identical to that already treated.

26. A Damped Absorber. The damping in the system of the foregoing section was located in the main part of the system

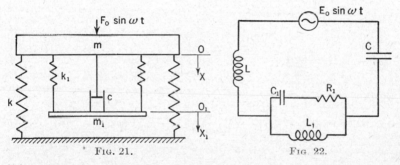

FIG. 21.   FIG. 22.

(Fig. 20). If it is located in the absorber instead, the system is essentially as shown in Fig. 21. Although the forced vibrations of m cannot be completely absorbed by any adjustment of the latter system, the coefficient of damping of the absorber can be adjusted to give the optimum range in amplitudes of the forced vibration for a range of frequencies ω of the impressed force. The corresponding electrical network is shown in Fig. 22.

Let the displacements $X(t)$ and $X_1(t)$ of the masses m and m_1 be measured from the positions of these masses when the system is in equilibrium, and let the initial displacements and velocities be zero. Then if the impressed force is $F_0 \sin \omega t$, the equations of motion are

$$m \frac{d^2X}{dt^2} = -kX + k_1(X_1 - X) + c\left(\frac{dX_1}{dt} - \frac{dX}{dt}\right) + F_0 \sin \omega t,$$

$$m_1 \frac{d^2X_1}{dt^2} = -k_1(X_1 - X) - c\left(\frac{dX_1}{dt} - \frac{dX}{dt}\right),$$

$$X(0) = X'(0) = X_1(0) = X_1'(0) = 0.$$

The transforms $x(s)$ and $x_1(s)$ therefore satisfy the equations

$$ms^2x = -kx + k_1(x_1 - x) + cs(x_1 - x) + \frac{\omega F_0}{s^2 + \omega^2},$$

$$m_1s^2x_1 = -k_1(x_1 - x) - cs(x_1 - x).$$

Therefore

$$x_1(s) = \frac{k_1 + cs}{m_1s^2 + cs + k_1} x(s)$$

and we find that

(1)
$$x(s) = \frac{\omega}{s^2 + \omega^2} \psi(s),$$

where

(2) $$\psi(s) = F_0 \frac{m_1s^2 + cs + k_1}{(m_1s^2 + cs + k_1)(ms^2 + cs + k + k_1) - (cs + k_1)^2}.$$

When $c \neq 0$, it is therefore clear that the factor $s^2 + \omega^2$ will always be present in the denominator of $x(s)$ and hence that the vibration $X(t)$ of the main mass will have a forced component of the type

(3)
$$A \sin (\omega t + \alpha).$$

Moreover, it follows from the expression (7), Sec. 17, that the amplitude A is $|\psi(i\omega)|$. This is easily computed from equation (2). We find that

(4) $$\frac{A^2}{F_0^2} = \frac{(m_1\omega^2 - k_1)^2 + c^2\omega^2}{[(m\omega^2 - k)(m_1\omega^2 - k_1) - m_1k_1\omega^2]^2 + c^2\omega^2[(m + m_1)\omega^2 - k]^2}.$$

The effectiveness of the damper can be studied from this equation.* The relation between A^2 and c^2 here, when ω and all other parameters are kept fixed, shows that A^2 is least either when c is zero or infinite, depending upon the magnitudes of m_1, ω, etc. But a study of A^2 as a function of ω^2 shows that there is a finite positive value of c for which the range of values of A^2

*See Den Hartog, *op. cit.*, pp. 118 ff., for a detailed disussion.

will be as small as possible for all frequencies ω. This optimum value of c is one of importance in the applications.

27. Motion of a Particle. As an example of another type of problem in mechanics leading to linear ordinary differential equations with constant coefficients, consider the following problem in the curvilinear motion of a particle in the XY-plane. A particle of unit mass is acted upon by two forces, one always directed toward the origin and proportional to the distance of the particle from the origin, and the other the force of gravity in the direction of the negative Y-axis (Fig. 23).

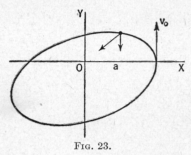

Fig. 23.

If the particle starts from the point $(a, 0)$ with a velocity v_0 in the vertical direction, the equations of motion are

$$X''(t) = -k^2 X(t), \qquad Y''(t) = -k^2 Y - g,$$
$$X(0) = a, \qquad X'(0) = 0, \qquad Y(0) = 0, \qquad Y'(0) = v_0.$$

The transforms of $X(t)$ and $Y(t)$, therefore, satisfy the equations

$$(s^2 + k^2)x(s) = sa, \qquad (s^2 + k^2)y(s) = v_0 - \frac{g}{s},$$

and it follows that

(1) $X(t) = a \cos kt, \qquad Y(t) = \dfrac{v_0}{k} \sin kt - \dfrac{g}{k^2}(1 - \cos kt).$

These are the parametric equations of the trajectory. If $v_0 \neq 0$ and $a \neq 0$, the trajectory is an ellipse whose major axis is not parallel to either coordinate axis.

PROBLEMS

1. Eliminate the parameter t from equations (1) above and show that when $v_0 \neq 0$ and $a \neq 0$ the trajectory is an ellipse.

2. A particle of mass m moves on a vertical X-axis under two forces: the force of gravity and a resistance proportional to the velocity. If the axis is taken positive downward, the equation of motion is

$$mX''(t) = mg - kX'(t).$$

Show that its solution, under the conditions $X(0) = 0$, $X'(0) = v_0$, is

$$X(t) = \frac{1}{b^2} [(bv_0 - g)(1 - e^{-bt}) + bgt],$$

where $b = k/m$, and discuss the motion.

28. Static Deflection of Beams.   We shall now illustrate the possibility of using the transformation in some problems with respect to a variable that has a finite range and also in which discontinuous functions are involved.

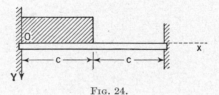

Fig. 24.

Let $Y(x)$ be the static transverse displacement at the point x in a uniform beam due to a load distributed in any manner along the beam.   It is shown in mechanics that

(1)
$$\frac{d^4Y}{dx^4} = aW(x),$$

where $a = 1/(EI)$, E being Young's modulus of elasticity and I being a moment of inertia of the cross section of the beam, and where $W(x)$ represents the load per unit length along the beam.   At any point where there is no support, not only the function Y but also its derivatives of the first three orders must be continuous.

Let both ends of a beam of length $2c$ be built in (Fig. 24), that is,

(2)
$$Y(0) = Y'(0) = Y(2c) = Y'(2c) = 0,$$

and let the load per unit length be zero over one half of the beam and a constant w_0 over the other half.   Thus

(3)
$$\begin{aligned} W(x) &= w_0 \quad &&\text{when } 0 < x < c, \\ &= 0 \quad &&\text{when } c < x < 2c. \end{aligned}$$

Let us extend the definition of the function $W(x)$ here, making it zero for all $x > 2c$.   Then the Laplace transform of this function, with respect to the variable x, is

$$w(s) = w_0 \left(\frac{1}{s} - \frac{1}{s} e^{-cs} \right).$$

Also let $y(s)$ denote the transform of the deflection $Y(x)$ in a beam extending infinitely far to the right, having the load zero on the extended part. Disregarding the conditions at the point $x = 2c$, and using the conditions at $x = 0$, the transform of equation (1) becomes

$$s^4 y(s) - s Y''(0) - Y'''(0) = \frac{aw_0}{s} (1 - e^{-cs}).$$

The constants $Y''(0)$ and $Y'''(0)$ which we shall write as A and B, respectively, will be determined from the conditions at the end $x = 2c$.

Since

$$y(s) = \frac{A}{s^3} + \frac{B}{s^4} + \frac{aw_0}{s^5} - \frac{aw_0}{s^5} e^{-cs}$$

we find that

(4) $$Y(x) = \frac{A}{2} x^2 + \frac{B}{6} x^3 + \frac{aw_0}{24} x^4 - \frac{aw_0}{24} \{x - c\}^4,$$

where the function $\{x - c\}$ has the following interpretation:

(5) $$\{x - c\} = 0 \qquad \text{when } x < c,$$
$$= x - c \qquad \text{when } x > c.$$

The conditions $Y(2c) = Y'(2c) = 0$ can now be applied to the function (4) to determine the constants A and B. After solving for A and B, our result is found to be

(6) $$\frac{Y(x)}{aw_0} = \frac{11}{96} c^2 x^2 - \frac{13}{96} cx^3 + \frac{1}{24} x^4 - \frac{1}{24} \{x - c\}^4,$$

where $0 \leqq x \leqq 2c$ and where the last function on the right is defined by equation (5).

The problem here is one that can be solved, of course, by successive integrations of equation (1). But the continuity conditions upon the first three derivatives of $Y(x)$ at $x = c$ which must be applied in that method make the method less direct than the transformation method.

PROBLEMS

1. Find the formula for the deflections in a uniform beam with both ends $x = 0$ and $x = 2c$ hinged, so that $Y(x)$ and $Y''(x)$ vanish at the ends, under a uniform load w_0 per unit length.

$$Ans.\ Y(x) = aw_0(\tfrac{1}{24}x^4 - \tfrac{1}{6}cx^3 + \tfrac{1}{3}c^3x).$$

2. Find the formula for the deflections in a uniform beam with the load bx per unit length on the interval $0 < x < c$ and $b(2c - x)$ on the interval $c < x < 2c$, if the end $x = 0$ is built in and the end $x = 2c$ is hinged.

$$Ans.\ \frac{Y(x)}{ab} = \frac{5}{32}c^3x^2 - \frac{7}{64}c^2x^3 + \frac{1}{120}x^5 - \frac{1}{60}\{x - c\}^5.$$

29. The Tautochrone.

We shall now discuss a problem in mechanics that leads to a simple integral equation of the convolution type.

The problem is that of determining a curve through the origin

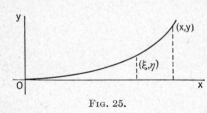

Fig. 25.

in a vertical xy-plane such that the time required for a particle to slide down the curve to the origin is independent of the starting position. The particle slides from rest under the action of its weight and the reaction of the curve on which it is constrained to move. The required curve is called the tautochrone.

Let σ denote the length of arc of the curve, measured from the origin O, and let (x, y) be the starting point and (ξ, η) any intermediate point (Fig. 25). Equating the gain in kinetic energy to the loss of potential energy, we have

$$\frac{1}{2}m\left(\frac{d\sigma}{dt}\right)^2 = mg(y - \eta),$$

where m is the mass of the particle and t is time.   Thus

$$d\sigma = -\sqrt{2g}\sqrt{y - \eta}\,dt,$$

and upon separating variables and integrating from $\eta = y$ to $\eta = 0$ we have

$$T\sqrt{2g} = \int_{\eta=0}^{\eta=y}\frac{d\sigma}{\sqrt{y - \eta}},$$

where T is the fixed time of descent.   Now

$$\sigma = H(y),$$

where the function $H(y)$ depends upon the curve, and therefore

(1) $$T\sqrt{2g} = \int_0^y (y - \eta)^{-\frac{1}{2}} H'(\eta)\, d\eta.$$

This is an integral equation of convolution type in the unknown function $H'(y)$.   We may write it in the form

$$T\sqrt{2g} = y^{-\frac{1}{2}} * H'(y).$$

Let $h(s)$ be the Laplace transform of $H(y)$ with respect to the variable y.   Recalling that $H(0) = 0$ and that the transform of the convolution of two functions is the product of the transforms, it follows formally from equation (1) that

$$T\sqrt{2g}\,\frac{1}{s} = sh(s)L\left\{\frac{1}{\sqrt{y}}\right\} = sh(s)\sqrt{\frac{\pi}{s}}.$$

That is,

$$sh(s) = T\sqrt{\frac{2g}{\pi}}\,\frac{1}{\sqrt{s}};$$

hence

(2) $$H'(y) = \frac{T}{\pi}\sqrt{2g}\,\frac{1}{\sqrt{y}}.$$

We can see that this function does satisfy our integral equation (1) by substituting it into that equation and performing the integration.

Since

$$H'(y) = \frac{d\sigma}{dy} = \sqrt{1 + \left(\frac{dx}{dy}\right)^2},$$

the differential equation of the curve in terms of the variables x and y is, according to equation (2),

$$1 + \left(\frac{dx}{dy}\right)^2 = \frac{2gT^2}{\pi^2 y} = \frac{a}{y},$$

where $a = 2gT^2/\pi^2$.   Separating variables here, we have

$$dx = \sqrt{\frac{a - y}{y}}\, dy,$$

and the necessary integration can be performed easily by substituting $y = a \sin^2 \tfrac{1}{2}\theta$, for we then find that

$$dx = a \cos^2 \frac{1}{2}\theta \; d\theta = \frac{a}{2}(1 + \cos \theta) \; d\theta.$$

Noting that $x = 0$ when $y = 0$, the parametric equations of the tautochrone are therefore

$$(3) \qquad x = \frac{a}{2}(\theta + \sin \theta), \qquad y = \frac{a}{2}(1 - \cos \theta).$$

These equations represent the cycloid generated by a point P on a circle of radius $\tfrac{1}{2}a$ as the circle rolls along the lower side of the line $y = a$. The parameter θ is the angle through which the radius drawn to the point P has turned, where the initial position of P is at the origin. Our tautochrone is of course just one arch of this cycloid. Since $a = 2gT^2/\pi^2$, the diameter of the generating circle is determined by the time T of descent.

The above problem can be generalized in various ways so as to lead to other interesting questions; in fact it was a generalization of the problem of the tautochrone that led the great Norwegian mathematician Niels Abel (1802–1829) to introduce the subject of integral equations.*

If the time T of descent is a function $F(y)$, for example, our integral equation (1) becomes

$$(4) \qquad \sqrt{2g}\, F(y) = \int_0^y (y - \eta)^{-\frac{1}{2}} H'(\eta)\; d\eta.$$

In case T is a linear function of the arc length,

$$(5) \qquad \sqrt{2g}\, T = a + b\sigma = a + bH(y),$$

our equation becomes the integrodifferential equation

$$(6) \qquad a + bH(y) = \int_0^y (y - \eta)^{-\frac{1}{2}} H'(\eta)\; d\eta.$$

The transformed equation is

$$\frac{a}{s} + bh(s) = \sqrt{\pi s}\; h(s).$$

This leads easily to a formula for $H'(y)$. In case $b = \sqrt{\pi}$, for

* See Bôcher, M., "Integral Equations," p. 6, 1909.

instance, we have

$$sh(s) = \frac{a}{\sqrt{\pi}} \frac{1}{\sqrt{s} - 1}$$

and, according to formula (10), Sec. 14,

$$H'(y) = \frac{a}{\pi \sqrt{y}} + \frac{a}{\sqrt{\pi}} [1 + \text{erf } (\sqrt{y})]e^y.$$

30. Mortality of Equipment. Let the function $F(t)$ denote the number of pieces of equipment on hand at time t, where the number is large enough that we can consider it as a continuous variable instead of a variable that takes on only integral values. The equipment wears out in time, or is lost from service for other reasons, so that out of $N(0)$ pieces introduced at time $t = 0$ the number $N(t)$ in service at time t is given by the formula

$$(1) \qquad\qquad N(t) = N(0)H(t),$$

where $H(t)$ is a function that determines the surviving equipment after t units of time. Note that $H(0) = 1$, necessarily.

If $R(\tau)$ is the total number of replacements up to time τ, then $R'(\tau) \, d\tau$ is the number of replacements during the time interval from $t = \tau$ to $t = \tau + d\tau$ and the number of survivals at any future time t, out of these replacements, is

$$R'(\tau)H(t - \tau) \, d\tau.$$

The total amount of equipment in service at time t is the sum of these survivals from the replacements during every time interval $d\tau$ between $\tau = 0$ and $\tau = t$, increased of course by the survivals from the new equipment on hand at time $t = 0$. Therefore

$$(2) \qquad\qquad F(t) = F(0)H(t) + \int_0^t R'(\tau)H(t - \tau) \, d\tau.$$

We have assumed here that the equipment $F(0)$ on hand at time $t = 0$ is all new; thus we take $R(0) = 0$.

If the amount $F(t)$ that must be in service at each instant is known and if the survival factor $H(t)$ is known, then equation (2) is an integral equation of convolution type in $R'(t)$. Its solution gives the formula by which replacements must be made.

The equation is an integrodifferential equation in the survival factor $H(t)$ when $F(t)$ and $R(t)$ are known.

In either case, the transformed equation is

$$(3) \qquad f(s) = F(0)h(s) + sr(s)h(s).$$

Then

$$(4) \qquad r(s) = \frac{f(s) - F(0)h(s)}{sh(s)},$$

and $R(t)$ is the inverse transform of this function.

Suppose the mortality is exponential in character so that

$$H(t) = e^{-kt}$$

and that the amount of equipment on hand is to be a constant,

$$F(t) = b.$$

Then $h(s) = 1/(s + k)$ and $f(s) = b/s$, and it follows from equation (4) that

$$r(s) = bk \frac{1}{s^2}.$$

Therefore replacements must be made at such a rate that the total equipment replaced at each time t is

$$R(t) = bkt,$$

a result that is easily verified as the solution of equation (2). Thus replacements must be made at the rate of bk pieces per unit time.

31. Evaluation of Integrals. Certain integrals containing parameters can be evaluated easily by means of the transformation. In order to give more interesting examples of such integrals, let us first note the transforms of a few functions that are of considerable importance.

We found in Sec. 18 that the transform of the sine-integral function is

$$L\{\text{Si}(t)\} = \frac{1}{s} \operatorname{arccot} s.$$

The *cosine-integral* function $\text{Ci}(t)$ is defined by the formula

$$(1) \qquad \text{Ci}(t) = -\int_t^\infty \frac{\cos \tau}{\tau} \, d\tau.$$

Substituting a new variable of integration $x = \tau/t$ here, we have

$$(2) \qquad \text{Ci}(t) = -\int_1^\infty \frac{\cos xt}{x} \, dx.$$

The Laplace transform of Ci(t) is therefore

$$L\{\mathrm{Ci}(t)\} = -s \int_1^\infty \frac{dx}{x(s^2 + x^2)} = -\frac{1}{s} \int_1^\infty \left(\frac{1}{x} - \frac{x}{s^2 + x^2}\right) dx$$

$$= -\frac{1}{2s} \log \frac{x^2}{s^2 + x^2}\Big]_1^\infty = \frac{1}{2s} \log \frac{1}{s^2 + 1},$$

provided it is permissible to interchange the order of integration of the repeated integral arising when we transform the function on the right of equation (2). That step can be shown to be valid.* Thus

(3) $$L\{\mathrm{Ci}(t)\} = -\frac{1}{2s} \log (s^2 + 1) \qquad (s > 0).$$

The *exponential-integral* function is usually defined as

(4)   *Disagreeon definition?* $$\mathrm{Ei}(t) = \int_{-\infty}^t \frac{e^\tau}{\tau} d\tau \qquad (t < 0),$$

and hence *doesn't exist*   *this is $E i(t)$ is well defined*

(5) $$-\mathrm{Ei}(-t) = \int_t^\infty \frac{e^{-\tau}}{\tau} d\tau = \int_1^\infty \frac{e^{-xt}}{x} dx \qquad (t > 0).$$

The transform of the function of t defined by (5) is therefore

$$\int_1^\infty \frac{dx}{x(s + x)} = \frac{1}{s} \int_1^\infty \left(\frac{1}{x} - \frac{1}{s + x}\right) dx = -\frac{1}{s} \log \frac{1}{s + 1};$$

that is,

(6) $$L\{-\mathrm{Ei}(-t)\} = \frac{1}{s} \log (s + 1) \qquad (s > 0).$$

As our first example in the evaluation of integrals, consider the integral

(7) $$\int_0^\infty \frac{\sin tx}{\sqrt{x}} dx = 2 \int_0^\infty \sin ty^2 \, dy = F(t) \qquad (t > 0).$$

The transform of $F(t)$ is

$$f(s) = 2 \int^\infty \frac{y^2}{s^2 + y^4} \, dy,$$

---

* For conditions under which the order of repeated infinite integrals can be changed see, for example, J. Pierpont, "Theory of Functions of Real Variables," Vol. 1, p. 488, 1905. In connection with the condition of uniform convergence involved here, see H. S. Carslaw, "Fourier Series and Integrals," p. 197, 1930.

since the interchange of order of integration can be justified as before.   By writing

$$s^2 + y^4 = (y^2 - y\sqrt{2s} + s)(y^2 + y\sqrt{2s} + s)$$

and breaking up the last integrand into its partial fractions and then integrating, we find that

$$f(s) = \frac{1}{\sqrt{2s}}\left[\arctan\left(y\sqrt{\frac{2}{s}} - 1\right) + \arctan\left(y\sqrt{\frac{2}{s}} + 1\right)\right]_0^{\infty}$$
$$= \frac{\pi}{\sqrt{2}}\frac{1}{\sqrt{s}}.$$

Therefore the integral (7) has the value

$$(8) \qquad\qquad F(t) = \sqrt{\frac{\pi}{2t}} \qquad\qquad (t > 0).$$

As another example let

$$(9) \qquad F(t) = \int_0^{\infty} \frac{\cos tx}{x^2 + b^2}\,dx.$$

Then

$$f(s) = s\int_0^{\infty} \frac{dx}{(s^2 + x^2)(x^2 + b^2)}$$
$$= \frac{s}{s^2 - b^2}\int_0^{\infty}\left(\frac{1}{x^2 + b^2} - \frac{1}{x^2 + s^2}\right)dx$$
$$= \frac{\pi}{2b}\frac{1}{s + b}.$$

Consequently the integral (9) has the value

$$(10) \qquad\qquad F(t) = \frac{\pi}{2b}e^{-bt} \qquad\qquad (t \geqq 0, b > 0).$$

Let us note that by writing

$$\cos t\,\mathrm{Si}(t) - \sin t\,\mathrm{Ci}(t) = \cos t\int_0^t \frac{\sin \tau}{\tau}\,d\tau + \sin t\int_t^{\infty} \frac{\cos \tau}{\tau}\,d\tau$$
$$= \cos t\int_0^{\infty} \frac{\sin \tau}{\tau}\,d\tau$$
$$- \int_t^{\infty} \frac{\cos t\,\sin \tau - \sin t\,\cos \tau}{\tau}\,d\tau$$

$$= \frac{\pi}{2} \cos t + \int_t^\infty \frac{\sin (t - \tau)}{\tau} d\tau$$

$$= \frac{\pi}{2} \cos t + \int_1^\infty \frac{\sin t(1 - x)}{x} dx,$$

and performing the transformation with respect to t, we can show that

(11) $$L\{\cos t \operatorname{Si}(t) - \sin t \operatorname{Ci}(t)\} = \frac{\log s}{s^2 + 1}.$$

Now the transform of the integral

(12) $$F(t) = \int_0^\infty \frac{e^{-tx}}{1 + x^2} dx$$

is

$$f(s) = \frac{\pi}{2} \frac{s}{s^2 + 1} - \frac{\log s}{s^2 + 1}.$$

In view of (11) therefore, the integral (12) has the value

(13) $$F(t) = \left[\frac{\pi}{2} - \operatorname{Si}(t)\right] \cos t + \operatorname{Ci}(t) \sin t.$$

Observing that the integral in (12) is a Laplace integral, we can write our result as

(14) $$L\left\{\frac{1}{1 + t^2}\right\} = \left[\frac{\pi}{2} - \operatorname{Si}(s)\right] \cos s + \operatorname{Ci}(s) \sin s.$$

PROBLEMS

Establish the following formulas:

1. $$\int_0^\infty \frac{\cos tx}{\sqrt{x}} dx = \sqrt{\frac{\pi}{2t}} \qquad\qquad (t > 0).$$

2. $$\int_{-\infty}^\infty \frac{x \sin tx}{a^2 + x^2} dx = \pi e^{-at} \qquad\qquad (a > 0, t > 0).$$

3. $$L\{-\operatorname{Ei}(-at)\} = \frac{1}{s} [\log (s + a) - \log (a)].$$

4. $$\int_0^\infty \frac{e^{-tx^2}}{1 + x^2} dx = \frac{\pi}{2} e^t \operatorname{erfc} (\sqrt{t}).$$

5. $$\int_0^\infty \frac{\sin tx}{x} dx = \frac{\pi}{2}. \qquad\qquad (t > 0).$$

CHAPTER IV

PROBLEMS IN PARTIAL DIFFERENTIAL EQUATIONS

32. Displacements in a Long Stretched String. Let a string be stretched along the x-axis, and let x and Y be the coordinates of any point of the string at time t. The function $Y(x, t)$ then represents the displacement of each point at time t. Whenever the displacement of any element is changing solely because of the effect of the tension exerted upon it by the adjacent elements of the string, it can be shown that $Y(x, t)$ satisfies the partial differential equation

$$(1) \qquad \frac{\partial^2 Y}{\partial t^2} = a^2 \frac{\partial^2 Y}{\partial x^2},$$

where $a^2 = P/\delta$, P being the tension and δ the mass per unit length.

In the derivation of the equation of motion (1), it is assumed that the string is perfectly flexible, that the displacements are small enough for the tension P to be considered constant, and that the slope of the string is always small. The derivation follows quite readily from the fact that the vertical component of the tension exerted at the point (x, Y) by the portion of the string on the left upon the portion on the right is*

$$(2) \qquad \text{Force} = -P \frac{\partial Y}{\partial x}.$$

Consider now a semi-infinite stretched string, that is, one whose fixed right-hand end lies so far out on the x-axis that it may be considered to be infinitely far away. Let the left-hand end be initially at the origin, and let that end then be moved in some prescribed manner along the Y-axis (Fig. 26); thus

$$Y = F(t) \qquad \text{when } x = 0,$$

---

* For a derivation of the equation of motion (1) see, for instance, the author's book "Fourier Series and Boundary Value Problems," pp. 21*ff.*, 1941.

where $F(t)$ is a prescribed continuous function and $F(0) = 0$. If the string lies initially along the x-axis with no initial velocity and if the distant end is kept fixed, then

$$Y = 0 \quad \text{and} \quad \frac{\partial Y}{\partial t} = 0 \quad \text{when } t = 0, \text{ and } \lim_{x \to \infty} Y = 0.$$

It is convenient to let $Y_t(x, t)$ denote the partial derivative of Y with respect to t and $Y_{tt}(x, t)$ denote $\partial^2 Y / \partial t^2$, etc. Then the above conditions on the unknown function $Y(x, t)$ can be written

(3) $\qquad Y_{tt}(x, t) = a^2 Y_{xx}(x, t) \qquad\qquad (x > 0, t > 0),$

(4) $\qquad Y(x, 0) = Y_t(x, 0) = 0,$

(5) $\qquad Y(0, t) = F(t), \qquad \lim_{x \to \infty} Y(x, t) = 0.$

A problem composed of such conditions is called a *boundary value problem* in partial differential equations. We shall use a

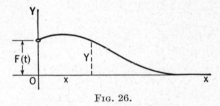

Fig. 26.

formal method to solve it and then indicate how our final result can be verified as a solution.

Let $y(x, s)$ denote the Laplace transform of $Y(x, t)$ with respect to the variable t. Then in view of the initial conditions (4),

$$L\{Y_{tt}(x, t)\} = s^2 y(x, s).$$

Also

$$L\{Y_{xx}(x, t)\} = \int_0^\infty \frac{\partial^2}{\partial x^2} [e^{-st} Y(x, t)] \, dt$$

$$= \frac{\partial^2}{\partial x^2} \int_0^\infty e^{-st} Y(x, t) \, dt = y_{xx}(x, s),$$

provided the function $e^{-st} Y(x, t)$ satisfies conditions under which the order of integration with respect to t and differentiation with respect to x can be interchanged as indicated. The variable x is independent of t, and it is therefore just a parameter in the Laplace integral. When the transformation is made on both members of the equation of motion (3), we therefore obtain the equation

$$s^2 y(x, s) = a^2 y_{xx}(x, s)$$

in the transform of our unknown function. We have also used the initial conditions (4) at this stage of our work.

Applying the transform to the members of equations (5), we have the conditions

$$y(0, s) = f(s), \qquad \lim_{x \to \infty} y(x, s) = 0,$$

provided it is permissible to interchange the order of taking the limit as $x \to \infty$ and integrating with respect to t.* The function $f(s)$ is the transform of $F(t)$.

The transformed boundary value problem thus becomes

(6) $$\frac{d^2 y}{dx^2} - \frac{s^2}{a^2} y = 0,$$

(7) $$y(0, s) = f(s), \qquad \lim_{x \to \infty} y(x, s) = 0,$$

where we have used the symbol for ordinary rather than partial differentiation since s is involved in the new problem only as a parameter. Differentiation occurs only with respect to x. The general solution of the ordinary differential equation (6) is

$$y(x, s) = C_1 e^{-\frac{sx}{a}} + C_2 e^{\frac{sx}{a}},$$

where C_1 and C_2 may be functions of s. This solution could of course be obtained by transforming the members of equation (6) with respect to the variable x. We consider s as positive since the Laplace integrals generally converge for all s greater than some fixed number. Since $y(x, s)$ is to approach zero as x tends to infinity, we must take $C_2 = 0$. The first of conditions (7) shows that $C_1 = f(s)$ and thus

(8) $$y(x, s) = e^{-\frac{sx}{a}} f(s).$$

---

* Since we can verify our final result, we need not be concerned about such conditions here. The simplest conditions under which this interchange of order of operations is valid, as well as the one above concerning partial differentiation with respect to x, involve the uniform convergence with respect to x of the Laplace integrals and the continuity of the integrals with respect to the two variables x and t.

Our translation property (Sec. 10) enables us to write the inverse transform of $y(x, s)$ at once, giving

$$(9) \qquad Y(x, t) = F\left(t - \frac{x}{a}\right) \qquad \text{if } t \geqq \frac{x}{a},$$

$$= 0 \qquad \text{if } t \leqq \frac{x}{a}.$$

This is the solution of our problem. Since any function of $at - x$ is easily shown to be a solution of the equation of motion (3) wherever the function has a derivative of the second order, the function (9) does satisfy our partial differential equation. The function clearly satisfies the boundary conditions (4) and (5).

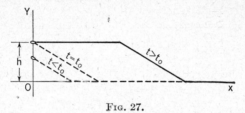

Fig. 27.

According to the solution (9), a point of the string x units from the origin remains at rest until the time $t = x/a$. Starting at that time, it executes the same motion as the left-hand end of the string. The time x/a by which the motion of the point x is retarded over the motion of the point $x = 0$ is the time it takes a disturbance to travel the distance x with the velocity a.

It is interesting to note various instantaneous positions of the string for particular end movements. Suppose for instance that

$$F(t) = \frac{h}{t_0} t \qquad \text{when } t \leqq t_0,$$

$$= h \qquad \text{when } t \geqq t_0;$$

that is, the end is raised at a constant velocity to the height h and then held there. Although $F(t)$ has a discontinuous derivative at $t = t_0$, our formula (9) is still the solution of the problem. The reader can show that in this case

$$Y(x, t) = 0 \qquad \text{when } x \geqq at,$$

$$= \frac{h}{at_0}(at - x) \qquad \text{when } a(t - t_0) \leqq x \leqq at,$$

$$= h \qquad \text{when } x \leqq a(t - t_0).$$

Three instantaneous positions of the string are shown in Fig. 27.

33. Other Interpretations of the Problem.

The function $Y(x, t)$ in the problem of the last section can have a number of physical interpretations in addition to the one already given it. It may denote, for instance, the longitudinal displacements of the sections of an elastic bar having the form of a prism or cylinder (Fig. 28). The variable x then denotes the distance from one end to the section when the bar is neither compressed nor elongated. The displacement per unit length, or the unit elongation or compression, is $\partial Y/\partial x$ and, assuming that Hooke's

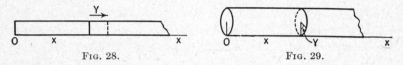

FIG. 28.   FIG. 29.

law applies, the force exerted by the left-hand portion of the bar across any section is

$$-EA\,\frac{\partial Y}{\partial x},$$

where E is Young's modulus of elasticity and A is the area of the cross section of the bar. It is not difficult then to show that $Y(x, t)$ satisfies the partial differential equation

(1) $$Y_{tt}(x, t) = a^2 Y_{xx}(x, t),$$

where $a^2 = E/\delta$ and δ is the mass of the material per unit volume.

The above problem is therefore the problem of determining the longitudinal displacements in a semi-infinite bar with the distant end kept fixed when the end $x = 0$ is pushed in or pulled out in some prescribed manner. The bar is initially unstrained and at rest.

If the bar is replaced by a column of air, the problem becomes one of importance in the theory of sound.

Again, the function Y may denote the angle through which a section of a cylindrical shaft, x units from the end, has turned at time t as a result of the elasticity of the shaft in torsion. The constant in equation (1) is, in this case,

$$a^2 = \frac{E_s}{\delta}$$

where E_s is the modulus of elasticity in shear and δ is the mass per unit volume (Fig. 29).

These interpretations of $Y(x, t)$ are more prominent in practical applications than that of the displacements in a string. Moreover, fewer assumptions are used in deriving the equation of motion (1) when $Y(x, t)$ denotes longitudinal or torsional displacements.*

Among other applications it should be noted that equation (1) is a special case of the telegraph equation

$$(2) \qquad \frac{\partial^2 v}{\partial x^2} = KL \frac{\partial^2 v}{\partial t^2} + (RK + SL) \frac{\partial v}{\partial t} + RSv,$$

where v is either the electric potential or the current in a long slender wire with resistance R, electrostatic capacity K, leakage conductance S, and self-inductance L, all per unit length of wire. When R and S are so small that their effect can be neglected, this equation has the same form as equation (1).

34. The Long String under Gravity. If the weight of a horizontal stretched string is to be taken into account, a force $-\delta g\, dx$ must be included in the vertical forces acting upon each element, where g is the acceleration of gravity. As a consequence, the equation of motion becomes

$$(1) \qquad Y_{tt} = a^2 Y_{xx} - g.$$

Let the end $x = 0$ of the string be held fast, and let the distant end be looped around a vertical support that cannot exert any vertical force upon the string, so that $Y_x(x, t)$ vanishes at that end. Let the string be initially supported along the x-axis, and let the support be removed at the instant $t = 0$. Then the boundary conditions accompanying equation (1) are

$$(2) \qquad Y(x, 0) = Y_t(x, 0) = 0 \qquad\qquad (x > 0),$$
$$(3) \qquad Y(0, t) = 0, \qquad \lim_{x \to \infty} Y_x(x, t) = 0.$$

The problem in the transform $y(x, s)$ is seen to be, formally,

$$(4) \qquad s^2 y(x, s) = a^2 y_{xx}(x, s) - \frac{g}{s},$$

---

* See, for example, Timoshenko, S., "Vibration Problems in Engineering," Chap. V, 1937; and Den Hartog, J. P., "Mechanical Vibrations," pp. 165–167, 1940.

(5) $$y(0, s) = 0, \qquad \lim_{x \to \infty} y_x(x, s) = 0.$$

The ordinary differential equation (4) has the solution

$$y(x, s) = C_1 e^{-\frac{sx}{a}} + C_2 e^{\frac{sx}{a}} - \frac{g}{s^3}.$$

In view of the second of conditions (5), $C_2 = 0$, and in view of the first, $C_1 = g/s^3$. Therefore

$$y(x, s) = -\frac{1}{2} g \left(\frac{2}{s^3} - \frac{2}{s^3} e^{-\frac{sx}{a}} \right),$$

and it follows that

$$Y(x, t) = -\frac{g}{2} \left[t^2 - \left(t - \frac{x}{a} \right)^2 \right] \quad \text{when } t \geqq \frac{x}{a},$$

$$= -\frac{1}{2} g t^2 \qquad\qquad \text{when } t \leqq \frac{x}{a}.$$

Our result can be written

(6) $$Y(x, t) = -\frac{g}{2a^2} (2axt - x^2) \quad \text{when } x \leqq at,$$

$$= -\frac{1}{2} g t^2 \qquad\qquad \text{when } x \geqq at.$$

It is easy to verify this as the solution of our problem. An instantaneous position of the string is shown in Fig. 30. We note

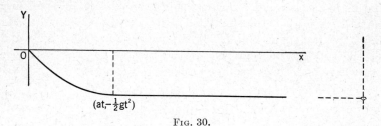

FIG. 30.

that at any time t all elements of the string to the right of the point $x = at$ have moved like freely falling bodies.

This is also the problem of the longitudinal displacements in a long bar with the end $x = 0$ held fixed, when a uniform force parallel to the bar acts on every element. This would be the case if the bar is hung vertically by one end.

If the external force per unit length of the string is $\delta F(t)$, the equation of motion is

(7) $$Y_{tt}(x, t) = a^2 Y_{xx}(x, t) + F(t).$$

When the boundary conditions (2) and (3) are used again, the solution of the transformed problem becomes

$$y(x, s) = \frac{1}{s^2} f(s) - \frac{1}{s^2} f(s) e^{-\frac{sx}{a}}.$$

If we let $G(t)$ denote the inverse transform of $f(s)/s^2$, so that

$$G(t) = \int_0^t \int_0^\tau F(\lambda) \, d\lambda \, d\tau,$$

we can write the formula for the displacements in the form

(8) $$Y(x, t) = G(t) - G\left(t - \frac{x}{a}\right) \quad \text{when } t \geqq \frac{x}{a},$$

$$= G(t) \quad \text{when } t \leqq \frac{x}{a}.$$

35. A Bar with a Prescribed Force on One End. Let the end $x = 0$ of an elastic bar of length c be kept fixed, and let $F(t)$ denote a prescribed force per unit area acting parallel to the bar at the end $x = c$ (Fig. 31). If the bar is initially unstrained and at rest, the boundary value problem in the longitudinal displacements $Y(x, t)$ is the following,

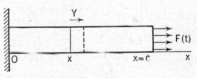

FIG. 31.

$$Y_{tt}(x, t) = a^2 Y_{xx}(x, t) \quad (0 < x < c, t > 0),$$
$$Y(x, 0) = Y_t(x, 0) = 0,$$
$$Y(0, t) = 0, \qquad EY_x(c, t) = F(t),$$

where $a^2 = E/\delta$, E is Young's modulus, and δ is the mass per unit volume.

The transform of $Y(x, t)$ therefore satisfies the conditions

$$s^2 y(x, s) = a^2 y_{xx}(x, s),$$
$$y(0, s) = 0, \qquad Ey_x(c, s) = f(s),$$

and the solution of this transformed problem is readily found to be

(1)
$$y(x, s) = \frac{a}{E} f(s) \frac{\sinh \dfrac{sx}{a}}{s \cosh \dfrac{sc}{a}}.$$

Consider first the case of a constant force,

(2)
$$F(t) = F_0.$$

Then

(3)
$$y(x, s) = \frac{aF_0}{E} \frac{\sinh \dfrac{sx}{a}}{s^2 \cosh \dfrac{sc}{a}}$$

and, when $x = c$,

$$y(c, s) = \frac{aF_0}{E} \frac{1}{s^2} \tanh \frac{sc}{a}.$$

In Sec. 19 we found that $s^{-2} \tanh (bs/2)$ is the transform of the periodic function $H(b, t)$ of period $2b$, whose graph is the zigzag

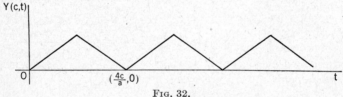

Y(c,t)

O $(\frac{4c}{a}, 0)$ t

FIG. 32.

line (Fig. 10) whose segments have slopes ± 1. Therefore the displacement of the end $x = c$ is

(4)
$$Y(c, t) = \frac{aF_0}{E} H\left(\frac{2c}{a}, t\right);$$

that is, the end moves by jerks as indicated in Fig. 32.

To find the displacement at an arbitrary point, let us write

$$2 \sinh \frac{sx}{a} = e^{\frac{sc}{a}} [e^{-\frac{(c-x)s}{a}} - e^{-\frac{(c+x)s}{a}}]$$

$$= \left(\cosh \frac{sc}{a} + \sinh \frac{sc}{a}\right) [e^{-\frac{(c-x)s}{a}} - e^{-\frac{(c+x)s}{a}}].$$

Then our formula (3) can be written .

(5) $\quad y(x, s) = \dfrac{aF_0}{E}\left(\dfrac{1}{s^2} + \dfrac{1}{s^2}\tanh\dfrac{sc}{a}\right)[e^{-\frac{(c-x)s}{a}} - e^{-\frac{(c+x)s}{a}}],$

and therefore our result can be written

$$(6) \quad Y(x, t) = \dfrac{aF_0}{2E}\left[\left\{t - \dfrac{c-x}{a}\right\} - \left\{t - \dfrac{c+x}{a}\right\}\right.$$
$$\left. + H\left(\dfrac{2c}{a}, t - \dfrac{c-x}{a}\right) - H\left(\dfrac{2c}{a}, t - \dfrac{c+x}{a}\right)\right],$$

provided it is understood that $\{t - k\} = 0$ when $t < k$ and that

$H\left(\dfrac{2c}{a}, t - k\right) = 0$ when $t < k$. Thus

$$\left\{t - \dfrac{c-x}{a}\right\} - \left\{t - \dfrac{c+x}{a}\right\} = 0 \qquad \text{when } t \leqq \dfrac{c-x}{a}$$

$$= t - \dfrac{c-x}{a} \quad \text{when } \dfrac{c-x}{a} \leqq t$$

$$\leqq \dfrac{c+x}{a},$$

$$= \dfrac{2x}{a} \qquad \text{when } t \geqq \dfrac{c+x}{a},$$

and it is not difficult to represent $Y(x, t)$ graphically (Fig. 33).

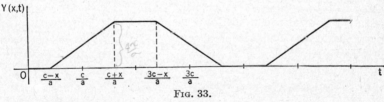

FIG. 33.

Let us illustrate another useful procedure for finding the inverse transformation in such problems. Referring to formula (3) for $y(x, s)$ again, we write

$$\dfrac{\sinh\dfrac{sx}{a}}{\cosh\dfrac{sc}{a}} = \dfrac{e^{-\frac{(c-x)s}{a}} - e^{-\frac{(c+x)s}{a}}}{1 + e^{-\frac{2cs}{a}}}$$

$$= [e^{-\frac{(c-x)s}{a}} - e^{-\frac{(c+x)s}{a}}]\sum_{n=0}^{\infty}(-1)^n e^{-\frac{2ncs}{a}},$$

since $(1 + z)^{-1} = \sum\limits_0^\infty (-1)^n z^n$ when $0 < z < 1$.   Therefore

$$y(x, s) = \frac{aF_0}{E} \sum_0^\infty (-1)^n \left\{ \frac{1}{s^2} \exp\left[-s \frac{(2n+1)c - x}{a} \right] \right.$$
$$\left. - \frac{1}{s^2} \exp\left[-s \frac{(2n+1)c + x}{a} \right] \right\}.$$

Formally applying the inverse transformation to the terms of the infinite series, we obtain the formula

$$(7) \quad Y(x, t) = \frac{aF_0}{E} \left[\left\{ t - \frac{c-x}{a} \right\} - \left\{ t - \frac{c+x}{a} \right\} \right.$$
$$- \left\{ t - \frac{3c-x}{a} \right\} + \left\{ t - \frac{3c+x}{a} \right\} + \left\{ t - \frac{5c-x}{a} \right\}$$
$$\left. - \left\{ t - \frac{5c+x}{a} \right\} - \cdots \right].$$

For any fixed t the series here is finite since each of the braces are to be replaced by zero when the quantity inside is negative. The number of nonvanishing terms in the series increases as t increases.

The result (7) can be verified directly as the solution of our problem.   The graph in Fig. 33 can be determined easily from formula (7).

In the case of a general force function $F(t)$, we can write the formula for the displacement with the aid of the property of convolution.   Referring to equation (1) and writing in the same manner as above,

$$p(x, s) = \frac{\sinh \dfrac{sx}{a}}{s \cosh \dfrac{sc}{a}}$$

$$= \sum_0^\infty (-1)^n \left\{ \frac{1}{s} \exp\left[-s \frac{(2n+1)c - x}{a} \right] \right.$$
$$\left. - \frac{1}{s} \exp\left[-s \frac{(2n+1)c + x}{a} \right] \right\},$$

we have

$$(8) \quad P(x, t) = S_{\frac{c-x}{a}}(t) - S_{\frac{c+x}{a}}(t) - S_{\frac{3c-x}{a}}(t) + S_{\frac{3c+x}{a}}(t) + \cdots$$

where $S_k(t)$ is the step function defined in Sec. 3 (Fig. 1). In view of formula (1) for $y(x, s)$, then

$$(9) \qquad Y(x, t) = \frac{a}{E} \int_0^t F(t - \tau) P(x, \tau) \, d\tau.$$

Consider finally the motion of the end $x = c$ when the force takes the form of an impulse. Let

$$F(t) = F_0 \qquad \text{when } t < t_0$$
$$= 0 \qquad \text{when } t > t_0,$$

so that

$$(10) \qquad f(s) = \frac{F_0}{s}(1 - e^{-t_0 s}),$$

and from formula (1) we obtain a fairly simple expression for $y(c, s)$. In the case of a pure impulse we set

$$F_0 t_0 = I$$

and, keeping I fixed, let F_0 increase and t_0 approach zero. We should find the limit of $Y(c, t)$ as this change takes place in $F(t)$; but the result turns out to be the same as that obtained by substituting the limit of $f(s)$ into formula (1). In view of equation (10)

$$\lim_{t_0 \to 0} f(s) = \frac{I}{s} \lim_{t_0 \to 0} \frac{1 - e^{-t_0 s}}{t_0} = I;$$

thus in view of (1),

$$y(c, s) = \frac{aI}{E} \frac{1}{s} \tanh \frac{sc}{a}.$$

The displacement of the end is therefore represented by the square wave function of Sec. 10 (Fig. 9),

$$(11) \qquad Y(c, t) = \frac{aI}{E} M\left(\frac{2c}{a}, t\right).$$

Thus the end jumps suddenly back and forth between two fixed positions. It is possible to demonstrate a close approximation to this behavior by substituting for the bar a loosely wound coil spring. If, when the spring is hanging from one end, the free lower end is given a sharp tap, the lower end tends to move as indicated.

PROBLEMS

1. Solve the following problem in partial differential equations, and verify your result.

$$Y_t(x, t) + xY_x(x, t) + Y(x, t) = xF(t),$$
$$Y(x, 0) = 0, \qquad Y(0, t) = 0,$$

where $F(t)$ is a prescribed function.

$$Ans.\ Y(x, t) = xe^{-2t} \int_0^t e^{2\tau}F(\tau)\ d\tau.$$

2. Solve the problem

$$2xY_t(x, t) + Y_x(x, t) = 2x,$$
$$Y(x, 0) = 1, \qquad Y(0, t) = 1.$$

$$Ans.\ Y(x, t) = 1 + t \quad \text{when } 0 \leqq t \leqq x^2,$$
$$= 1 + x^2 \quad \text{when } t \geqq x^2.$$

3. The force per unit area on the end $x = 0$ of a semi-infinite prismatic bar is $F(t)$ (Fig. 34), so that $-EY_x(0, t) = F(t)$. If the infinite

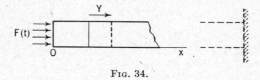

F(t)

Y

O

x

FIG. 34.

end is fixed and the initial displacement and velocity of each section is zero, set up the boundary value problem for the longitudinal displacements $Y(x, t)$ and derive the solution

$$Y(x, t) = \frac{a}{E} G\left(t - \frac{x}{a}\right) \qquad \text{when } t \geqq \frac{x}{a},$$
$$= 0 \qquad \text{when } t \leqq \frac{x}{a},$$

where

$$G(t) = \int_0^t F(\tau)\ d\tau.$$

Note that the displacement at the end $x = 0$ is

$$Y(0, t) = \frac{a}{E} G(t).$$

4. In Prob. 3 let the force be

$$F(t) = F_0 \qquad \text{when } t < t_0,$$
$$= 0 \qquad \text{when } t > t_0,$$

and show that

$$Y(x, t) = 0 \qquad \text{when } t \leqq \frac{x}{a},$$

$$= \frac{F_0}{E}(at - x) \quad \text{when } \frac{x}{a} \leqq t \leqq t_0 + \frac{x}{a},$$

$$= \frac{F_0 a t_0}{E} \qquad \text{when } t \geqq t_0 + \frac{x}{a}.$$

Study this function graphically.

5. In Prob. 4 let

$$F_0 t_0 = I,$$

and let t_0 tend to zero and F_0 increase in such a manner that I remains constant. Either from the result of Prob. 4 or by replacing $f(s)$ in Prob. 3 by

$$\lim_{t_0 \to 0} f(s) = I,$$

show that the displacement in this case of an impulse at $x = 0$ is

$$Y(x, t) = \frac{aI}{E} S_{\frac{x}{a}}(t),$$

where $S_k(t)$ is the step function defined in Sec. 3 (Fig. 1). Also note that $Y(0, t) = aI/E$, $(t > 0)$, in this idealized case of the instantaneous impulse.

6. A semi-infinite elastic bar is moving endwise with velocity $-v_0$ when one end is suddenly brought to rest, the other end remaining free

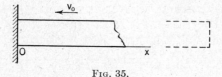

Fig. 35.

(Fig. 35). The displacement $Y(x, t)$ of its sections then satisfies the conditions

$$Y_{tt}(x, t) = a^2 Y_{xx}(x, t) \qquad (x > 0, t > 0),$$
$$Y(x, 0) = 0, \qquad Y_t(x, 0) = -v_0 \qquad (x > 0),$$
$$Y(0, t) = 0, \qquad \lim_{x \to \infty} Y_x(x, t) = 0 \qquad (t > 0).$$

Show that the solution of the transformed problem is

$$y(x, s) = -v_0 \left(\frac{1}{s^2} - \frac{1}{s^2} e^{-\frac{sx}{a}} \right)$$

and hence that

$$Y(x, t) = -v_0 t \qquad \text{when } t \leqq \frac{x}{a},$$
$$= -\frac{v_0 x}{a} \qquad \text{when } t \geqq \frac{x}{a}.$$

Also note that the force per unit area exerted by the support at $x = 0$ upon the end of the bar is Ev_0/a.

7. A constant force F_0 per unit area acts upon the end $x = c$ of an elastic bar (Fig. 36). If the end $x = 0$ is free and the initial displace-

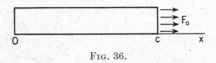

FIG. 36.

ment and velocity are both zero, set up the boundary value problem for the displacements $Y(x, t)$ and show that the solution of the transformed problem is

$$y(x, s) = \frac{aF_0}{E} \frac{1}{s^2} \frac{\cosh \dfrac{xs}{a}}{\sinh \dfrac{cs}{a}}.$$

(a) Find a formula for $Y(x, t)$.

(b) Writing

$$y(c, s) = \frac{aF_0}{E} \frac{1}{s} \left[\frac{1}{s} \left(1 + \coth \frac{sc}{a} \right) - \frac{1}{s} \right],$$

and noting from Sec. 11 the transform of the staircase function $S(h, t)$, show that the displacement of the end $x = c$ is

$$Y(c, t) = \frac{aF_0}{E} \int_0^t \left[2S \left(\frac{2c}{a}, \tau \right) - 1 \right] d\tau.$$

Examine this function graphically, and note that the end moves with a uniform velocity up to the time $t = 2c/a$, then with a greater uniform velocity up to the time $t = 4c/a$, and so on.

8. Let the force per unit area on the bar of Prob. 7 be

$$F(t) = F_0 \cos \omega t,$$

and show that when $\omega = \pi a/(2c)$,

$$y(c, s) = \frac{2cF_0}{\pi E} L \left\{ \sin \frac{\pi a t}{2c} \right\} \coth \frac{sc}{a}.$$

Hence, in view of formula (12) of Sec. 19, show that the displacement of the end is

$$Y(c, t) = \frac{2cF_0}{\pi E} \left| \sin \frac{\pi a t}{2c} \right|.$$

9. When the force at the end $x = c$ of the bar of Sec. 35 (Fig. 31) is constant, $F(t) = F_0$, determine with the aid of equation (3) the force exerted by the bar upon the support at $x = 0$. Note that

$$E y_x(0, s) = F_0 \frac{1}{s \cosh \dfrac{sc}{a}} = F_0 e^{-\frac{sc}{a}} \frac{2}{s(1 + e^{-\frac{2sc}{a}})};$$

thus, according to formula (4) of Sec. 19, the force is

$$EY_x(0, t) = 0 \qquad\qquad \text{when } t < \frac{c}{a},$$

$$= F_0 \left[1 + M\left(\frac{2c}{a}, t - \frac{c}{a}\right) \right] \quad \text{when } t > \frac{c}{a}.$$

Hence note that the force becomes twice the applied force during regular intervals of time (Fig. 37).

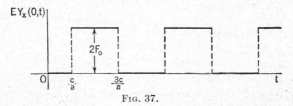

FIG. 37.

10. When the end $x = c$ of the bar of Sec. 35 (Fig. 31) is subjected to the force per unit area

$$F(t) = F_0 \qquad \text{when } t < t_0,$$
$$= 0 \qquad \text{when } t > t_0,$$

with the end $x = 0$ fixed, show that the displacement of the end $x = c$ is

$$Y(c, t) = \frac{aF_0}{E} \left[H\left(\frac{2c}{a}, t\right) - H\left(\frac{2c}{a}, t - t_0\right) \right],$$

where the function $(aF_0/E)H(2c/a, t)$ is shown in Fig. 32, and where $H(2c/a, t - t_0) = 0$ when $t \leqq t_0$. Consequently, show that when

$$t_0 = \frac{4c}{a}$$

the displacement $Y(c, t)$ consists of the single oscillation shown in Fig. 38.

11. The end $x = 0$ of a bar or heavy coil spring (Fig. 39) is free, and the end $x = c$ is displaced longitudinally in a prescribed manner,

$$Y(c, t) = G(t).$$

If the bar is initially unstrained and at rest, set up the boundary value

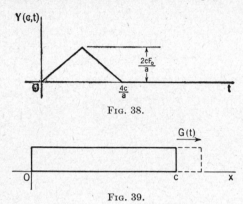

Fɪɢ. 38.

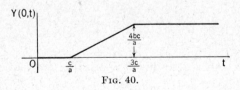

Fɪɢ. 39.

problem for the displacements $Y(x, t)$, and show that

$$y(x, s) = g(s) \frac{\cosh \dfrac{sx}{a}}{\cosh \dfrac{ac}{a}}.$$

(*a*) When $G(t) = F_0 t$ where F_0 is a constant, show that the displacement $Y(0, t)$ of the free end is the function obtained by integrating the function $EY_x(0, t)$ of Fig. 37 from 0 to t.

Y(0,t)

Fɪɢ. 40.

(*b*) If

$$G(t) = bt \qquad \text{when } t \leqq \frac{4c}{a},$$
$$= \frac{4bc}{a} \qquad \text{when } t \geqq \frac{4c}{a},$$

show that the free end moves with a uniform velocity $2b$ to a new position and remains there (Fig. 40).

(c) When $G(t)$ is arbitrary, derive the solution

$$Y(x, t) = \sum_{0}^{\infty} (-1)^n \left\{ G\left[t - \frac{(2n + 1)c - x}{a} \right] \right.$$

$$\left. + G\left[t - \frac{(2n + 1)c + x}{a} \right] \right\},$$

where the function G is zero when its argument is negative, and hence the series here is finite for each fixed t.

36. The Long String Initially Displaced.

We now apply our method to a very well-known problem in order to display further manipulations.

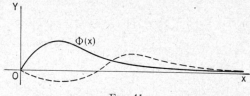

Fig. 41.

The formal manner of procedure is justified at the end, since our result can be fully verified as the solution. Let the ends of a semi-infinite string stretched along the positive x-axis be kept fixed, and let the string be given some prescribed transverse displacement $Y = \Phi(x)$ initially and released from that position with initial velocity zero (Fig. 41). Then the boundary value problem in the displacement $Y(x, t)$ is the following.

(1)
$$Y_{tt}(x, t) = a^2 Y_{xx}(x, t) \qquad (x > 0, t > 0),$$
$$Y(x, 0) = \Phi(x), \qquad Y_t(x, 0) = 0,$$
$$Y(0, t) = 0, \qquad \lim_{x \to \infty} Y(x, t) = 0.$$

The problem in the transform $y(x, s)$ is therefore

(2) $\qquad s^2 y(x, s) - s\Phi(x) = a^2 y_{xx}(x, s) \qquad (x > 0),$

(3) $\qquad y(0, s) = 0, \qquad \lim_{x \to \infty} y(x, s) = 0.$

We shall solve the ordinary differential equation (2) by using the Laplace transformation with respect to x. Let $u(z, s)$ denote that transform of $y(x, s)$; that is,

$$u(z, s) = \int_0^\infty e^{-zx} y(x, s) \, dx.$$

Since $y(0, s) = 0$, when we transform both members of equation (2) we obtain the equation

$$s^2 u(z, s) - s\varphi(z) = a^2[z^2 u(z, s) - y_x(0, s)],$$

where $\varphi(z)$ is the transform of $\Phi(x)$. Let the unknown function of s, $y_x(0, s)$ be denoted by C. Then the solution of the last equation can be written

$$u(z, s) = \frac{C}{z^2 - \dfrac{s^2}{a^2}} - \frac{s}{a^2} \varphi(z) \frac{1}{z^2 - \dfrac{s^2}{a^2}},$$

and performing the inverse transformation with respect to z, with the aid of the convolution, we have

$$(4) \qquad y(x, s) = \frac{aC}{s} \sinh \frac{sx}{a} - \frac{1}{a} \int_0^x \Phi(\xi) \sinh \frac{s}{a} (x - \xi) \, d\xi.$$

In view of the condition requiring $y(x, s)$ to vanish as x tends to infinity, it is necessary that the coefficient of $e^{sx/a}$ on the right of equation (4) should vanish as x becomes infinite. Writing the hyperbolic sines in terms of exponential functions, that coefficient is seen to be

$$\frac{aC}{2s} - \frac{1}{2a} \int_0^x \Phi(\xi) e^{-\frac{s\xi}{a}} \, d\xi.$$

Since the limit of this function is to be zero as $x \to \infty$, we have

$$\frac{aC}{s} = \frac{1}{a} \int_0^\infty \Phi(\xi) e^{-\frac{s\xi}{a}} \, d\xi.$$

Substituting this into equation (4) we can write the result in the form

$$2ay(x, s) = \int_x^\infty \Phi(\xi) e^{-\frac{s(\xi - x)}{a}} \, d\xi - \int_0^\infty \Phi(\xi) e^{-\frac{s(x + \xi)}{a}} \, d\xi$$
$$+ \int_0^x \Phi(\xi) e^{-\frac{s(x - \xi)}{a}} \, d\xi.$$

Let us integrate each integral here by parts in order to introduce a factor $1/s$. Since $\Phi(0) = 0$, this gives the formula

(5) $$y(x, s) = \frac{1}{2s} \Phi(x) + \frac{1}{2s} \int_x^\infty \Phi'(\xi) e^{-\frac{s(\xi - x)}{a}} \, d\xi$$

$$- \frac{1}{2s} \int_0^\infty \Phi'(\xi) e^{-\frac{s(x + \xi)}{a}} \, d\xi - \frac{1}{2s} \int_0^x \Phi'(\xi) e^{-\frac{s(x - \xi)}{a}} \, d\xi.$$

Now

$$L^{-1} \left\{ \frac{1}{s} e^{-\frac{s(\xi - x)}{a}} \right\} = 1 \quad \text{when } at > \xi - x,$$

$$= 0 \quad \text{when } at < \xi - x;$$

that is, this function of ξ vanishes except when $\xi < x + at$, and the inverse transform of the second term of the right-hand member of equation (5) becomes

$$\tfrac{1}{2} \int_x^{x+at} \Phi'(\xi) \, d\xi = \tfrac{1}{2}\Phi(x + at) - \tfrac{1}{2}\Phi(x).$$

Similarly,

$$L^{-1} \left\{ \frac{1}{s} e^{-\frac{s(x + \xi)}{a}} \right\} = 1 \quad \text{if } at > x + \xi,$$

$$= 0 \quad \text{if } at < x + \xi;$$

so that if $at > x$ this is unity when $0 < \xi < at - x$, and if $at < x$ it is zero for all positive ξ. Hence the third term on the right of (5) has the inverse transform

$$- \tfrac{1}{2} \int_0^{at-x} \Phi'(\xi) \, d\xi = - \tfrac{1}{2}\Phi(at - x) \quad \text{when } at > x,$$

$$0 \quad \text{when } at < x.$$

Likewise we find that the inverse transform of the last term in equation (5) is

$$- \tfrac{1}{2}\Phi(x) \qquad\qquad \text{when } at > x,$$

$$- \tfrac{1}{2}\Phi(x) + \tfrac{1}{2}\Phi(x - at) \qquad \text{when } at < x.$$

Our formula for the displacements is therefore

(6) $$Y(x, t) = \tfrac{1}{2}[\Phi(at + x) - \Phi(at - x)] \quad \text{when } t > \frac{x}{a},$$

$$= \tfrac{1}{2}[\Phi(x + at) + \Phi(x - at)] \quad \text{when } t < \frac{x}{a}.$$

It is not difficult to see that this function satisfies all the conditions of our boundary value problem.

It is interesting to note that instantaneous positions of the string can be sketched easily with the aid of this formula when $\Phi(x)$ is prescribed. The graph of the function $\Phi(x - at)$ for $x > at$, for example, is obtained by translating the graph of $\Phi(x)$ to the right through the distance at.

PROBLEMS

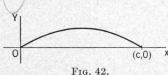

1. A string is stretched between two fixed points $(0, 0)$ and $(c, 0)$. If it is displaced into the curve $Y = b \sin (\pi x/c)$ and released from rest in that position (Fig. 42), set up the boundary value problem for the displacements and derive the formula for the displacement $Y(x, t)$. Verify the result; that is, show that it satisfies all the conditions of the problem. Also describe the motion of the string.

Fig. 42.

$$Ans. \ Y(x, t) = b \cos \frac{\pi a t}{c} \sin \frac{\pi x}{c}.$$

2. If the initial displacement of the string in Prob. 1 is changed to

$$Y(x, 0) = b \sin \frac{n\pi x}{c} \qquad (0 \leqq x \leqq c),$$

where n is any integer, derive the formula

$$Y(x, t) = b \cos \frac{n\pi a t}{c} \sin \frac{n\pi x}{c}.$$

Note that the sum of two or more of these functions with different values of n and b is a solution of the equation of motion that satisfies all the boundary conditions except one. What is the initial displacement $Y(x, 0)$ corresponding to such a superposition of solutions?

3. A string is stretched between the fixed points $(0, 0)$ and $(c, 0)$ and its points are given initial velocities $v_0 \sin (\pi x/c)$, so that the initial conditions are

$$Y(x, 0) = 0, \qquad Y_t(x, 0) = v_0 \sin \frac{\pi x}{c} \qquad (0 \leqq x \leqq c).$$

Derive the formula

$$Y(x, t) = \frac{v_0 c}{\pi a} \sin \frac{\pi a t}{c} \sin \frac{\pi x}{c},$$

and describe the motion.

4. A cylindrical shaft is rotating with an angular velocity ω when its ends $x = c$ and $x = -c$ are suddenly clamped (Fig. 43). The angular displacement $\Theta(x, t)$ then satisfies the conditions

$$\Theta_{tt}(x, t) = a^2\Theta_{xx}(x, t) \qquad (-c < x < c, t > 0),$$
$$\Theta(x, 0) = 0, \qquad \Theta_t(x, 0) = \omega,$$
$$\Theta(-c, t) = \Theta(c, t) = 0,$$

where $a^2 = E_s/\delta$ (Sec. 33). Derive the formula

$$\theta(x, s) = \frac{\omega}{s^2}\left(1 - \frac{\cosh \dfrac{sx}{a}}{\cosh \dfrac{sc}{a}}\right)$$

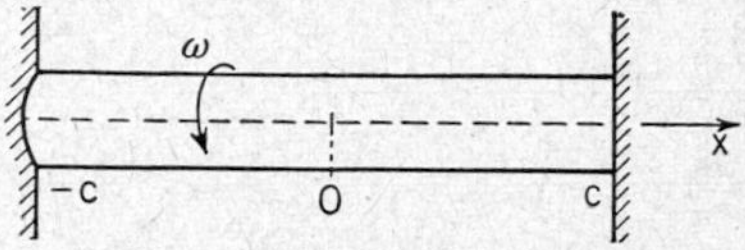

for the transform of $\Theta(x, t)$.

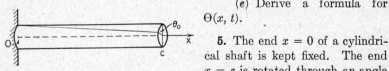

FIG. 43.

(a) Show that the formula for the displacement of the middle section is

$$\Theta(0, t) = \omega t \qquad\qquad \text{when } t \leqq \frac{c}{a}$$

$$= \omega\frac{c}{a} - \omega H\left(\frac{2c}{a}, t - \frac{c}{a}\right) \qquad \text{when } t \geqq \frac{c}{a},$$

where H is the triangular wave function of Sec. 19 (Fig. 10). Show $\Theta(0, t)$ graphically.

(b) The torque T across any section is $-E_s I\Theta_x$, where I is the moment of inertia of the section with respect to the axis of the shaft. Show that the torque acting on the support at $x = c$ is

$$T(c, t) = \frac{E_s I\omega}{a} M\left(\frac{2c}{a}, t\right),$$

where M is the square wave function of Sec. 19 (Fig. 9).

(e) Derive a formula for $\Theta(x, t)$.

5. The end $x = 0$ of a cylindrical shaft is kept fixed. The end $x = c$ is rotated through an angle θ_0 and, when all parts of the bar have come to rest, this end is released (Fig. 44). Thus the angular displacement $\Theta(x, t)$ satisfies the boundary conditions

FIG. 44.

$$\Theta(x, 0) = \theta_0\frac{x}{c}, \qquad \Theta_t(x, 0) = 0,$$
$$\Theta(0, t) = 0, \qquad \Theta_x(c, t) = 0.$$

Show that the displacement of the free end at each instant is

$$\Theta(c, t) = \theta_0 - \theta_0 \frac{a}{c} H\left(\frac{2c}{a}, t\right),$$

where H is the triangular wave function (Fig. 10).

6. An unstrained elastic bar is moving lengthwise with velocity v_0 when its end $x = c$ is suddenly clamped (Fig. 45). Show that the force on the support at $x = c$ is

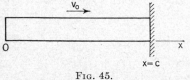

$$\frac{v_0 E A}{a} M\left(\frac{2c}{a}, t\right),$$

Fig. 45.

where A is the area of the cross section of the bar and M is the square wave function (Fig. 9).

7. An infinite string stretched along the x-axis is given a prescribed initial displacement and released from rest in that position. Thus

$$Y_{tt}(x, t) = a^2 Y_{xx}(x, t) \quad (-\infty < x < \infty, t > 0),$$
$$Y(x, 0) = \Phi(x), \qquad Y_t(x, 0) = 0 \quad (-\infty < x < \infty),$$
$$\lim_{x \to -\infty} Y(x, t) = 0, \qquad \lim_{x \to \infty} Y(x, t) = 0.$$

Derive the formula

$$Y(x, t) = \tfrac{1}{2}[\Phi(x + at) + \Phi(x - at)],$$

and verify this solution.

8. Let the points of the infinite string of Prob. 7 be given a prescribed initial velocity $\psi(x)$ instead of an initial displacement; that is,

$$Y(x, 0) = 0, \qquad Y_t(x, 0) = \psi(x) \quad (-\infty < x < \infty).$$

Derive the solution

$$Y(x, t) = \frac{1}{2a} [\Phi(x + at) - \Phi(x - at)],$$

where

$$\Phi(x) = \int_0^x \psi(\xi) \, d\xi.$$

37. Temperatures in a Semi-infinite Solid. Let $U(x, t)$ denote the temperature at each point of a homogeneous solid at time t when conditions are such that at each instant the temperature depends only on x, the distance of the point from a fixed plane. If K is the thermal conductivity, the time rate of flow of heat per unit area, or the flux of heat, by conduction across any plane perpendicular to the x-axis is

(1)
$$\Phi = -K \frac{\partial U}{\partial x};$$

that is, the flux is proportional to the gradient of the temperature. As a consequence, it is not difficult to show that when the variations in the function $U(x, t)$ are the result of heat transfer by conduction the function must satisfy the equation

(2)
$$\frac{\partial U}{\partial t} = k \frac{\partial^2 U}{\partial x^2},$$

where $k = K/(c\delta)$. The coefficient k is called the diffusivity, c is the specific heat, and δ is the density. We have assumed that K is constant.

This equation is a simple form of the equation of conduction, or the heat equation.* It is also called the equation of diffusion since it is satisfied by the concentration U of a substance that is diffusing into a porous solid.

Let us now derive the formula for the temperature $U(x, t)$ in a semi-infinite solid $x \geqq 0$, initially at temperature zero, when a constant flux of heat is maintained at the boundary $x = 0$ (Fig. 46). In this idealized case of a thick slab of material, we shall substitute, for the thermal condition at the right-hand boundary, the condition that U tends to zero as x tends to infinity.

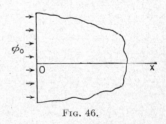

FIG. 46.

The boundary value problem is then

(3) $\qquad U_t(x, t) = kU_{xx}(x, t) \qquad (x > 0, t > 0),$

(4) $\qquad U(x, 0) = 0 \qquad\qquad\qquad (x > 0),$

(5) $\qquad -KU_x'(0, t) = \phi_0, \quad \lim_{x \to \infty} U(x, t) = 0 \qquad (t > 0).$

As in our earlier problems, it is advantageous to use a formal procedure to obtain the required formula, that is, a procedure in which we do not fully justify all steps, and then verify our final result as the required solution.

---

* For a derivation of the heat equation see, for example, the author's "Fourier Series and Boundary Value Problems," Chap. 2.

Let $u(x, s)$ be the transform, with respect to t, of the temperature function $U(x, t)$. Transforming the members of equations (3) and (5), we have the following problem in ordinary differential equations which $u(x, s)$ must satisfy:

$$su(x, s) = ku_{xx}(x, s) \qquad (x > 0),$$

$$-Ku_x(0, s) = \frac{\phi_0}{s}, \qquad \lim_{x \to \infty} u(x, s) = 0.$$

The solution of this problem is

$$u(x, s) = \frac{\phi_0 \sqrt{k}}{Ks \sqrt{s}} e^{-x\sqrt{\frac{s}{k}}}.$$

According to formula (5), Sec. 20, we can write

$$L^{-1}\left\{\frac{1}{\sqrt{s}} e^{-x\sqrt{\frac{s}{k}}}\right\} = \frac{1}{\sqrt{\pi t}} e^{-\frac{x^2}{4kt}},$$

and in view of the factor $1/s$ in our formula for $u(x, s)$ it follows that

$$U(x, t) = \frac{\phi_0}{K} \sqrt{\frac{k}{\pi}} \int_0^t e^{-\frac{x^2}{4k\tau}} \frac{d\tau}{\sqrt{\tau}}$$

$$= \frac{\phi_0 x}{K \sqrt{\pi}} \int_{\frac{x}{2\sqrt{kt}}}^{\infty} \frac{1}{\lambda^2} e^{-\lambda^2} d\lambda,$$

where the second integral is obtained from the first by the substitution $\lambda = x/(2\sqrt{k\tau})$. Upon integrating the last integral by parts, we find that

$$U(x, t) = \frac{\phi_0}{K \sqrt{\pi}} \left(2 \sqrt{kt} e^{-\frac{x^2}{4kt}} - 2x \int_{\frac{x}{2\sqrt{kt}}}^{\infty} e^{-\lambda^2} d\lambda\right).$$

We can therefore write our formula in terms of the complementary error function (Sec. 20) in the form

$$(6) \qquad U(x, t) = \frac{\phi_0}{K}\left[2 \sqrt{\frac{kt}{\pi}} e^{-\frac{x^2}{4kt}} - x \operatorname{erfc}\left(\frac{x}{2\sqrt{kt}}\right)\right].$$

We can show that the function (6) satisfies all our conditions (3), (4), and (5). Note, for instance, that

$$U_x(x, t) = \frac{\phi_0}{K}\left[-\frac{x}{\sqrt{\pi kt}} e^{-\frac{x^2}{4kt}} - \text{erfc}\left(\frac{x}{2\sqrt{kt}}\right) + \frac{x}{\sqrt{\pi kt}} e^{-\frac{x^2}{4kt}} \right]$$

$$= -\frac{\phi_0}{K}\text{erfc}\left(\frac{x}{2\sqrt{kt}}\right),$$

and since erfc $0 = 1$ it follows that condition (5) is satisfied. Also

$$U_{xx}(x, t) = \frac{\varphi_0}{K}\frac{1}{\sqrt{\pi kt}} e^{-\frac{x^2}{4kt}},$$

and the product of this function by k is the same as $\partial U/\partial t$ found from formula (6). Therefore our function satisfies the heat equation. It is easy to see that the condition (4) in the form $U(x, +0) = 0$ and the second of conditions (5) is satisfied by our function (6).

We observe that

$$U(0, t) = \frac{2\phi_0 \sqrt{k}}{K \sqrt{\pi}} \sqrt{t}.$$

Thus the temperature of the face of the solid must vary as $\sqrt{t}$ in order that the flux of heat through the face shall be constant.

38. The Flux under Variable Surface Temperature. Let the temperature of the face of a semi-infinite solid $x \geq 0$ be a prescribed function $F(t)$ of time. If the initial temperature is zero, the temperature function $U(x, t)$ is the solution of the boundary value problem

$$U_t(x, t) = kU_{xx}(x, t) \qquad (x > 0, t > 0),$$
$$U(x, 0) = 0 \qquad (x > 0),$$
$$U(0, t) = F(t), \quad \lim_{x \to \infty} U(x, t) = 0 \qquad (t > 0).$$

The transform $u(x, s)$ of $U(x, t)$, therefore, satisfies the conditions

$$su(x, s) = ku_{xx}(x, s) \qquad (x > 0),$$
$$u(0, s) = f(s), \quad \lim_{x \to \infty} u(x, s) = 0,$$

where $f(s)$ is the transform of $F(t)$. It follows that

(1) $$u(x, s) = f(s) e^{-x\sqrt{\frac{s}{k}}}.$$

Let us first study the flux of heat through the face of the solid,

$$\Phi(t) = -KU_x(0, t).$$

The transform of this function, $-Ku_x(0, s)$, according to formula (1), is

$$(2) \qquad \varphi(s) = \frac{K}{\sqrt{k}} \sqrt{s}\, f(s) = \frac{K}{\sqrt{k}} \, sf(s) \, \frac{1}{\sqrt{s}}.$$

Since $s^{-\frac{1}{2}} = L\{(\pi t)^{-\frac{1}{2}}\}$ and $sf(s) = L\{F'(t)\} + F(+0)$, assuming that $F(t)$ is a continuous function, then

$$\varphi(s) = \frac{K}{\sqrt{k}} \left[\frac{F(+0)}{\sqrt{s}} + L\{F'(t)\} \, \frac{1}{\sqrt{s}} \right]$$

and with the aid of the convolution it follows that

$$(3) \qquad \Phi(t) = \frac{K}{\sqrt{\pi k}} \left[\frac{F(+0)}{\sqrt{t}} + \int_0^t \frac{F'(t-\tau)}{\sqrt{\tau}} \, d\tau \right],$$

when $F(t)$ is continuous.

Whenever $F(+0) \neq 0$, then the flux is infinite initially; in fact it is of the order of $t^{-\frac{1}{2}}$ as t approaches zero. When $F(t)$ is a constant F_0, for example,

$$\Phi(t) = \frac{KF_0}{\sqrt{\pi k}} \frac{1}{\sqrt{t}}.$$

The total amount of heat absorbed by the solid through a unit area of the face at time t is

$$Q(t) = \int_0^t \Phi(\tau) \, d\tau.$$

Hence

$$q(s) = \frac{1}{s} \, \varphi(s) = \frac{K}{\sqrt{k}} \frac{1}{\sqrt{s}} f(s),$$

and therefore

$$(4) \quad Q(t) = \frac{K}{\sqrt{\pi k}} \int_0^t \frac{F(\tau)}{\sqrt{t-\tau}} \, d\tau = \frac{K}{\sqrt{\pi k}} \int_0^t \frac{F(t-\tau)}{\sqrt{\tau}} \, d\tau.$$

For example, if

$$(5) \qquad\qquad F(t) = F_0 \qquad \text{when } t < t_0,$$
$$= 0 \qquad \text{when } t > t_0,$$

it follows from formula (4) that

$$(6) \qquad\qquad Q(t) = \frac{2KF_0}{\sqrt{\pi k}} \sqrt{t} \qquad\qquad \text{when } t \leqq t_0,$$

$$= \frac{2KF_0}{\sqrt{\pi k}} (\sqrt{t} - \sqrt{t - t_0}) \quad \text{when } t \geqq t_0.$$

This function is shown in Fig. 47.   Its greatest value is

$$2KF_0 \sqrt{t_0/(\pi k)},$$

which is assumed at the instant $t = t_0$.

Returning to formula (1) for $u(x, s)$ and noting that, according to formula (4) of Sec. 20,

$$e^{-x \sqrt{\frac{s}{k}}} = L \left\{ \frac{x}{2 \sqrt{\pi k t^3}} e^{-\frac{x^2}{4kt}} \right\},$$

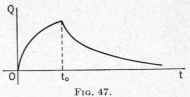

FIG. 47.

we can write, with the aid of the convolution,

$$U(x, t) = \frac{x}{2 \sqrt{\pi k}} \int_0^t \frac{F(t - \tau)}{\tau^{\frac{3}{2}}} e^{-\frac{x^2}{4k\tau}} d\tau.$$

Substituting a new variable of integration, we have for the general temperature formula

$$(7) \qquad U(x, t) = \frac{2}{\sqrt{\pi}} \int_{\frac{x}{2\sqrt{kt}}}^{\infty} F\left(t - \frac{x^2}{4k\lambda^2} \right) e^{-\lambda^2} d\lambda.$$

When the temperature of the surface is constant,

$$(8) \qquad F(t) = F_0,$$

the temperature within the solid is therefore

$$(9) \qquad U(x, t) = F_0 \, \text{erfc} \left(\frac{x}{2 \sqrt{kt}} \right).$$

Since this is a function of F_0 and $x/\sqrt{kt}$ only, it follows that the rate of heating is proportional to k, for if k had been increased and t decreased so that kt is unchanged, the temperature at any given distance x from the face is the same.   It is also interesting to note that for a fixed k two points x_1 and x_2 will have equal temperatures at times t_1 and t_2 provided $x_1/\sqrt{t_1} = x_2/\sqrt{t_2}$, that is, if

$$\frac{x_1}{x_2} = \sqrt{\frac{t_1}{t_2}}.$$

This is sometimes called the law of times in the conduction of heat in semi-infinite solids.

When the surface temperature is

$$(10) \qquad\qquad F(t) = F_0 \qquad \text{when } 0 < t < t_0,$$
$$= 0 \qquad \text{when } t > t_0,$$

then $F(t - x^2/4k\lambda^2) = F_0$ when λ is such that

$$0 < t - \frac{x^2}{4k\lambda^2} < t_0,$$

and it is zero for other values of λ. If $t < t_0$, this inequality is true for every λ, and if $t > t_0$, it is true if $\lambda < x/\sqrt{4k(t - t_0)}$. Thus it follows from formula (7) that

$$(11) \quad U(x, t) = F_0 \, \text{erfc} \left(\frac{x}{2 \sqrt{kt}} \right) \qquad\qquad \text{when } t < t_0,$$

$$= F_0 \left[\text{erf} \left(\frac{x}{2 \sqrt{k(t - t_0)}} \right) - \text{erf} \left(\frac{x}{2 \sqrt{kt}} \right) \right]$$
$$\text{when } t > t_0.$$

PROBLEMS

1. A thick slab of iron with thermal diffusivity $k = 0.15$ c.g.s. (centimeter-gram-second) unit is initially at 0°C. throughout. Its surface is suddenly heated to a temperature of 500°C. and maintained at that temperature for 5 min., after which the surface is kept chilled to 0°C. Find the temperature to the nearest degree at a depth of 10 cm. below the surface (*a*) at the end of 5 min.; (*b*) at the end of 10 min.

$\qquad\qquad\qquad\qquad\qquad$ *Ans.* (*a*) 146°C.; (*b*) 82°C.

2. Solve Prob. 1 if the slab is made of firebrick with $k = 0.007$ c.g.s. unit. $\qquad\qquad\qquad\qquad\qquad$ *Ans.* (*a*) 0°C.; (*b*) 0°C.

3. The surface of a thick slab of concrete with $k = 0.005$ c.g.s. unit, initially at 0°C., undergoes the temperature changes described in Prob. 1. Show that at each instant the temperature at any depth x_1 in the concrete slab is the same as the temperature at the depth $x_2 = 10 \sqrt{3} \, x_1$ in the iron slab. Generalize this result for materials with diffusivities k_1 and k_2 and any common time interval t_0 of heating the surfaces of the slabs.

4. At time $t = 0$, the brakes of an automobile are applied, bringing the automobile to a stop at time t_0. Assuming that the rate of generating heat at the surface of the brake bands varies linearly with the time, then

$$U_x(0, t) = A(t - t_0),$$

where A is a positive constant and x is the distance from the face of the band. If t_0 is not large, the band can be assumed to be a semi-infinite solid $x \geqq 0$. If the initial temperature of the band is taken as zero, show that the temperature at the face is

$$U(0, t) = \frac{2A}{3} \sqrt{\frac{k}{\pi}} \sqrt{t} \, (3t_0 - 2t) \qquad (0 \leqq t \leqq t_0).$$

Hence show that this temperature is greatest at the instant $t = \frac{1}{2}t_0$ and that this maximum temperature is

$$\sqrt{2} \, U(0, t_0).$$

39. Temperatures in a Slab. The initial temperature of a slab of homogeneous material bounded by the planes $x = 0$ and $x = l$ is u_0. Let us find the formula for the temperatures in this solid

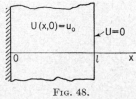

FIG. 48.

after the face $x = 0$ is insulated and the temperature of the face $x = l$ is reduced to zero (Fig. 48).

The temperature function $U(x, t)$ satisfies the following conditions

$$U_t(x, t) = kU_{xx}(x, t) \qquad (0 < x < l, t > 0),$$
$$U(x, 0) = u_0 \qquad (0 < x < l),$$
$$U_x(0, t) = 0, \qquad U(l, t) = 0 \qquad (t > 0).$$

The transform therefore satisfies the conditions

(1) $$su(x, s) - u_0 = ku_{xx}(x, s),$$
(2) $$u_x(0, s) = 0, \qquad u(l, s) = 0.$$

The solution of the ordinary differential equation (1) that satisfies the first of the conditions (2) is

$$u(x, s) = \frac{u_0}{s} + C \cosh x \sqrt{\frac{s}{k}},$$

where C is an arbitrary function of s. Since $u(l, s) = 0$, it follows that

$$C = -\frac{u_0}{s} \frac{1}{\cosh l \sqrt{\frac{s}{k}}},$$

and therefore

(3) $$u(x, s) = u_0 \left[\frac{1}{s} - \frac{1}{s} \frac{\cosh x \sqrt{\frac{s}{k}}}{\cosh l \sqrt{\frac{s}{k}}} \right].$$

Let us write

$$q = \sqrt{\frac{s}{k}},$$

and note that

$$\frac{\cosh xq}{\cosh lq} = e^{-lq}(e^{xq} + e^{-xq})\frac{1}{1 + e^{-2lq}}$$

$$= [e^{-(l-x)q} + e^{-(l+x)q}]\sum_{0}^{\infty}(-1)^n e^{-2nlq}$$

$$= \sum_{n=0}^{\infty}(-1)^n\{\exp[-q(ml - x)] + \exp[-q(ml + x)]\},$$

where $m = 2n + 1$. We have seen (Sec. 20) that

$$\frac{1}{s}e^{-\alpha\sqrt{s}} = L\left\{\operatorname{erfc}\left(\frac{\alpha}{2\sqrt{t}}\right)\right\}, \qquad (\alpha \geqq 0).$$

Therefore

$$\frac{1}{s}\exp[-q(ml \pm x)] = L\left\{\operatorname{erfc}\left(\frac{ml \pm x}{2\sqrt{kt}}\right)\right\},$$

and it follows formally from equation (3) that

$$(4) \quad U(x, t) = u_0 - u_0\sum_{n=0}^{\infty}(-1)^n\left\{\operatorname{erfc}\left[\frac{(2n+1)l - x}{2\sqrt{kt}}\right]\right.$$

$$\left. + \operatorname{erfc}\left[\frac{(2n+1)l + x}{2\sqrt{kt}}\right]\right\}.$$

We shall not take up the verification of this formula since a complete discussion would be lengthy. However, it is not difficult to show with the aid of the ratio test that the series converges uniformly with respect to x and t and that the series can be differentiated term by term. Since the value of the complementary error function here decreases rapidly as n increases, the convergence of the series is rapid, especially when t is small. Moreover the error function is one that is tabulated so that the series is well adapted to computation.

40. A Bar with Variable End Temperature. Let us determine the formula for the temperature $U(x, t)$ in a bar with its lateral surface insulated against the flow of heat when the initial temperature is zero and one end is kept at temperature zero while the temperature of the other end is a prescribed function of t.

If we take the unit of length as the length of the bar (Fig. 49) and select the unit of time such that $(1/k)\, \partial U/\partial t'$ becomes $\partial U/\partial t$,

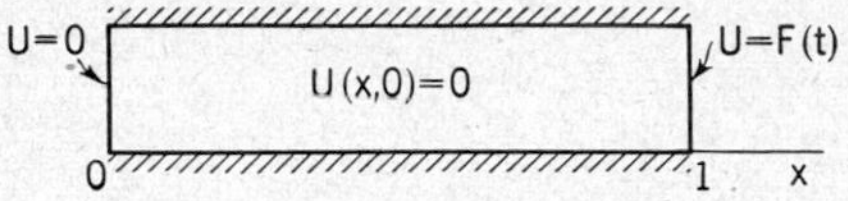

FIG. 49.

that is, so that $t = kt'$ where t' is the original and t the new variable, our boundary value problem can be written as follows.

$$
\begin{aligned}
U_t(x, t) &= U_{xx}(x, t) & (0 < x < 1,\, t > 0),\\
U(x, 0) &= 0 & (0 < x < 1),\\
U(0, t) &= 0, \qquad U(1, t) = F(t) & (t > 0).
\end{aligned}
$$

The problem in the transform of $U(x, t)$ is therefore

$$
su(x, s) = u_{xx}(x, s),
$$
$$
u(0, s) = 0, \qquad u(1, s) = f(s),
$$

and the solution of this problem is

$$
u(x, s) = f(s)\, \frac{\sinh x \sqrt{s}}{\sinh \sqrt{s}}.
$$

Proceeding as in the last section, we can write

$$
\frac{\sinh x \sqrt{s}}{\sinh \sqrt{s}} = \sum_{0}^{\infty} \left[e^{-(2n+1-x)\sqrt{s}} - e^{-(2n+1+x)\sqrt{s}} \right]
$$

and thus, when $0 \le x < 1$,

$$
L^{-1} \left\{ \frac{\sinh x \sqrt{s}}{\sinh \sqrt{s}} \right\} = \frac{1}{2\sqrt{\pi t^3}} \sum_{n=0}^{\infty} \left[(m - x)e^{-\frac{(m-x)^2}{4t}} \right.
$$
$$
\left. - (m + x)e^{-\frac{(m+x)^2}{4t}} \right],
$$

where $m = 2n + 1$. With the aid of a convolution, we can now write the inverse transform of $u(x, s)$. After the usual change in the variable of integration, our result can be written

(1) $\quad U(x, t) = \dfrac{2}{\sqrt{\pi}} \sum_{n=0}^{\infty} \left\{ \int_{\frac{m-x}{2\sqrt{t}}}^{\infty} F\left[t - \dfrac{(m - x)^2}{4\lambda^2}\right] e^{-\lambda^2}\, d\lambda \right.$

$\qquad\qquad \left. - \int_{\frac{m+x}{2\sqrt{t}}}^{\infty} F\left[t - \dfrac{(m + x)^2}{4\lambda^2}\right] e^{-\lambda^2}\, d\lambda \right\} \quad (m = 2n + 1).$

When the temperature of the face $x = 1$ is constant,

(2) $\qquad\qquad\qquad F(t) = F_0,$

our formula can be written

(3) $\quad U(x, t) = F_0 \sum_{0}^{\infty} \left[\operatorname{erf}\left(\dfrac{2n + 1 + x}{2\sqrt{t}}\right) - \operatorname{erf}\left(\dfrac{2n + 1 - x}{2\sqrt{t}}\right)\right],$

a result that is not difficult to verify as a solution. Note in particular that

$$U(1, t) = \dfrac{2}{\sqrt{\pi}} F_0 \sum_{0}^{\infty} \int_{\frac{n}{\sqrt{t}}}^{\frac{n+1}{\sqrt{t}}} e^{-\lambda^2}\, d\lambda$$

$$= \dfrac{2}{\sqrt{\pi}} F_0 \int_{0}^{\infty} e^{-\lambda^2}\, d\lambda = F_0.$$

PROBLEMS

1. The initial temperature of a semi-infinite solid $x \geqq 0$ is zero, and the flux of heat through the face is a prescribed function of time

$$-KU_x(0, t) = \Phi(t).$$

Derive the temperature formula

$$U(x, t) = \dfrac{x}{K\sqrt{\pi}} \int_{\frac{x}{2\sqrt{kt}}}^{\infty} \Phi\left(t - \dfrac{x^2}{4k\lambda^2}\right) \dfrac{e^{-\lambda^2}}{\lambda^2}\, d\lambda \qquad (x > 0).$$

Also show that the temperature of the face must be

$$U(0, t) = \dfrac{1}{K}\sqrt{\dfrac{k}{\pi}} \int_{0}^{t} \Phi(\tau)(t - \tau)^{-\frac{1}{2}}\, d\tau.$$

2. Let the flux of heat through the face of the semi-infinite solid of Prob. 1 be

$$\Phi(t) = \phi_0 \qquad \text{when } t < t_0,$$
$$= 0 \qquad \text{when } t > t_0,$$

and let $\phi_0 t_0 = Q_0$ be kept fixed while t_0 approaches zero and ϕ_0 grows. Show that under these conditions

$$\lim_{t_0 \to 0} u(x, s) = \frac{Q_0 \sqrt{k}}{K} \frac{1}{\sqrt{s}} e^{-x \sqrt{\frac{s}{k}}},$$

and thus obtain formally the formula

$$\lim_{t_0 \to 0} U(x, t) = \frac{Q_0}{K} \sqrt{\frac{k}{\pi t}} e^{-\frac{x^2}{4kt}}.$$

3. Assuming the temperature function $U(x, t)$ is such that the following integral exists, the total quantity of heat that passes through a unit area of a plane perpendicular to the x-axis is

$$Q(x) = -K \int_0^\infty U_x(x, t) \, dt.$$

Note that the integral here is the Laplace transform of $U_x(x, t)$ when $s = 0$, and hence, formally, that

$$Q(x) = -Ku_x(x, 0) = -K \lim_{s \to 0} u_x(x, s).$$

In the semi-infinite solid of Sec. 38, show that

$$Q(x) = \frac{K}{\sqrt{k}} \lim_{s \to 0} \sqrt{s} \, f(s),$$

provided this limit exists. For the slab of Sec. 39, show that

$$Q(l) = \frac{Ku_0}{\sqrt{k}} \lim_{s \to 0} \frac{\tanh l \sqrt{\frac{s}{k}}}{\sqrt{s}} - \frac{Ku_0 l}{k}.$$

4. The initial temperature of a semi-infinite solid $x \geqq 0$ is

$$U(x, 0) = U_0(x),$$

where the function $U_0(x)$ is prescribed. If the face $x = 0$ is kept at temperature zero $(t > 0)$ and if $U(x, t)$ approaches zero as $x \to \infty$, derive the formula

$$U(x, t) = \frac{1}{2\sqrt{\pi kt}} \int_0^\infty U_0(\xi) [e^{-\frac{(\xi - x)^2}{4kt}} - e^{-\frac{(\xi + x)^2}{4kt}}] \, d\xi \quad (t > 0).$$

5. Show that the sum of the temperature function found in Prob. 4 and of the function (7) of Sec. 38 represents the temperature in the solid $x \geqq 0$ when the temperature of the face is $F(t)$ and the initial temperature is $U_0(x)$.

6. If heat is being generated in a long wire $x \geqq 0$ at the rate of $c\rho R(t)$ units per unit length, so that $c\rho R(t)$ has such dimensions as

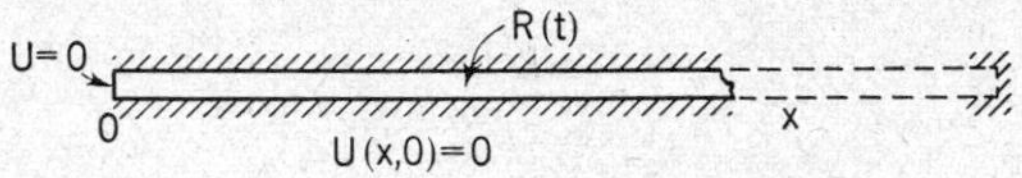

FIG. 50.

calories per centimeter per second, and if the lateral surface of the wire is insulated, the heat equation becomes

$$U_t(x, t) = kU_{xx}(x, t) + R(t).$$

Let the initial temperature be zero and the end $x = 0$ be kept at that temperature, and let the distant end be insulated (Fig. 50); that is,

$$U(x, 0) = 0, \qquad U(0, t) = 0, \qquad \lim_{x \to \infty} U_x(x, t) = 0.$$

Derive the formula

$$U(x, t) = Q(t) - \frac{2}{\sqrt{\pi}} \int_{\frac{x}{2\sqrt{kt}}}^{\infty} Q\left(t - \frac{x^2}{4k\lambda^2}\right) e^{-\lambda^2} \, d\lambda,$$

where

$$Q(t) = \int_0^t R(\tau) \, d\tau.$$

7. In Prob. 6 let the rate of generation of heat be constant,

$$R(t) = R_0,$$

and derive the formula

$$U(x, t) = R_0 \int_0^t \operatorname{erf}\left(\frac{x}{2\sqrt{k\tau}}\right) d\tau.$$

8. In Prob. 6 let the heat be generated as follows:

$$
\begin{aligned}
R(t) &= R_0 & &\text{when } t < t_0, \\
&= 0 & &\text{when } t > t_0.
\end{aligned}
$$

Show formally that if $R_0 t_0 = A$ where A is fixed, and R_0 is permitted to increase, then

$$\lim_{t_0 \to 0} U(x, t) = A \operatorname{erf}\left(\frac{x}{2\sqrt{kt}}\right).$$

9. The convex surface of a wire of unit length is insulated while its ends $x = 0$ and $x = 1$ are kept at temperature zero. Heat is being generated at a constant rate in the wire so that the heat equation takes the form

$$U_t(x, t) = kU_{xx}(x, t) + B \quad (0 < x < 1, t > 0).$$

If the initial temperature is

$$U(x, 0) = \frac{B}{2k} (x - x^2),$$

derive the temperature formula

$$U(x, t) = \frac{B}{2k} (x - x^2).$$

10. The initial temperature of a bar of unit length is zero, and the end $x = 1$ is kept at that temperature (Fig. 51). The convex surface and the end $x = 0$ are insulated, and the unit of time is taken so that $k = 1$. If heat is generated in the bar such that the heat equation is

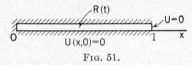

FIG. 51.

$$U_t(x, t) = U_{xx}(x, t) + R(t), \quad (0 < x < 1, t > 0),$$

derive the temperature formula

$$U(x, t) = \int_0^t R(\tau)\, d\tau - \int_0^t R(t - \tau)E(x, \tau)\, d\tau,$$

where

$$E(x, t) = \sum_0^\infty (-1)^n \left[\operatorname{erfc} \left(\frac{2n + 1 + x}{2\sqrt{t}} \right) + \operatorname{erfc} \left(\frac{2n + 1 - x}{2\sqrt{t}} \right) \right].$$

41. A Semi-infinite Radiating Wire. If there is heat transfer at the surface of a long slender wire according to Newton's law of transfer, that is, such that the rate of heat loss is proportional to the difference between the temperature of the wire and the temperature of the surroundings, and if the temperature of the surroundings is taken as zero, the heat equation becomes

$$(1) \qquad U_t(x, t) = kU_{xx}(x, t) - hU(x, t).$$

The constant h is sometimes called the relative emissivity. Let the initial temperature be zero, and let the distant end be kept at that temperature. Then if the end $x = 0$ is kept at the con-

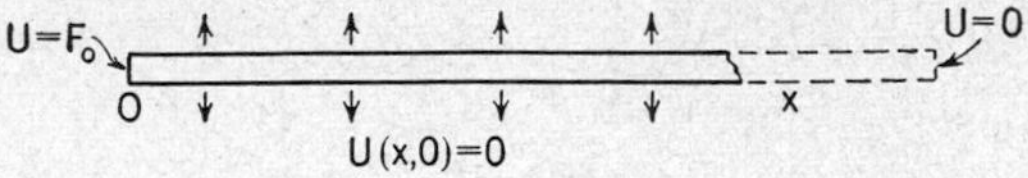

$$U = F_0$$

$$O$$ $$x$$

$$U(x,0) = 0$$ $$U = 0$$

Fig. 52.

stant temperature F_0 (Fig. 52), the boundary conditions are

$$U(x, 0) = 0 \qquad (x > 0),$$
$$U(0, t) = F_0, \qquad \lim_{x \to \infty} U(x, t) = 0 \qquad (t > 0).$$

The problem in the transform is then

$$ku_{xx}(x, s) - (s + h)u(x, s) = 0 \qquad (x > 0),$$
$$u(0, s) = \frac{F_0}{s}, \qquad \lim_{x \to \infty} u(x, s) = 0.$$

The solution of this problem is

$$(2) \qquad u(x, s) = \frac{F_0}{s} e^{-x \sqrt{\frac{(s+h)}{k}}}.$$

Knowing the inverse transform of $e^{-x\sqrt{s/k}}$ we can write, with the aid of our property on substitution of $s + h$ for s (Sec. 7),

$$L^{-1}\{e^{-x \sqrt{\frac{(s+h)}{k}}}\} = \frac{xe^{-ht}}{2\sqrt{\pi k t^3}} e^{-\frac{x^2}{4kt}}.$$

It follows from formula (2) that

$$U(x, t) = \frac{F_0 x}{2\sqrt{\pi k}} \int_0^t e^{-h\tau} e^{-\frac{x^2}{4k\tau}} \tau^{-\frac{3}{2}} d\tau$$

$$(3) \qquad = \frac{2F_0}{\sqrt{\pi}} \int_{\frac{x}{2\sqrt{kt}}}^{\infty} e^{-\left(\lambda^2 + \frac{hx^2}{4k\lambda^2}\right)} d\lambda,$$

where the second integral is obtained by the substitution $\lambda = \frac{1}{2}x/\sqrt{k\tau}$.

The formula (3) can be changed to a more useful form with the aid of the integration formula

$$(4) \qquad \frac{2}{\sqrt{\pi}} \int_{\frac{a}{b}}^{\infty} e^{-\left(\lambda^2 + \frac{a^2}{\lambda^2}\right)} d\lambda = \cosh 2a - \frac{1}{2} \left[e^{2a} \operatorname{erf}\left(b + \frac{a}{b}\right) \right.$$

$$\left. - e^{-2a} \operatorname{erf}\left(b - \frac{a}{b}\right) \right],$$

where a and b are constants or parameters independent of λ. This formula can be verified by noting that the derivative, when the parameter a is fixed, of the left-hand member with respect to b, namely,

$$\frac{2a}{\sqrt{\pi}\, b^2}\, e^{-\left(\frac{a^2}{b^2}+b^2\right)},$$

is identical to the derivative of the right-hand member with respect to b, also that both members vanish as $b \to 0$. Setting $a = \frac{1}{2}x\sqrt{h/k}$ and $b = \sqrt{ht}$ in formula (4), we see that our temperature formula (3) can be written

$$(5) \quad U(x, t) = \frac{F_0}{2}\left[2\cosh x\sqrt{\frac{h}{k}} - e^{x\sqrt{\frac{h}{k}}}\operatorname{erf}\left(\sqrt{ht} + \frac{x}{2\sqrt{kt}}\right) \right.$$
$$\left. + e^{-x\sqrt{\frac{h}{k}}}\operatorname{erf}\left(\sqrt{ht} - \frac{x}{2\sqrt{kt}}\right)\right].$$

It is not difficult to verify this as the solution of our problem. In obtaining formula (5) we have found a desirable form of the inverse transform of the function $u(x, s)$ defined by equation (2).

PROBLEMS

1. Let the initial temperature of the long radiating wire ($x \geqq 0$) be u_0, and let the end $x = 0$ be kept at temperature zero while the distant

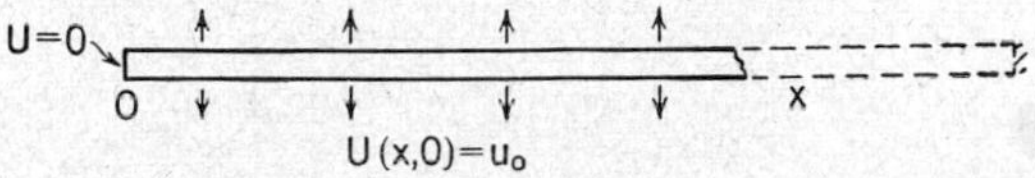

FIG. 53.

end is insulated (Fig. 53). Derive the temperature formula

$$U(x, t) = u_0 e^{-ht}\operatorname{erf}\left(\frac{x}{2\sqrt{kt}}\right).$$

2. Let the long radiating wire ($x \geqq 0$) contain a constant source of heat so that the heat equation is

$$U_t(x, t) = kU_{xx}(x, t) - hU(x, t) + R_0 \quad (x > 0, t > 0).$$

If the initial temperature of the wire is zero and if the end $x = 0$ is kept at temperature zero while the distant end is insulated, derive the temperature formula

$$U(x, t) = R_0\int_0^t e^{-h\tau}\operatorname{erf}\left(\frac{x}{2\sqrt{k\tau}}\right)d\tau.$$

Integrate the integral here by parts, and use the method or the results of Sec. 41 to obtain a more useful formula for $U(x, t)$.

3. The initial temperature of a solid sphere of unit radius is zero, and all points of the surface are kept at the temperature $F(t)$ (Fig. 54). If $U_1(r, t)$ is the temperature at time t at a point whose distance from the center of the sphere is r, the heat equation is

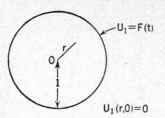

FIG. 54.

$$\frac{\partial U_1}{\partial t} = \frac{1}{r}\frac{\partial^2 (rU_1)}{\partial r^2} \qquad (0 \leqq r < 1, t > 0),$$

where the time unit has been selected so that $k = 1$. The boundary conditions are

$$U_1(r, 0) = 0, \qquad (0 \leqq r < 1); \qquad U_1(1, t) = F(t), \qquad (t > 0).$$

Assuming that $U_1(0, t)$ has a finite transform, show that

$$u_1(r, s) = \frac{1}{r} f(s) \frac{\sinh r \sqrt{s}}{\sinh \sqrt{s}}$$

and hence that

$$U_1(r, t) = \frac{1}{r} U(r, t)$$

where $U(x, t)$ is the function given by formula (1), Sec. 40.

42. Temperatures in a Semi-infinite Composite Solid.

Let us find the formual for the temperatures in a solid $x \geqq 0$ composed of a layer $0 \leqq x \leqq a$ of one material initially at the uniform temperature A in contact with a semi-infinite solid $x \geqq a$ of another material initially at temperature zero, when the face $x = 0$ is kept insulated (Fig. 55).

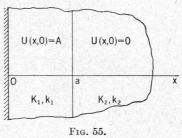

FIG. 55.

Let $U(x, t)$ denote the temperature in the solid. If the thermal conductivity and diffusivity are K_1 and k_1, respectively, in the first part and K_2 and k_2 in the second part, the boundary value problem is the following one:

(1) $\qquad\qquad U_t(x, t) = k_1 U_{xx}(x, t) \quad (0 < x < a, t > 0),$

(2) $\qquad\qquad U_t(x, t) = k_2 U_{xx}(x; t) \qquad (x > a, t > 0),$

(3) $\qquad U(x, 0) = A (0 < x < a), \qquad U(x, 0) = 0 \quad (x > a),$

$$(4) \qquad U_x(0, t) = 0, \qquad \lim_{x \to \infty} U(x, t) = 0 \qquad (t > 0),$$

$$(5) \qquad U(a - 0, t) = U(a + 0, t) \qquad (t > 0),$$

$$(6) \qquad K_1 U_x(a - 0, t) = K_2 U_x(a + 0, t) \qquad (t > 0).$$

Condition (5) states that the temperature at the interface $x = a$ is the same after $t = 0$ when the point approaches the interface from either direction. Condition (6) states that the flux of heat out of the first part through the interface must be equal to the flux into the second part, at each instant.

The problem in the transform of $U(x, t)$ is then

$$(7) \qquad su(x, s) - A = k_1 u_{xx}(x, s) \qquad (0 < x < a),$$

$$(8) \qquad su(x, s) = k_2 u_{xx}(x, s) \qquad (x > a),$$

$$(9) \qquad u_x(0, s) = 0, \qquad \lim_{x \to \infty} u(x, s) = 0,$$

$$(10) \qquad u(a - 0, s) = u(a + 0, s),$$
$$K_1 u_x(a - 0, s) = K_2 u_x(a + 0, s).$$

The solution of equation (7) that satisfies the first of conditions (9) is

$$u(x, s) = C_1 \cosh x \sqrt{\frac{s}{k_1}} + \frac{A}{s} \qquad (0 \leqq x < a),$$

and the solution of (8) that satisfies the second of conditions (9) is

$$u(x, s) = C_2 e^{-x \sqrt{\frac{s}{k_2}}} \qquad (x > a).$$

By applying the conditions (10) to these functions, the values of C_1 and C_2 are easily found. The formulas for $u(x, s)$ can then be written

$$(11) \quad u(x, s) = \frac{A}{s} \left[1 - \frac{1 - \lambda}{2} \frac{e^{-\sigma(a-x)} + e^{-\sigma(a+x)}}{1 - \lambda e^{-2\sigma a}} \right] \qquad (0 < x < a),$$

$$(12) \quad u(x, s) = \frac{A(1 + \lambda)}{2s} \frac{e^{-\sigma \mu(x-a)} - e^{-\sigma(2a+\mu x - \mu a)}}{1 - \lambda e^{-2\sigma a}} \qquad (x > a),$$

where we have put

$$\sigma = \sqrt{\frac{s}{k_1}}, \qquad \mu = \sqrt{\frac{k_1}{k_2}}, \qquad \lambda = \frac{K_1 \sqrt{k_2} - K_2 \sqrt{k_1}}{K_1 \sqrt{k_2} + K_2 \sqrt{k_1}},$$

and therefore $\sigma \mu = \sqrt{s/k_2}$ and $|\lambda| < 1$.

Since $\sigma > 0$,

$$\frac{1}{1 - \lambda e^{-2\sigma a}} = \sum_0^\infty \lambda^n e^{-2n\sigma a},$$

and equation (11) can be written

$$\frac{u(x, s)}{A} = \frac{1}{s} - \frac{1 - \lambda}{2} \sum_{n=0}^\infty \frac{\lambda^n}{s} \left[e^{-\sigma(ma-x)} + e^{-\sigma(ma+x)} \right] \quad (0 < x < a),$$

where $m = 2n + 1$, and (12) can be written

$$\frac{u(x, s)}{A} = \frac{1 + \lambda}{2} \sum_{n=0}^\infty \frac{\lambda^n}{s} \left[e^{-\sigma(2na+\mu x-\mu a)} - e^{-\sigma(2na+2a+\mu x-\mu a)} \right] \quad (x > a).$$

When b is a positive number independent of s, we know that

$$\frac{1}{s} e^{-\sigma b} = \frac{1}{s} e^{-b \sqrt{\frac{s}{k_1}}} = L \left\{ \mathrm{erfc} \left(\frac{b}{2 \sqrt{k_1 t}} \right) \right\}.$$

It therefore follows from the last two expressions for $u(x, s)$ that

$$(13) \quad U(x, t) = A - A \frac{1 - \lambda}{2} \sum_0^\infty \lambda^n \left\{ \mathrm{erfc} \left[\frac{(2n + 1)a - x}{2 \sqrt{k_1 t}} \right] \right.$$

$$\left. + \mathrm{erfc} \left[\frac{(2n + 1)a + x}{2 \sqrt{k_1 t}} \right] \right\} \quad (0 < x < a),$$

$$(14) \quad U(x, t) = A \frac{1 + \lambda}{2} \sum_0^\infty \lambda^n \left\{ \mathrm{erfc} \left[\frac{2na + \mu(x - a)}{2 \sqrt{k_1 t}} \right] \right.$$

$$\left. - \mathrm{erfc} \left[\frac{(2n + 2)a + \mu(x - a)}{2 \sqrt{k_1 t}} \right] \right\} \quad (x > a).$$

This is the formal solution of the problem. It can be verified as the actual solution.* The convergence of the series here is quite rapid, especially when t is small.

PROBLEM

The entire surface of a long bar is insulated. The bar is composed of two semi-infinite bars, the first $(-\infty < x < 0)$ made of material with thermal coefficients K_1 and k_1, and the second $(0 < x < \infty)$ of material

---

* This verification together with a discussion of the uniqueness of the solution is included in a paper by the author in the *Philosophical Magazine*, Ser. 7, Vol. 31, pp. 81–87, 1941.

with coefficients K_2 and k_2 (Fig. 56). If the initial temperature of the first part is zero and of the second part is u_0, the boundary value problem

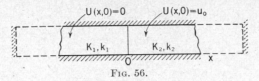

FIG. 56.

in the temperature function is

$$U_t(x, t) = k_1 U_{xx}(x, t) \qquad (x < 0, t > 0),$$
$$= k_2 U_{xx}(x, t) \qquad (x > 0, t > 0),$$
$$U(x, 0) = 0 \qquad (x < 0),$$
$$= u_0 \qquad (x > 0),$$
$$U(-0, t) = U(+0, t), \qquad K_1 U_x(-0, t) = K_2 U_x(+0, t) \qquad (t > 0),$$
$$\lim_{x \to -\infty} U(x, t) = 0, \qquad \lim_{x \to \infty} U(x, t) = 0.$$

Derive the temperature formula

$$U(x, t) = \frac{u_0}{1 + \lambda} \, \text{erfc}\left(\frac{-x}{2\sqrt{k_1 t}}\right) \qquad (x < 0),$$

$$= \frac{u_0}{1 + \lambda}\left[1 + \lambda \, \text{erf}\left(\frac{x}{2\sqrt{k_2 t}}\right)\right] \qquad (x > 0),$$

where

$$\lambda = \frac{K_1}{K_2}\sqrt{\frac{k_2}{k_1}}.$$

This problem is of considerable importance as a diffusion problem, in which case $U(x, t)$ is the concentration of the diffusing substance.

43. Observations on the Method. All the problems treated in this chapter involve partial differential equations and boundary conditions that are *linear*, that is, of first degree in the unknown function and its derivatives. The limitation of our operational method to the treatment of such linear boundary value problems is a natural one, since we have presented no formula giving the Laplace transform of the product of two functions in terms of the transforms of the individual functions. It is known that the transform of the product of two arbitrary functions can be expressed by a convolution integral of the two transforms, where the integration is one in the complex plane of s. But it is safe to say that no advantage can be anticipated in replacing nonlinear differential forms by complex nonlinear integral forms.

We have dealt essentially in problems with constant coefficients. If the coefficients are functions of t, the variable with respect to which the transformation is made, the transformed problem is not likely to be simpler than the original one. For even when the coefficients are polynomials in t, the transformed problem involves derivatives with respect to s in place of the derivatives with respect to t present in the original one. If the coefficients are not functions of t, the transformed problem will be simpler; but it may still be a difficult problem.

We have made the transformation with respect to time t in all our problems in partial differential equations. If the physical problem involved the first derivative U_t, the initial value $U(x, 0)$ was prescribed; if it involved Y_{tt}, then $Y(x, 0)$ and $Y_t(x, 0)$ were both prescribed. Consequently, when we applied the formula for the transformation of these derivatives, for example,

$$L\{U_t(x, t)\} = su(x, s) - U(x, 0),$$

$u(x, s)$ was the only unknown function arising. But suppose the transformation with respect to x had been applied in the temperature problems. Then if $L\{U(x, t)\} = u(z, t)$,

$$L\{U_{xx}(x, t)\} = z^2 u(z, t) - zU(0, t) - U_x(0, t),$$

and ordinarily not both of the functions $U(0, t)$ and $U_x(0, t)$ would be prescribed, since both the temperature and the flux of heat at the surface $x = 0$ are not usually prescribed. Thus one of these unknown functions may have to be determined with the aid of other boundary conditions, and that determination is often awkward. There are problems, however, in which a transformation with respect to a variable other than time t is useful.

In case there are more than two independent variables, say x, y, and t, a transformation of the equation with respect to t still leaves us with a partial differential equation in the independent variables x and y. This may be attacked by one of the classical methods, such as the method of separation of variables, by one of the Fourier transformations with respect to x or y, or by a Laplace transformation with respect to x or y. The choice should depend on the particular problem.

The operational method of solving partial differential equations is of course not limited to equations of the second order. We shall soon take up a more powerful method of obtaining inverse transforms, and then we can attack problems whose solutions depend upon more involved inverse transformations than those in this chapter.

Finally, it is worth noting that the operational method is well adapted to the solution of problems in differential equations in which some of the given functions or their derivatives are discontinuous. This has been illustrated in the last two chapters. It is one of the remarkable features of the method.

CHAPTER V

FUNCTIONS OF A COMPLEX VARIABLE

For the reader's convenience, we present in this chapter a synopsis of some important definitions and theorems that are needed in the further development of the theory of the Laplace transformation. For a more extensive study of these topics and for proofs of the theorems, the reader may refer to books on the theory of functions of a complex variable. A partial list of such books will be found at the end of the chapter.

44. Complex Numbers. Let i denote the unit imaginary number $\sqrt{-1}$ having the property $i^2 = -1$. If x and y are real numbers, the number

$$z = x + iy$$

is called a complex number with real part x and imaginary coefficient y, written

$$\Re(z) = x, \qquad \Im(z) = y.$$

The conjugate of the complex number z, denoted by $\bar{z}$, is the number

$$\bar{z} = x - iy.$$

Two complex numbers are equal if and only if their real parts are the same and their imaginary parts are the same, and hence

$$x + iy = 0$$

if and only if $x = y = 0$. Addition, subtraction, multiplication, and division of two complex numbers $x_1 + iy_1$ and $x_2 + iy_2$ are based on the rules

$$(x_1 + iy_1) \pm (x_2 + iy_2) = (x_1 \pm x_2) + i(y_1 \pm y_2),$$
$$(x_1 + iy_1)(x_2 + iy_2) = (x_1 x_2 - y_1 y_2) + i(x_1 y_2 + x_2 y_1),$$
$$\frac{x_1 + iy_1}{x_2 + iy_2} = \frac{(x_1 + iy_1)(x_2 - iy_2)}{x_2^2 + y_2^2} = \frac{x_1 x_2 + y_1 y_2}{x_2^2 + y_2^2} + \frac{x_2 y_1 - x_1 y_2}{x_2^2 + y_2^2} i.$$

A complex number $z_1 = x_1 + iy_1$ is represented geometrically either by the point (x_1, y_1) or by the vector from the origin to the point (x_1, y_1) in the complex plane (Fig. 57). In view of the above rule for the addition of two complex numbers, $z_1 + z_2$ is represented by the vector sum of the two vectors representing

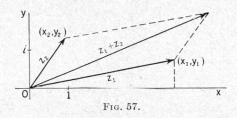

FIG. 57.

z_1 and z_2. The length of the vector representing z is called the absolute value of z,

$$|z| = \sqrt{x^2 + y^2} = \sqrt{z\bar{z}}.$$

Let (r, θ) be the polar coordinates of the point (x, y). Then $|z| = r$ and

$$z = x + iy = r(\cos \theta + i \sin \theta).$$

For two complex numbers in polar form, it can be shown that

$$z_1 z_2 = r_1 r_2 [\cos (\theta_1 + \theta_2) + i \sin (\theta_1 + \theta_2)],$$
$$\frac{z_1}{z_2} = \frac{r_1}{r_2} [\cos (\theta_1 - \theta_2) + i \sin (\theta_1 - \theta_2)];$$

also,

$$z^n = r^n(\cos n\theta + i \sin n\theta),$$

where n is any rational number. It follows that

$$|z_1 z_2| = |z_1||z_2|, \qquad \left|\frac{z_1}{z_2}\right| = \frac{|z_1|}{|z_2|}, \qquad |z^n| = |z|^n.$$

45. Analytic Functions. Let w be a complex variable whose value is uniquely determined by the value of the variable $z = x + iy$; that is, w is a single-valued function of z,

$$w - f(z) = u(x, y) + iv(x, y),$$

where u and v are the real and imaginary parts of w. Thus if

$w = z^2$, then

$$f(z) = (x + iy)^2 = (x^2 - y^2) + 2xyi$$

so that $u = x^2 - y^2$ and $v = 2xy$.

The derivative of w at a point z is

$$\frac{dw}{dz} = f'(z) = \lim_{\Delta z \to 0} \frac{\Delta w}{\Delta z} = \lim_{\Delta z \to 0} \frac{f(z + \Delta z) - f(z)}{\Delta z},$$

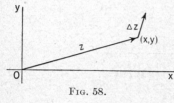

Fig. 58.

provided this limit exists. But here $\Delta z = \Delta x + i\,\Delta y$ and the value of the limit may depend upon the direction of the vector representing Δz (Fig. 58). Suppose, for instance, that $\Delta y = 0$ so that $\Delta z = \Delta x$. Then since $\Delta w = \Delta u + i\,\Delta v$,

$$\frac{dw}{dz} = \lim_{\Delta x \to 0} \left(\frac{\Delta u}{\Delta x} + i\frac{\Delta v}{\Delta x} \right) = \frac{\partial u}{\partial x} + i\frac{\partial v}{\partial x}.$$

But if $\Delta x = 0$ so that $\Delta z = i\,\Delta y$, then

$$\frac{dw}{dz} = -i\frac{\partial u}{\partial y} + \frac{\partial v}{\partial y}.$$

If the two values of dw/dz so found are to be the same, it is therefore necessary that u and v satisfy the two conditions

$$\frac{\partial u}{\partial x} = \frac{\partial v}{\partial y}, \qquad \frac{\partial v}{\partial x} = -\frac{\partial u}{\partial y}.$$

These are known as the *Cauchy-Riemann* conditions.

Let u and v be functions whose partial derivatives $\partial u/\partial x, \partial u/\partial y, \partial v/\partial x$, and $\partial v/\partial y$ are continuous functions of x and y and satisfy the Cauchy-Riemann conditions, in some region a point (x, y). Then it can be shown that the derivative dw/dz of the function

$$w = u + iv$$

exists at that point and has the same value regardless of the manner in which Δz tends to zero.

A single-valued function $f(z)$ having a unique derivative at each point in some region of the xy-plane that includes the point z in its interior is called *analytic* at the point z. If $f(z) = u + iv$ is an analytic function, then the partial derivatives of u and v

of the first order are continuous and satisfy the Cauchy-Riemann conditions. Conversely, when these conditions on u and v are satisfied, $u + iv$ is an analytic function.

Consider, for example, the function

$$f(z) = z^2 = x^2 - y^2 + 2xyi.$$

Here

$$\frac{\partial u}{\partial x} = 2x = \frac{\partial v}{\partial y}, \qquad \frac{\partial v}{\partial x} = 2y = -\frac{\partial u}{\partial y},$$

and it follows that the function z^2 is analytic at every point z, where z is finite. Just as in the case of real functions it follows from the definition of the derivative that $f'(z) = 2z$.

If n is any positive integer, the function $f(z) = z^n$ is analytic at each finite point z, and $f'(z) = nz^{n-1}$.

Similarly it can be seen that the function

$$f(z) = \frac{1}{z} = \frac{1}{x + iy} = \frac{x}{x^2 + y^2} - \frac{y}{x^2 + y^2} i$$

is analytic except at $z = 0$, where u and v and their derivatives do not exist. Also, $f'(z) = -1/z^2$ $(z \neq 0)$.

The sum or product of any two analytic functions is an analytic function, and the quotient is analytic except at those points where the denominator vanishes. Consequently, every polynomial

$$a_0 + a_1z + a_2z^2 + \cdots + a_nz^n$$

is an analytic function, and the quotient of any two polynomials is analytic except at the points for which the polynomial in the denominator vanishes. In fact, it can be shown that an analytic function of an analytic function is analytic. Given, for example, that $\sin z$ is analytic it follows that $\sin (1 + z^2)$ is analytic and that $\sin (1/z)$ is analytic except at $z = 0$.

Consider now some examples of single-valued functions that are not analytic. The conjugate of z,

$$\bar{z} = x - iy,$$

is a function of z since its value is determined by z. In this case $u = x$ and $v = -y$; hence

$$\frac{\partial u}{\partial x} = 1, \qquad \frac{\partial v}{\partial y} = -1$$

and the Cauchy-Riemann conditions are not satisfied. Therefore $f(z) = \bar{z}$ is not analytic at any point. The reader may find it instructive to apply the definition of the derivative to this function and show directly that the value of $f'(z)$ in this case depends upon the manner in which Δz tends to zero.

As another example, let

$$f(z) = |z|^2 = x^2 + y^2.$$

Here $v \equiv 0$, and $\partial u/\partial x = 2x$, $\partial u/\partial y = 2y$, so that the Cauchy-Riemann conditions are not satisfied. There is no region in which this function of z is analytic.

The functions $\mathfrak{R}(z) = x$, $\mathfrak{I}(z) = y$, the sum or difference of these functions, and such a function as

$$f(z) = x^2 + iy^2,$$

are further examples of single-valued nonanalytic functions of z.

46. Exponential and Trigonometric Functions. The exponential function with imaginary exponent may be defined by the equation

$$(1) \qquad e^{iy} = \cos y + i \sin y.$$

This definition is suggested by formally replacing t by iy in the power series expansion $\sum\limits_{0}^{\infty} t^n/n!$ of e^t. Thus

$$e^{iy} = \sum_{0}^{\infty} \frac{i^n y^n}{n!} = 1 - \frac{y^2}{2!} + \frac{y^4}{4!} - \cdots + i\left(y - \frac{y^3}{3!} + \frac{y^5}{5!} - \cdots\right)$$
$$= \cos y + i \sin y.$$

If the exponent is complex, we write

$$(2) \qquad e^z = e^{(x+iy)} = e^x(\cos y + i \sin y).$$

The reader can show that the Cauchy-Riemann conditions are satisfied by the real and imaginary parts of the function e^z, so that the function is analytic for every finite z.

According to the above definition of e^{iy},

$$(3) \qquad e^{-iy} = \cos y - i \sin y$$

and by eliminating first $\sin y$ and then $\cos y$ between equations (1) and (3) we find that

$$\cos y = \frac{e^{iy} + e^{-iy}}{2} = \cosh (iy),$$

$$\sin y = \frac{e^{iy} - e^{-iy}}{2i} = -i \sinh (iy),$$

where, by definition,

$$\cosh z = \frac{e^z + e^{-z}}{2}, \qquad \sinh z = \frac{e^z - e^{-z}}{2}.$$

It is not difficult to show that

$$\cosh z = \cosh x \cos y + i \sinh x \sin y,$$
$$\sinh z = \sinh x \cos y + i \cosh x \sin y.$$

These are analytic functions for every finite z. Each of the remaining hyperbolic functions of z,

$$\tanh z = \frac{\sinh z}{\cosh z}, \qquad \coth z = \frac{1}{\tanh z},$$
$$\text{sech } z = \frac{1}{\cosh z}, \qquad \text{csch } z = \frac{1}{\sinh z},$$

is analytic except at those points where the denominator on the right-hand side vanishes.

The circular functions of z can be defined as follows:

$$\cos z = \frac{e^{iz} + e^{-iz}}{2}, \qquad \sin z = \frac{e^{iz} - e^{-iz}}{2i}, \qquad \tan z = \frac{\sin z}{\cos z},$$

the remaining three being the reciprocals of these. The functions $\cos z$ and $\sin z$ are analytic for every finite z. In view of these definitions, it follows that

$$\cos iy = \cosh y, \qquad \sin iy = i \sinh y.$$

All trigonometric identities for the functions with real arguments can be extended without change of form to the functions with complex arguments; for example,

$$\sin^2 z + \cos^2 z = 1, \qquad \sin (z_1 + z_2) = \sin z_1 \cos z_2$$
$$+ \cos z_1 \sin z_2.$$

The same is true for the relations between the six hyperbolic functions. Furthermore, the formulas for the derivatives of all these functions, including e^z, retain the same form when the argument is complex as they have when the argument is real; thus

$$\frac{d}{dz} e^z = e^z, \qquad \frac{d}{dz} \sin z = \cos z, \qquad \frac{d}{dz} \cos z = - \sin z,$$

and so on.

PROBLEMS

1. Show that

(a) $|z_1 + z_2| \leqq |z_1| + |z_2|$;   (b) $|z_1 - z_2| \geqq ||z_1| - |z_2||$;

(c) $\left| \displaystyle\sum_{n=1}^{m} z_n \right| \leqq \displaystyle\sum_{n=1}^{m} |z_n|.$

2. If w_1 and w_2 are analytic functions of z, use the definition of the derivative to show that

(a) $\dfrac{d}{dz} (w_1 + w_2) = \dfrac{dw_1}{dz} + \dfrac{dw_2}{dz}$;   (b) $\dfrac{d}{dz} (w_1 w_2) = w_1 \dfrac{dw_2}{dz} + w_2 \dfrac{dw_1}{dz}$;

(c) $\dfrac{d}{dz} \left(\dfrac{w_1}{w_2} \right) = \dfrac{\left(w_2 \dfrac{dw_1}{dz} - w_1 \dfrac{dw_2}{dz} \right)}{w_2^2}$;

(d) $\dfrac{d}{dz} w_1(w_2) = \dfrac{dw_1}{dw_2} \dfrac{dw_2}{dz}.$

3. A function $f(z)$ is continuous at $z = z_0$ if $f(z_0)$ exists and $\lim_{\Delta z \to 0} f(z_0 + \Delta z) = f(z_0)$. Show that if $f(z)$ is analytic at z_0 it is necessarily continuous there; but not conversely.

4. For all finite z, show that the function

$$f(z) = a_1 x + b_1 y + c_1 + i(a_2 x + b_2 y + c_2),$$

where the coefficients a_n and b_n are real, is analytic if and only if the coefficients are such that

$$f(z) = (a_1 - ib_1)z + c_1 + ic_2.$$

5. Show that

(a) $|e^z| = e^x$;   (b) $e^{-z} = \dfrac{1}{e^z}$;   (c) $e^{(z_1 + z_2)} = e^{z_1} e^{z_2}.$

6. Show that

(a) $\sin z = \sin x \cosh y + i \cos x \sinh y$;
(b) $\cos z = \cos x \cosh y - i \sin x \sinh y$;
(c) $\sin 2z = 2 \sin z \cos z$;
(d) $\cos (z_1 + z_2) = \cos z_1 \cos z_2 - \sin z_1 \sin z_2$;
(e) $\cosh (z_1 + z_2) = \cosh z_1 \cosh z_2 + \sinh z_1 \sinh z_2.$

7. Prove (a) that the zeros of sin z, that is, the values of z for which the function is zero, are $z = \pm n\pi$ $(n = 0, 1, 2, \cdots)$; (b) that the zeros of sinh z are $z = \pm n\pi i$.

8. Show that tanh z is analytic except at the points $z = \pm (2n - 1)\pi i/2$ $(n = 1, 2, \cdots)$.

9. If w is an analytic function of z, show that

(a) $\dfrac{d}{dz} e^w = e^w \dfrac{dw}{dz}$;   (b) $\dfrac{d}{dz} \sin w = \cos w \dfrac{dw}{dz}$;

(c) $\dfrac{d}{dz} \sinh w = \cosh w \dfrac{dw}{dz}$;   (d) $\dfrac{d}{dz} w^n = n w^{n-1} \dfrac{dw}{dz}$.

47. Branches of Multiple-valued Functions.

According to Sec. 44, if n is a positive integer then

$$z^{\frac{1}{n}} = r^{\frac{1}{n}}\left(\cos \frac{\theta}{n} + i \sin \frac{\theta}{n}\right);$$

here $r^{1/n}$ represents the positive nth root of r. Since

$$z = r(\cos \theta + i \sin \theta) = r[\cos (\theta + 2\pi m) + i \sin (\theta + 2\pi m)],$$

where m is any positive integer, the function $z^{1/n}$ has n distinct values

$$z^{\frac{1}{n}} = r^{\frac{1}{n}}\left(\cos \frac{\theta + 2\pi m}{n} + i \sin \frac{\theta + 2\pi m}{n}\right) \quad (m = 0, 1, \cdots, n - 1).$$

When $n = 2$, for example, we have the function $\sqrt{z}$ with the two values

$$f_1(z) = \sqrt{r}\left(\cos \frac{\theta}{2} + i \sin \frac{\theta}{2}\right),$$

$$f_2(z) = \sqrt{r}\left[\cos \left(\frac{\theta}{2} + \pi\right) + i \sin \left(\frac{\theta}{2} + \pi\right)\right] = -f_1(z)$$

for each z. We may select a definite range for θ, say

$$-\pi \leqq \theta < \pi;$$

then $\pi \leqq \theta + 2\pi < 3\pi$ and $f_1(z)$ is a complex number in either the fourth or first quadrant of the complex plane, since

$$-\frac{\pi}{2} \leqq \frac{\theta}{2} < \frac{\pi}{2},$$

while $f_2(z)$ is a number in either the second or third quadrant. The functions $f_1(z)$ and $f_2(z)$ are called *branches* of $\sqrt{z}$.

If we restrict the polar representation of z by writing, for instance,

$$z = r(\cos \phi + i \sin \phi) \qquad (-\pi \leqq \phi < \pi)$$

with the agreement that the angle in the polar representation will be confined to the range $-\pi$ to π, and if we write

$$\sqrt{z} = \sqrt{r}\left(\cos \frac{\phi}{2} + i \sin \frac{\phi}{2}\right),$$

the function $\sqrt{z}$ so prescribed is single valued. It is the branch $f_1(z)$ of the double-valued function. This function is analytic in the region $r > 0$, $-\pi < \phi < \pi$. The region of the plane of z in which this function is single valued and analytic can be indicated by running a line, called a branch cut, from O along the negative half of the real axis and requiring that z is not to fall on or cross that line (Fig. 59).

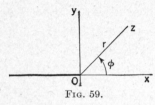

Fig. 59.

Any other ray through O making an angle ϕ_0 with Ox, so that $\phi_0 < \phi < \phi_0 + 2\pi$, would similarly prescribe a definite branch of $\sqrt{z}$. The point O is called a branch point of $\sqrt{z}$.

The function $\sqrt[n]{z}$ has n branches one of which is prescribed by writing

$$z = r(\cos \phi + i \sin \phi) \qquad (\phi_0 \leqq \phi < \phi_0 + 2\pi)$$

for any fixed ϕ_0, and

$$\sqrt[n]{z} = \sqrt[n]{r}\left(\cos \frac{\phi}{n} + i \sin \frac{\phi}{n}\right).$$

The single-valued function so defined is analytic when $r > 0$, $\phi_0 < \phi < \phi_0 + 2\pi$, also,

$$\frac{d}{dz} z^{\frac{1}{n}} = \frac{1}{n} z^{\left(\frac{1}{n}-1\right)}.$$

We may define $\log z$ by writing

$$z = r(\cos \theta + i \sin \theta) = re^{i\theta}$$

where $-\pi \leqq \theta < \pi$, say, and

$$\log z = \log r + \log e^{i\theta} = \log r + i\theta.$$

But z is not affected by adding a multiple of 2π to θ, and thus, without limiting the range of θ, the function is multiple valued,

$$\log z = \log r + i(\theta + 2n\pi) \quad (n = 0, 1, 2, \cdots).$$

Each one of the branches of this function is an inverse of the exponential function; that is, if

$$w = \log z \qquad \text{then } z = e^w.$$

Any one of the single-valued branches $\theta_0 < \theta < \theta_0 + 2\pi$ is analytic for $r > 0$, and

$$\frac{d}{dz} \log z = \frac{1}{z}.$$

The inverse trigonometric and inverse hyperbolic functions are also multiple valued. They can be expressed in terms of square roots and logarithms, and hence they are single valued in suitably restricted regions.

48. Properties of Analytic Functions. Let C be a circle $r = a$. The integral of the function z^2 around this circle can be written in terms of real integrals,

$$\int_C z^2 \, dz = \int_0^{2\pi} a^2 e^{2i\theta} ae^{2i\theta} 2i \, d\theta$$

$$= 2a^3 i \int_0^{2\pi} \cos 4\theta \, d\theta - 2a^3 \int_0^{2\pi} \sin 4\theta \, d\theta,$$

and therefore

$$\int_C z^2 \, dz - 0.$$

Similarly, if C is any closed curve, the integral can be expressed in terms of real variables with the aid of the equation of the curve, and the value of the integral is zero. Suppose, for example, that C is a square with $(0, 0)$ and $(1, 1)$ as opposite vertices (Fig. 60). Then $z = x$ on the lower side, $z = 1 + iy$ on the right-hand side, etc., and integrating in the counterclockwise direction around C we have

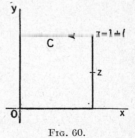

Fig. 60.

$$\int_C z^2 \, dz = \int_0^1 x^2 \, dx + \int_0^1 (1 + iy)^2 i \, dy + \int_1^0 (x + i)^2 \, dx$$

$$+ \int_1^0 (iy)^2 i \, dy.$$

The second integral on the right can be written

$$\int_0^1 (1 + iy)^2 i \, dy = -2 \int_0^1 y \, dy + i \int_0^1 (1 - y^2) \, dy,$$

and in this way it can be seen that the integral of z^2 around the square is zero.

If any function $f(z)$ is analytic in a region R of the complex plane, then

$$\int_C f(z) \, dz = 0,$$

where C is any closed curve lying entirely within the region R. This is the *Cauchy-Goursat* theorem. Moreover, if the integral of a single-valued continuous function around every closed curve in some region R is zero, that function is analytic in R, so that this property is a characteristic one for analytic functions.

As an immediate consequence of the theorem, the line integral

$$\int_{z_0}^z f(\xi) \, d\xi = F(z)$$

along any path joining z_0 to z is independent of the path as long as the path lies within a region in which $f(z)$ is analytic. Also $F'(z) = f(z)$ so that $F(z)$ is the indefinite integral of $f(z)$ when z_0 is an arbitrary constant.

The contour integral of the function z^{-1} must therefore vanish when taken around any closed curve not containing $z = 0$. But if the curve is, for example, the circle $r = a$ enclosing $z = 0$, then

$$\int_C \frac{dz}{z} = \int^{2\pi} \frac{1}{ae^{i\theta}} ae^{i\theta} i \, d\theta = i \int_0^{2\pi} d\theta = 2\pi i.$$

The value of a function $f(z)$, analytic in a region R, is determined at a point z_0 by the values of the function at the points on any curve C lying within R and enclosing the point z_0 (Fig. 61) as follows:

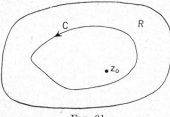

FIG. 61.

$$f(z_0) = \frac{1}{2\pi i} \int_C \frac{f(z) \, dz}{z - z_0},$$

where the z traverses C in the counterclockwise direction. This is *Cauchy's integral formula*. Note that the integrand is not analytic at $z = z_0$.

One of the most important characteristics of analytic functions is that they can be represented by convergent power series. A necessary and sufficient condition that $f(z)$ be analytic at $z = z_0$ is that

$$f(z) = a_0 + a_1(z - z_0) + a_2(z - z_0)^2 + \cdots$$
$$+ a_n(z - z_0)^n + \cdots,$$

where the coefficients a_n are complex constants depending on the function and on the point z_0, and where the series converges for all z within some circle about z_0.   The series can be differentiated term by term, and the new series represents $f'(z)$ within that circle.   Consequently the derivative of any order $f^{(n)}(z)$ is also analytic at z_0.   In fact the coefficients in the above series have the values

$$a_0 = f(z_0), \qquad a_n = \frac{1}{n!}\, f^{(n)}(z_0);$$

that is, the series is Taylor's series for $f(z)$.

The power series representations of the elementary functions have the same forms when their arguments are complex as they have when their arguments are real.   For example,

$$e^z = \sum_0^\infty \frac{z^n}{n!}, \qquad \sin z = \sum_1^\infty \frac{z^{2n-1}}{(2n - 1)!},$$

where we have taken $z_0 = 0$. These two series converge and represent their functions for every finite z, so the radius of the circle of convergence is infinite.

We have noted various possible methods of determining whether a single-valued function is analytic.   It may be an analytic function of a function that is known to be analytic. It may be represented by a convergent power series.   We may show that its real and imaginary parts satisfy the Cauchy-Riemann conditions, or that $f'(z)$ exists and is unique, or that the function satisfies the conditions of the Cauchy-Goursat theorem.

49. Poles and Residues.   A point at which a single-valued function fails to be analytic is called a *singular point*.   An *isolated* singular point is a point interior to a region throughout which the function is analytic except at the point itself.   The function $(1 - z)^{-1}$, for example, has an isolated singularity at $z = 1$.   The function

$$f(z) = \frac{\sin z}{z} = \frac{1}{z}\left(z - \frac{z^3}{3!} + \frac{z^5}{5!} - \cdots\right)$$

has such a singularity at $z = 0$. But if we define this function at $z = 0$ as $f(0) = 1$, then at all points

$$f(z) = 1 - \frac{z^2}{3!} + \frac{z^4}{5!} - \cdots;$$

this function is analytic at $z = 0$. Any such singular point that can be removed by properly defining the function at the point is called a *removable* singular point.

The circle of convergence of the power series representation of an analytic function extends to the nearest singularity. Thus the circle of convergence of the series in powers of z for the function $(z - 1)^{-1}$ is the circle $r = 1$.

If a function $f(z)$ becomes infinite at $z = z_0$ in such a manner that, for some positive integer n, the function

$$\phi(z) = (z - z_0)^n f(z)$$

has a removable singularity at z_0 and $\phi(z_0) \neq 0$, then z_0 is called a *pole* of *order n* of $f(z)$. Here $\phi(z_0)$ denotes the value that must be assigned to $\phi(z)$ at z_0 in order to make the function $\phi(z)$ analytic at z_0. If $n = 1$, the pole is a *simple* pole.

The simplest examples of functions with poles are quotients of polynomials. Thus the function z^{-2} has a pole of order 2 at $z = 0$. The function

$$f(z) = \frac{z^2 + 1}{z^2 - 1} = \frac{z^2 + 1}{(z - 1)(z + 1)}$$

has simple poles at $z = 1$ and $z = -1$. Here the function $\phi(z)$ corresponding to the pole $z = 1$ is $(z^2 + 1)/(z + 1)$.

The function

$$\coth z = \frac{\cosh z}{\sinh z}$$

has simple poles at $z = 0$, $\pm\pi i$, $\pm 2\pi i$, $\cdots$. For the pole at $z = 0$,

$$\phi(z) = z \coth z = \frac{\cosh z}{1 + \frac{z^2}{3!} + \frac{z^4}{5!} + \cdots},$$

provided $\phi(0) = 1$, and the function on the right is analytic at $z = 0$, since it is the quotient of two analytic functions and the denominator does not vanish at $z = 0$. Likewise it can be shown that $z = \pi i$ is a simple pole by expanding sinh z in powers of $(z - \pi i)$. For

$$\sinh z = \sinh \pi i + (z - \pi i) \cosh \pi i + \frac{1}{2!}(z - \pi i)^2 \sinh \pi i + \cdots$$

$$= -(z - \pi i) - \frac{1}{3!}(z - \pi i)^3 - \frac{1}{5!}(z - \pi i)^5 - \cdots$$

and it follows that $(z - \pi i) \coth z$ is analytic at $z = \pi i$ provided this product is defined to be 1 when $z = \pi i$. In the same way, it can be shown that $z = \pm n\pi i$ are simple poles.

Let z_0 be a simple pole of the function $f(z)$. Then

$$\phi(z) = (z - z_0)f(z) = A_{-1} + A_0(z - z_0) + A_1(z - z_0)^2 + \cdots$$

where $A_{-1} = \phi(z_0)$ is the value $\phi(z)$ must have at z_0 in order to be analytic there. This value can be written

$$(1) \qquad A_{-1} = \phi(z_0) = \lim_{z \to z_0} (z - z_0)f(z).$$

We therefore have the representation

$$(2) \quad f(z) = \frac{A_{-1}}{z - z_0} + A_0 + A_1(z - z_0) + A_2(z - z_0)^2 + \cdots.$$

The number A_{-1} is called the *residue* of $f(z)$ at the pole z_0. In case $f(z)$ is the quotient $p(z)/q(z)$ of two analytic functions, where $p(z_0) \neq 0$, formula (1) for the residue at the simple pole z_0 can be written

$$(3) \qquad A_{-1} = \lim_{z \to z_0} \frac{(z - z_0)p(z)}{q(z)} = \frac{p(z_0)}{q'(z_0)}.$$

The function $e^z/(z^2 - 4)$, for instance, has simple poles at $z = \pm 2$. The residue at the pole $z = 2$ is $e^2/4$, and at $z = -2$ the residue is $-e^{-2}/4$.

If z_0 is a pole of order n of the function $f(z)$, then

$$(4) \quad \phi(z) = (z - z_0)^n f(z) = A_{-n} + A_{-n+1}(z - z_0) + \cdots$$
$$+ A_{-1}(z - z_0)^{n-1} + \cdots$$

in some circle about z_0, and thus

(5) $\quad f(z) = \dfrac{A_{-n}}{(z - z_0)^n} + \dfrac{A_{-n+1}}{(z - z_0)^{n-1}} + \cdots$

$$+ \frac{A_{-1}}{z - z_0} + \sum_{\nu = 0}^{\infty} A_\nu (z - z_0)^\nu.$$

The number A_{-1} is the *residue* of $f(z)$ at z_0. Its numerical value may be found in any particular case by writing out the expansion (4), or by the formula

(6) $\qquad\qquad \phi^{(n-1)}(z_0) = (n - 1)!A_{-1},$

obtained by differentiating (4) successively and setting $z = z_0$.

Let R be a region in which $f(z)$ is analytic except for a pole at z_0 with residue A_{-1}. Then if C is a closed curve in R enclosing z_0, it can be shown that

$$\frac{1}{2\pi i} \int_C f(z)\, dz = A_{-1},$$

where the point z describes C in the counterclockwise direction.

This important result can be generalized to any number of poles. Let $\rho_1, \rho_2, \cdots, \rho_m$ denote the residues of $f(z)$ at the poles $z_1, z_2, \cdots, z_m$, respectively, and let R be a region in which $f(z)$ is analytic except at those poles. Then if C is any closed curve in R enclosing all those poles,

(7) $\qquad\qquad \int_C f(z)\, dz = 2\pi i \sum_{\nu = 1}^{m} \rho_\nu,$

where C is described in the counterclockwise direction. This is Cauchy's *residue theorem*.

As an example, the integral of z^{-1} around any closed path enclosing $z = 0$ is $2\pi i$. As another illustration consider the function

$$f(z) = \frac{1 + z}{z^2(1 - z)},$$

which has a pole of order 2 at $z = 0$ and a simple pole at $z = 1$. To find the residue at the first pole, we may write

$$f(z) = \frac{1 + z}{z^2}(1 + z + z^2 + \cdots)$$

$$= (1 + z)\left(\frac{1}{z^2} + \frac{1}{z} + 1 + z + z^2 + \cdots\right),$$

so that the total coefficient of $1/z$ on the right, or the residue at $z = 0$, is 2. The residue at $z = 1$ is -2 since

$$\lim_{z \to 1} (z - 1)f(z) = \lim_{z \to 1} - \frac{1 + z}{z^2} = -2.$$

According to the residue theorem then, the integral of $f(z)$ over any closed path enclosing both $z = 0$ and $z = 1$ is zero.

An isolated singular point of $f(z)$ that is not removable and not a pole is called an *essential* singularity. For example, the point $z = 0$ is an essential singularity of the function $e^{1/z}$.

We have noted that any single-valued function that is analytic in a region R including z_0 is represented by its Taylor series about z_0 throughout any circle, with center at z_0, lying entirely within R. If the function has an isolated singularity at z_0 and is otherwise analytic in R, the function can be represented by a series of positive and negative powers of $(z - z_0)$, in any circle with center at z_0 lying entirely within R, except of course at z_0 itself. The series is *Laurent's series:*

$$(8) \qquad f(z) = \sum_{-\infty}^{\infty} A_n(z - z_0)^n \qquad (z \neq z_0).$$

The coefficients have the values

$$A_n = \frac{1}{2\pi i} \int_C \frac{f(z)\, dz}{(z - z_0)^{n+1}},$$

where C is any closed curve about z_0 lying entirely within R, and where z describes C in the counterclockwise direction.

If z_0 is a simple pole, the coefficients A_n ($n = -2, -3, \cdots$) in formula (8) are zero and the expansion is that given by equation (2). Equation (5) is another special case of (8).

PROBLEMS

1. Let $p(z)$ denote a polynomial in z. Show that the residues of the function

$$\frac{p(z)}{(z - z_1)(z - z_2)}$$

at the poles z_1 and z_2, when $z_1 \neq z_2$, are $p(z_1)/(z_1 - z_2)$ and $p(z_2)/(z_2 - z_1)$, respectively.

2. The function $f(z) = 1/z^2$ is already written as a Laurent series, with all coefficients zero except one. Hence its residue at $z = 0$ is zero.

In the converse of the Cauchy-Goursat theorem (Sec. 48), what condition is not satisfied by $f(z)$ at $z = 0$? What are the residues of the functions z^{-n} ($n = 3, 4, \cdots$) at the pole $z = 0$?

3. Find the value of the integral of the function $(a + bz + cz^2)/z^3$ around the circle $r = 1$ (a) directly; (b) by using the residue theorem.

Ans. $2\pi ci$.

4. Show that the function $\tan z$ is analytic except for simple poles at $z = \pm(2n - 1)\pi/2$ and that its integral around the square bounded by the lines $x = \pm 2$, $y = \pm 2$ has the value $-4\pi i$.

5. Show that the integral of $\tanh z$ around the circle $r = \pi$ has the value $4\pi i$.

6. Show that $z = 0$ is an essential singularity of the functions $\sin(1/z)$ and $\cos(1/z)$.

7. Using the Cauchy-Riemann conditions, show that if $f(z) = u + iv$ is analytic at a point then u and v satisfy Laplace's equation in two variables there,

$$\frac{\partial^2 u}{\partial x^2} + \frac{\partial^2 u}{\partial y^2} = 0, \qquad \frac{\partial^2 v}{\partial x^2} + \frac{\partial^2 v}{\partial y^2} = 0.$$

50. Analytic Continuation. If a function, known to be analytic in a region R, is defined at all points on an arc of some curve interior to R, the function is uniquely determined throughout R. If the function is zero on the arc, it must therefore vanish throughout R since $f(z) \equiv 0$ is an analytic function.

The function

$$\phi(z) = 1 + z + z^2 + z^3 + \cdots$$

is defined by the series and is analytic for all z within the circle of convergence $r = 1$. Its value there is $(1 - z)^{-1}$. Now the function

$$f(z) = \frac{1}{1 - z}$$

is everywhere analytic except at $z = 1$ and $f(z) \equiv \phi(z)$ when $|z| < 1$. There can be no other function analytic outside the circle $r = 1$ that is identical to $\phi(z)$ inside the circle. The function $f(z)$ is called the *analytic continuation* of $\phi(z)$.

As another example, consider the function

$$\phi(z) = \int_0^\infty e^{-zt} \, dt.$$

Since $e^{-zt} = e^{-xt-iyt}$, the integral converges and the function $\phi(z)$

is defined only if $x > 0$. Its value is $1/z$. Now the function

$$f(z) = \frac{1}{z}$$

is everywhere analytic except at $z = 0$, and it is identical to $\phi(z)$ when $\Re(z) > 0$. Hence $f(z)$ is the analytic continuation of $\phi(z)$. In either example, $\phi(z)$ is called an *element* of the function $f(z)$.

51. An Extension of Cauchy's Integral Formula. In Sec. 48 we noted that the value of an analytic function $f(z)$ at any point z_0 inside a closed curve C is given in terms of the value of the function on C by Cauchy's integral formula

$$f(z_0) = \frac{1}{2\pi i} \int_C \frac{f(z)\,dz}{z - z_0}.$$

In the next chapter we shall need an extension of this formula to the case in which C is replaced by a straight line parallel to the axis of imaginaries and z_0 is any point to the right of that line. To establish such an extension of the theorem, let us first introduce the notion of order of a function of a complex variable. A function $f(z)$ is of the order of z^k as z tends to infinity, written

$$f(z) = O(z^k) \qquad \text{as } z \to \infty,$$

if some positive numbers M and r_0 exist such that $|z^{-k}f(z)| < M$ when $|z| > r_0$; that is, if

$$|f(z)| < M|z|^k$$

for all $|z|$ sufficiently large.

Theorem. *Let the function $f(z)$ be analytic when $R(z) \geqq \gamma$ and of the order $O(z^{-k})$ as $|z| \to \infty$ in that half-plane, where γ and k are real constants and $k > 0$. Then if z_0 is any complex number with $\Re(z_0) > \gamma$,*

$$(1) \qquad f(z_0) = -\frac{1}{2\pi i} \lim_{\beta \to \infty} \int_{\gamma - i\beta}^{\gamma + i\beta} \frac{f(z)\,dz}{z - z_0}.$$

The notation here is intended to imply that the integration takes place along the line $x = \gamma$, where $z = x + iy$, from the point $\gamma - i\beta$ to $\gamma + i\beta$. The limit of this integral as $\beta \to \infty$ is called the Cauchy *principal value* of the integral from $y = -\infty$ to $y = \infty$ along the line.

Consider the rectangle (Fig. 62) with vertices $\gamma \pm i\beta$, $\beta \pm i\beta$, where $\beta > |\gamma|$ and β is large enough that the fixed point z_0 lies inside the rectangle. Let S denote the path consisting of the open rectangle obtained by removing the left-hand side of our rectangle, where z traverses S in the counterclockwise direction.

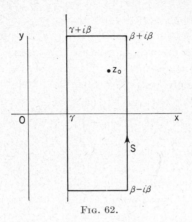

FIG. 62.

Applying Cauchy's integral formula to the closed rectangle, we can write

$$(2) \qquad \frac{1}{2\pi i} \left[-\int_{\gamma-i\beta}^{\gamma+i\beta} \frac{f(z)\,dz}{z - z_0} + \int_S \frac{f(z)\,dz}{z - z_0} \right] = f(z_0).$$

It is not difficult to show that the integral of a function $\phi(z)$ of a complex variable over a path Q satisfies the inequality

$$\left| \int_Q \phi(z)\,dz \right| \leqq \int_Q |\phi(z)\,dz|,$$

also that $\int_Q |dz|$ is the length of the path Q. Now the absolute value of the integrand of the second integral in equation (2) satisfies the following inequality, in view of the order condition on $f(z)$:

$$\left| \frac{f(z)}{z - z_0} \right| < \frac{M}{|z^k||z - z_0|} = \frac{M}{|z|^{k+1}\left|1 - \dfrac{z_0}{z}\right|}.$$

Since z is on S, we can take β large enough to make $|z_0/z| < \frac{1}{2}$; then $|1 - z_0/z| > \frac{1}{2}$. Also $|z| \geqq \beta$ on the path S, and therefore

$$\left|\frac{f(z)}{z - z_0}\right| < \frac{2M}{\beta^{k+1}}.$$

It follows that

$$\left|\int_S \frac{f(z)\,dz}{z - z_0}\right| < \frac{2M}{\beta^{k+1}} \int_S |dz| = \frac{2M}{\beta^k}\left(4 - \frac{2\gamma}{\beta}\right)$$

since the length of S is $4\beta - 2\gamma$. Since $k > 0$, the expression on the right vanishes as $\beta \to \infty$.

Consequently, the second integral in equation (2) tends to zero as $\beta \to \infty$, and since the first integral is the one in our theorem the theorem is proved.

Under the conditions in the theorem, it can be seen that the infinite integral along the line $x = \gamma$ exists; that is, our formula (1) could be written

$$f(z_0) = -\frac{1}{2\pi}\int_{-\infty}^{\infty} \frac{f(\gamma + iy)\,dy}{\gamma + iy - z_0}.$$

REFERENCES

Curtiss, D. R.: "Analytic Functions of a Complex Variable," 1926.

Franklin, Philip: "A Treatise on Advanced Calculus," 1940.

Townsend, E. J.: "Functions of a Complex Variable," 1915.

MacRobert, T. M.: "Functions of a Complex Variable," 1933.

Rothe, F., F. Ollendorff, and K. Pohlausen: "Theory of Functions as Applied to Engineering Problems," 1933.

Phillips, E. G.: "Functions of a Complex Variable with Applications," 1940.

Pierpont, J.: "Functions of a Complex Variable," 1914.

Titchmarsh, E. C.: "Theory of Functions," 1939.

CHAPTER VI

THE INVERSION INTEGRAL

We shall now extend our theory of the Laplace transform by letting the letter s in the transform $f(s)$ represent a complex variable. As before, $F(t)$ represents a real function of the positive real variable t; but the transform $f(s)$ can assume complex values. We shall see that the properties of the transformation already obtained by assuming that s is real carry over to the case in which s is complex.

Some of the properties derived in this chapter could have been found when s is real without the use of complex variables; but of course once these have been established for complex s they are valid in the special case when s is real. Others involve such concepts as analytic functions, residues, and line integrals in the complex plane. The complex variable is of course essential for the derivation and use of such properties.

52. Analytic Transforms. When s is the complex variable

$$s = x + iy,$$

the Laplace transform of the real function $F(t)$,

$$f(s) = \int_0^\infty e^{-st} F(t)\, dt = \int_0^\infty e^{-xt} e^{-iyt} F(t)\, dt,$$

can be written at once in terms of real integrals,

(1) $\quad f(s) = \int_0^\infty e^{-xt} \cos yt\, F(t)\, dt - i \int_0^\infty e^{-xt} \sin yt\, F(t)\, dt.$

Thus

$$f(s) = u(x, y) + iv(x, y)$$

where

(2) $\quad u(x, y) = \int_0^\infty e^{-xt} \cos yt\, F(t)\, dt,$

$$v(x, y) = - \int_0^\infty e^{-xt} \sin yt\, F(t)\, dt.$$

148

Replacing s by its conjugate, we see that

$$f(x - iy) = u(x, y) - iv(x, y),$$

which is the conjugate of $f(s)$. Hence the conjugate $\overline{f(s)}$ of the transform is the same as the transform with its argument replaced by the conjugate:

(3) $$\overline{f(s)} = f(\bar{s}),$$

whenever the Laplace integral converges.

If $F(t)$ is a sectionally continuous function in each finite interval, for $t \geqq 0$, and if it is of exponential order as $t \to \infty$, then a positive constant M and a constant x_0 exist such that for all $t \geqq 0$

$$|F(t)| < Me^{x_0 t}.$$

The function

$$\phi(x, y, t) = e^{-xt} \cos yt\, F(t),$$

which is the integrand of the integral representing $u(x, y)$, then satisfies the inequality

$$|\phi(x, y, t)| \leqq e^{-xt}|F(t)| < Me^{-(x-x_0)t}.$$

Let x be confined to a range $x \geqq x_1$ where x_1 is a constant greater than x_0. Then $x - x_0 \geqq x_1 - x_0 > 0$ and

$$|\phi(x, y, t)| < Me^{-(x_1-x_0)t}.$$

The function $e^{-(x_1-x_0)t}$ is independent of x and y, and its integral from zero to infinity converges. According to the Weierstrass test* for the convergence of infinite integrals the integral

$$\int_0^\infty \phi(x, y, t)\, dt,$$

representing $u(x, y, t)$, is uniformly convergent with respect to x and y when $x \geqq x_1$ and for all y. The integral is also absolutely convergent.

Now $\phi(x, y, t)$ is the product of the sectionally continuous function $F(t)$ by a continuous function of x, y, and t, and the

---

* This test is derived in most books on advanced calculus or on the theory of functions. For a careful statement of the conditions when the integrand is a function of two variables, the reader may refer to H. S. Carslaw, "Fourier's Series and Integrals," p. 196, 1930. The case in which the integrand contains three variables is an immediate extension of this test.

integral of ϕ is uniformly convergent with respect to x and y. Under these conditions,* the integral represents a continuous function of x and y; that is, $u(x, y)$ is a continuous function of its two variables for every y and for every $x > x_0$. This conclusion clearly applies to $v(x, y)$ as well since the integrand there differs from that of $u(x, y)$ only to the extent of containing the factor sin yt instead of cos yt. Thus $f(s)$ is a continuous function of x and y and, therefore, of s.

Let us now show that

$$(4) \qquad \frac{\partial u}{\partial x} = - \int_0^\infty e^{-xt} \cos (yt) tF(t) \; dt,$$

where the integral is obtained by differentiating the first integral in equations (2) under the integral sign. The integral here is the same as that representing $u(x, y)$ except that $tF(t)$ has replaced $F(t)$. Since $F(t)$ is of exponential order $O(e^{x_0 t})$, we can write

$$|tF(t)| < Mte^{x_0 t} = Mte^{-\epsilon t} e^{(x_0 + \epsilon)t},$$

and if we take $\epsilon > 0$, the function $Mte^{-\epsilon t}$ has a maximum value, say M', for all positive t so that

$$|tF(t)| < M' e^{(x_0 + \epsilon)t}.$$

That is, $tF(t)$ is of order $O(e^{\alpha t})$ for every $\alpha > x_0$.

The argument used above on $u(x, t)$ therefore shows that the integral in equation (4) is uniformly convergent with respect to x and y and represents a continuous function of those variables whenever $x > x_0$. The uniform convergence of the integral and the sectional continuity of $F(t)$ ensure the validity of the differentiation under the integral sign† so that formula (4) is valid and $\partial u/\partial x$ is continuous, when $x > x_0$.

Likewise, the functions $\partial u/\partial y$, $\partial v/\partial x$, and $\partial v/\partial y$ are continuous when $x > x_0$, and since

$$\frac{\partial v}{\partial y} = - \int_0^\infty e^{-xt} \cos (yt) tF(t) \; dt,$$

it follows that $\partial u/\partial x = \partial v/\partial y$. Similarly, $\partial u/\partial y = -\partial v/\partial x$. Since the Cauchy-Riemann conditions are satisfied, the function $f(s)$ is analytic when $x > x_0$.

---

* See, for instance, Carslaw, *op. cit.*, p. 198.
† *Op. cit.*, p. 200.

The derivative of an analytic function $f(s)$ is independent of the manner in which Δs tends to zero. If we keep y constant, then

$$f'(s) = \frac{\partial f}{\partial x} = \frac{\partial u}{\partial x} + i\,\frac{\partial v}{\partial x} = -\int_0^\infty te^{-xt}(\cos yt - i \sin yt)F(t)\,dt;$$

that is,

$$f'(s) = -\int_0^\infty te^{-st}F(t)\,dt = -L\{tF(t)\}.$$

Since $tF(t)$ is sectionally continuous and of exponential order, our result can be applied to that function as well as to $F(t)$, so that

$$f''(s) = L\{t^2F(t)\} \qquad\qquad (x > x_0).$$

The same is true for $t^n F(t)$, and our results can be stated as follows:

Theorem 1. *Let the function $F(t)$ be sectionally continuous in each finite interval and of the order $O(e^{x_0 t})$, for $t \geqq 0$. Then the Laplace transform of $F(t)$,*

$$f(s) = \int_0^\infty e^{-st}F(t)\,dt = L\{F(t)\} \qquad (s = x + iy),$$

is an analytic function of s in the half plane $x > x_0$. The Laplace integral converges absolutely and uniformly with respect to x and y in that half plane. The derivatives of $f(s)$ are given by the formula

$$(5) \qquad\qquad f^{(n)}(s) = L\{(-t)^n F(t)\} \qquad\qquad (x > x_0).$$

Formula (5) was found in Sec. 12 (Theorem 4) for the special case in which s is a real variable.

The conditions in Theorem 1 can be made less narrow. For instance, let $F(t)$ satisfy the conditions as stated except that it becomes infinite at $t = t_0 \geqq 0$ in such a way that $|(t - t_0)^k F(t)|$ remains bounded as $t \to t_0$, where $k < 1$. Then the conclusions in the theorem are still valid. As an example, the transform of $F(t) = t^{-\frac{1}{2}}$ is analytic in the half plane $x > 0$ and formula (5) applies to it.

53. Permanence of Forms. We have seen that the Laplace integral of $F(t)$ leads to a function $f(s)$ that is analytic in the half plane $x > x_0$, where $s = x + iy$. If the integration is performed when $s = x$, a real function $\phi(x)$ is obtained that is identical to $f(s)$ to the right of x_0 along the real axis; that is, $\phi(x) = f(x)$ when

$x > x_0$. If $\phi(s)$ is an analytic function in the half plane, then it must be identical to $f(s)$ since two different analytic functions cannot be identical along a line in the complex plane (Sec. 50).

It follows that transforms can be found by carrying out the integration as if s were a real variable. That the function $f(s)$ so found is analytic when $\Re(s) > x_0$ can be seen in the particular cases; but it is true in general because the integration formulas are the same whether the parameter in the integral is complex or real. The transform of $F(t) = t^2$, for instance, was found to be $2s^{-3}$ when s is real. Now t^2 is of the order $O(e^{x_0 t})$ for any $x_0 > 0$, and $2s^{-3}$ is analytic except at $s = 0$. Therefore

$$L\{t^2\} = \frac{2}{s^3}$$

for all complex s in the half plane $x > 0$.

All our transforms of particular functions, tabulated in Appendix III, are valid when s is complex. We seldom need the value of x_0 which determines the half plane in which s lies; the existence of the number x_0 usually suffices.

The operational properties of the transform developed in the first two chapters and tabulated in Appendix II are likewise valid when s is a complex variable in the half plane $x > x_0$. For the sake of simplicity, we may make an exception of operation 10, Appendix II:

$$L\left\{\frac{1}{t} F(t)\right\} = \int_s^\infty f(\lambda)\, d\lambda,$$

and agree that s is real here.

The permanence of the forms of those properties is again a consequence of the fact that the steps used in their derivations are independent of the real or complex character of the parameter s. However, the derivations could be rewritten with $s = x + iy$ by proceeding as we did in the derivation of formula (5), Sec. 52.

In deriving the formula for the transform of the derivative, for example, we can write

$$L\{F'(t)\} = \int_0^\infty e^{-xt} \cos yt\, F'(t)\, dt - i \int_0^\infty e^{-xt} \sin yt\, F'(t)\, dt.$$

The integrals here are real. Upon integrating each of them by parts, we find that

$$L\{F'(t)\} = e^{-xt}(\cos yt - i \sin yt)F(t)\Big]_0^\infty$$

$$- \int_0^\infty \frac{\partial}{\partial t}(e^{-xt}\cos yt)F(t)\,dt + i\int_0^\infty \frac{\partial}{\partial t}(e^{-xt}\sin yt)F(t)\,dt.$$

Carrying out the indicated differentiations and collecting terms, we get the familiar result

$$L\{F'(t)\} = -F(+0) + (x + iy)\int_0^\infty e^{-xt}(\cos yt - i \sin yt)F(t)\,dt$$

$$= sL\{F(t)\} - F(+0) \qquad\qquad (x > x_0).$$

We have assumed in this derivation that $F(t)$ is of the order of $e^{x_0 t}$ as $t \to \infty$ and that s is confined to the half plane $x > x_0$. We have also assumed that $F(t)$ is continuous. As pointed out in Sec. 4, the derivative $F'(t)$ may be a sectionally continuous function.

54. Order Properties of Transforms. We have seen that the transform of every sectionally continuous function of exponential order is an analytic function $f(s)$ in a right half plane. We shall now show that the behavior of $f(s)$ as either $|s|$ or $\Re(s)$ increases is subject to restrictions.

Theorem 2. *If $F(t)$ is sectionally continuous and of exponential order $O(e^{x_0 t})$, then its transform is of the order $O(1/x)$ in the half plane $x \geqq x_1$ where x_1 is any number greater than x_0 and where $s = x + iy$; that is, a constant M exists such that for all s in the half plane,*

$$(1) \qquad\qquad |xf(x + iy)| < M \qquad\qquad (x \geqq x_1).$$

Note that it follows from the theorem that the analytic function $f(s)$ satisfies the condition

$$(2) \qquad\qquad \lim_{x \to \infty} f(x + iy) = 0.$$

The function $f(s) = s$, for instance, does not satisfy this condition; hence it cannot be the transform of any function $F(t)$ that is sectionally continuous and of exponential order. Actually, it is not the transform of any function. The same is true of $f(s) = 1$.

To prove the theorem, we may first write

$$(3) \quad f(x + iy) = \int_0^\infty e^{-xt}\cos yt\,F(t)\,dt - i\int_0^\infty e^{-xt}\sin yt\,F(t)\,dt.$$

Using the fact that the absolute value of an integral is not greater than the integral of the absolute value of its integrand, we have

$$\left| \int_0^\infty e^{-xt} \cos yt\, F(t)\, dt \right| \leqq \int_0^\infty e^{-xt} |\cos yt\, F(t)|\, dt$$

$$< \int_0^\infty e^{-xt} M_1 e^{x_0 t}\, dt = \frac{M_1}{x - x_0} \qquad (x > x_0),$$

where M_1 is such that $|F(t)| < M_1 e^{x_0 t}$ when $x \geqq x_0$. The second integral in equation (3) satisfies the same inequality, and thus if $x_0 \geqq 0$,

$$(4) \qquad x|f(x + iy)| < \frac{2M_1 x}{x - x_0} \leqq \frac{2M_1}{1 - \dfrac{x_0}{x}}.$$

If $x \geqq x_1$ where $x_1 > x_0$, the smallest possible value of the quantity $1 - x_0/x$ is $1 - x_0/x_1$ and therefore

$$x|f(x + iy)| < \frac{2M_1}{1 - \dfrac{x_0}{x_1}} \qquad (x \geqq x_1).$$

The fraction on the right can be taken as the number M in the theorem. The demonstration is similar if $x_0 < 0$. Thus Theorem 2 is proved.

According to this theorem, $f(s)$ tends to zero as the point s moves to the right in the half plane. Under slightly different conditions on the function $F(t)$, the transform $f(s)$ tends to zero as s moves farther out in the half plane in any direction. One set of conditions under which this is true is contained in the following theorem:

Theorem 3. *Let the function $F(t)$ be continuous with a sectionally continuous derivative $F'(t)$, and let $F(t)$ and $F'(t)$ be of order $O(e^{x_0 t})$. Then $f(s)$ is of the order $O(1/s)$ in the half plane $x \geqq x_1$ where $x_1 > x_0$; that is, a constant M exists such that*

$$(5) \qquad |sf(s)| < M \qquad (x \geqq x_1).$$

Under the conditions of this theorem, we know that

$$L\{F'(t)\} = sf(s) - F(+0) \qquad (x > x_0);$$

therefore

$$sf(s) = L\{F'(t)\} + F(+0).$$

Since $F'(t)$ is sectionally continuous and of exponential order, it follows from the inequality (4) that when $x_1 > x_0$ a number M_1

exists such that

$$|L\{F'(t)\}| < \frac{2M_1}{x - x_0} \leqq \frac{2M_1}{x_1 - x_0}.$$

Consequently for all $x \geqq x_1$,

$$|sf(s)| < \frac{2M_1}{x_1 - x_0} + |F(+0)|.$$

The quantity in the right-hand member here can be taken as the number M in the inequality (5), and the theorem is proved.

Note, for instance, that the functions $F(t) = 1$, $F(t) = t$, and $F(t) = \cos kt$ satisfy the conditions in the theorem when x_0 is any positive number. Their transforms, which are

$$\frac{1}{s}, \frac{1}{s^2}, \frac{s}{s^2 + k^2},$$

respectively, are of the order of $1/s$ in any half plane $x \geqq x_1 > 0$. In fact, the second of these transforms is of the order of $1/s^2$, a conclusion that would follow from the character of the function $F(t) = t$ alone, with the aid of the following extension of Theorem 3.

Theorem 4. *If the functions $F(t)$, $F'(t)$, and $F''(t)$ are of the order $O(e^{x_0 t})$, if $F'(t)$ is continuous, and if $F''(t)$ is sectionally continuous, then*

$$(6) \qquad\qquad |s^2 f(s) - sF(+0)| < M \qquad (x \geqq x_1 > x_0);$$

if, in addition, $F(+0) = 0$ then $f(s) = O(1/s^2)$; that is

$$(7) \qquad\qquad |s^2 f(s)| < M \qquad\qquad (x \geqq x_1).$$

Under the conditions on $F(t)$ and its derivatives, we know that

$$L\{F''(t)\} = s^2 f(s) - sF(+0) - F'(+0) \qquad (x > x_0).$$

Since $L\{F''(t)\}$ is a bounded function of s in the half plane $x \geqq x_1$, when $x_1 > x_0$, the function

$$s^2 f(s) - sF(+0) = L\{F''(t)\} + F'(+0)$$

is bounded. This is the statement (6). When $F(+0) = 0$, the inequality (7) follows at once.

The extension to higher orders is immediate. For instance,

$$f(s) = O\left(\frac{1}{s^3}\right) \qquad\qquad (x \geqq x_1)$$

provided that $F(t)$ and its derivatives of the first three orders are of exponential order, that $F'''(t)$ is continuous and $F''''(t)$ is sectionally continuous, and that

$$F(+0) = F'(+0) = 0.$$

The function $F(t) = t^2$, for example, satisfies these conditions.

In Theorem 3 the condition that $F(t)$ be continuous is introduced in order to have a simple proof of the order property $f(s) = O(1/s)$. By using the second theorem of the mean for definite integrals, it can be shown that this order property is true if for some $x_0 \geqq 0$ the function $F(t)$ is such that the product $e^{-x_0 t}F(t)$ is bounded and sectionally monotonic for all $t \geqq 0$.* A sectionally monotonic function is one such that the positive t-axis can be divided into segments $0 \leqq t \leqq t_1$, $t_1 \leqq t \leqq t_2$, $\cdots$, none of whose lengths is less than some fixed positive number ϵ, such that in each segment the function is either nonincreasing or nondecreasing as t increases. The step function $S_k(t)$, for example, satisfies these conditions with $x_0 = 0$. Its transform e^{-ks}/s is of the order of s^{-1} in any half plane $x \geqq x_1 > 0$.

The conditions on $F(t)$ under which $f(s)$ is of the order of s^{-n} can be relaxed in the same manner by using the above result in conjunction with the transformation of derivatives. Conditions that are more elegant and more efficient than those given here can be found in the literature on the theory of the transformation; but the concepts involved in their statements are somewhat more advanced than those used here.

PROBLEMS

1. Determine an order property of $f(s)$ from the character of the function $F(t)$ in each of the following cases, and verify your result by writing $f(s)$:

(a) $F(t) = \sin kt$;   (b) $F(t) = \cos kt$;

(c) $F(t) = t \sinh t$;   (d) $F(t) = \begin{cases} 0 & \text{when } 0 < t < k, \\ t - k & \text{when } t > k. \end{cases}$

2. Show that under the conditions of Theorem 3 it is true that $|xsf(s)|$ is bounded in the half-plane $x \geqq x_1$ provided $F(+0) = 0$.

---

* A proof will be found in a paper by the author entitled "The Solution of Linear Boundary-value Problems in Physics by Means of the Laplace Transformation, Part 1," *Mathematische Annalen*, Vol. 114, p. 597, 1937.

55. The Complex Inversion Integral. According to the extension of Cauchy's integral formula presented in Sec. 51, a function $f(s)$ that is analytic in a half plane $\Re(s) \geqq \gamma$ and of the order $O(s^{-k})$ there, where $k > 0$, can be expressed in terms of its values along a vertical line by a line integral:

$$f(s) = \frac{1}{2\pi i} \lim_{\beta \to \infty} \int_{\gamma - i\beta}^{\gamma + i\beta} \frac{f(z)\,dz}{s - z},$$

where $\Re(s) > \gamma$. Let us formally apply the inverse Laplace transformation to the function of s on either side of this equation assuming that, on the right, the order of the operator L^{-1} and the integration along the line $\Re(z) = \gamma$ can be interchanged. Then

$$L^{-1}\{f(s)\} = \frac{1}{2\pi i} \lim_{\beta \to \infty} \int_{\gamma - i\beta}^{\gamma + i\beta} f(z) L^{-1}\left\{\frac{1}{s - z}\right\}\,dz.$$

If $f(s)$ is the Laplace transform of a function $F(t)$, then, since the inverse transform of $1/(s - z)$ is e^{zt}, it would follow that

$$(1) \qquad F(t) = \frac{1}{2\pi i} \lim_{\beta \to \infty} \int_{\gamma - i\beta}^{\gamma + i\beta} e^{zt} f(z)\,dz.$$

The expression in the right-hand member is called the *complex inversion integral* of the Laplace transformation. We introduce the symbol L_i^{-1} here for the transformation of $f(s)$ represented by the inversion integral; that is,

$$(2) \quad L_i^{-1}\{f(s)\} =$$

$$\frac{1}{2\pi i} \lim_{\beta \to \infty} \int_{\gamma - i\beta}^{\gamma + i\beta} e^{zt} f(z)\,dz.$$

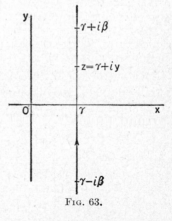

Fig. 63.

It is intended that the symbol will carry the suggestion of an integration as well as that of an inverse Laplace transformation.

Although the inversion integral is an integral in the complex plane along a line parallel to the axis of imaginaries (Fig. 63), it can be written as a real infinite integral. The variable of integration is $z = \gamma + iy$ where γ is fixed; hence we can write

$$\int_{\gamma-i\beta}^{\gamma+i\beta} e^{zt}f(z)\ dz = e^{\gamma t}\int_{-\beta}^{\beta} e^{iyt}f(\gamma + iy)i\ dy$$

$$= ie^{\gamma t}\left[\int_{-\beta}^{0} e^{iyt}f(\gamma + iy)\ dy + \int_{0}^{\beta} e^{iyt}f(\gamma + iy)\ dy\right].$$

In the first integral of the last line, we replace the variable of integration y by $-y$. Then the sum of the two integrals becomes

$$\int_{0}^{\beta} [e^{-iyt}f(\gamma - iy) + e^{iyt}f(\gamma + iy)]\ dy.$$

Now e^{-iyt} is the complex conjugate of e^{iyt}. When $f(s)$ is a transform, we noted in Sec. 52 that $f(\gamma - iy)$ is the conjugate of $f(\gamma + iy)$. Therefore the product $e^{-iyt}f(\gamma - iy)$ is the conjugate of the product $e^{iyt}f(\gamma + iy)$ so that the sum of the two products is twice the real part of one of them. Let

$$f(x + iy) = u(x, y) + iv(x, y).$$

Then

$$\Re[e^{iyt}f(\gamma + iy)] = u(\gamma, y)\cos yt - v(\gamma, y)\sin yt.$$

Consequently, the inversion integral (2) can be written

$$(3)\quad L_i^{-1}\{f(s)\} = \frac{e^{\gamma t}}{\pi}\int_{0}^{\infty} [u(\gamma, y)\cos yt - v(\gamma, y)\sin yt]\ dy.$$

This is the real form of the inversion integral. We shall see that the function of t represented by this formula is independent of the constant γ as long as that constant is taken sufficiently large. The form (3) is presented here for the purpose of showing that the inversion integral is subject to the rules of operation that apply to real integrals. The integration involved in this real form, even for very simple functions $f(s)$, is generally too difficult to perform. For the purpose of evaluating $L_i^{-1}\{f(s)\}$, we shall use the complex form (2) in conjunction with certain auxiliary line integrals and the theory of residues.

In the following sections, conditions on either $f(s)$ or $F(t)$ will be established under which the function $L_i^{-1}\{f(s)\}$ is the inverse Laplace transform $F(t)$ of $f(s)$; thus our equation (1), which can be written

$$(4)\qquad\qquad F(t) = L_i^{-1}\{f(s)\},$$

becomes an explicit formula giving $F(t)$ in terms of $f(s)$.

Other formulas for the inverse transformation are known. The reader will find accounts of them in the books by Doetsch and Widder.* The form (4) is, however, the only one that has been found useful, up to the present time, in the actual determination of inverse transforms of particular functions.

56. Conditions on f(s). The following theorem gives conditions on the function $f(s)$ sufficient to ensure the validity of the inversion integral formula of the last section. Certain properties that the function $F(t)$ must satisfy as a result of the order condition imposed on $f(s)$ are also noted.

Theorem 5. *Let $f(s)$ be any function of the complex variable s that is analytic and of the order $O(s^{-k})$, in some half plane $\Re(s) \geqq x_0$, where x_0 and k are real constants and $k > 1$. Then the inversion integral $L_i^{-1}\{f(s)\}$ along any line $x = \gamma$, where $\gamma \geqq x_0$, converges to a function $F(t)$ that is independent of γ,*

$$(1) \qquad\qquad F(t) = L_i^{-1}\{f(s)\},$$

whose Laplace transform is $f(s)$:

$$(2) \qquad\qquad L\{F(t)\} = f(s) \qquad\qquad (\Re(s) > \gamma).$$

Furthermore the function $F(t)$ is continuous for each $t \geqq 0$ and

$$(3) \qquad\qquad F(0) = 0;$$

also $F(t)$ is of the order $O(e^{\gamma t})$ for all $t \geqq 0$.

In view of the order property on $f(z)$ a constant M exists such that $|f(z)| < M|z|^{-k}$ in the half plane. Let $f(z) = u + iv$. Then on the line $\Re(z) = \gamma$,

$$\sqrt{u^2 + v^2} < \frac{M}{(\gamma^2 + y^2)^{\frac{1}{2}k}} \qquad\qquad (k > 1).$$

Consequently $|u(\gamma, y)|$ and $|v(\gamma, y)|$ separately are less than $M(\gamma^2 + y^2)^{-\frac{1}{2}k}$, and hence the integrand in the real form (3), Sec. 55, of $L_i^{-1}\{f(s)\}$ satisfies the inequality

$$(4) \qquad |u(\gamma, y) \cos yt - v(\gamma, y) \sin yt| < \frac{2M}{(\gamma^2 + y^2)^{\frac{1}{2}k}}.$$

When $k > 1$, the function of y on the right has a convergent integral from zero to infinity, and since the function is independent of t the inversion integral converges uniformly with

---

* Doetsch, G., "Theorie und Anwendung der Laplace-Transformation," 1937; Widder, D. V., "The Laplace Transform," 1941.

respect to t in every finite interval $a \leq t \leq b$. It is also absolutely convergent. Since the integrand of the integral is a continuous function of y and t, the function $F(t)$ represented by the inversion integral is continuous for every t, positive or negative.

It also follows from the inequality (4) that

$$|L_i^{-1}\{f(s)\}| < e^{\gamma t} \frac{M}{\pi} \int_0^\infty \frac{dy}{(\gamma^2 + y^2)^{\frac{1}{2}k}} \qquad (k > 1),$$

and since the coefficient of $e^{\gamma t}$ here is a constant our function $F(t)$ is of the order of $e^{\gamma t}$.

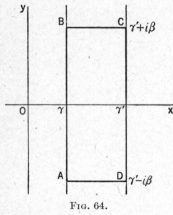

Fig. 64.

Let us show next that the value of the inversion integral is independent of γ as long as $\gamma \geq x_0$. Consider a second path $x = \gamma'$ where $\gamma' > \gamma$. Since $e^{zt}f(z)$ is analytic when $x \geq \gamma$, the integral of that function around the boundary of the rectangle $ABCD$ (Fig. 64) is zero. On the side BC, $z = x + i\beta$, and in view of the fact that $|f(z)| < M|z|^{-k}$,

$$|e^{zt}f(z)| < e^{xt}\frac{M}{\beta^k}.$$

Consequently the integral on that line satisfies the inequality

$$\left| \int_{\gamma+i\beta}^{\gamma'+i\beta} e^{zt}f(z) \, dz \right| < \frac{M}{\beta^k} \int_\gamma^{\gamma'} e^{xt} \, dx.$$

Hence as $\beta \to \infty$ that integral tends to zero. The same argument applies to the integral along the side AD. We have used only the fact that $k > 0$ here.

Since the sum of the integrals over the paths AB, BC, CD, and DA is zero, it follows that

$$\lim_{\beta \to \infty} \left[\int_{\gamma-i\beta}^{\gamma+i\beta} e^{zt}f(z) \, dz + \int_{\gamma'+i\beta}^{\gamma'-i\beta} e^{zt}f(z) \, dz \right] = 0,$$

or

$$\lim_{\beta \to \infty} \int_{\gamma-i\beta}^{\gamma+i\beta} e^{zt}f(z) \, dz = \lim_{\beta \to \infty} \int_{\gamma'-i\beta}^{\gamma'+i\beta} e^{zt}f(z) \, dz.$$

The function $L_i^{-1}\{f(s)\}$ is therefore independent of γ.

To establish the formula (2), that is, to show that $F(t)$ is the inverse transform of $f(s)$, we can write

$$(5) \quad L\{F(t)\} = \frac{1}{\pi} \int_0^\infty e^{-st} e^{\gamma t} \int_0^\infty (u \cos yt - v \sin yt)\, dy\, dt$$

where u is written for $u(\gamma, y)$ and v for $v(\gamma, y)$. Let $s = a + ib$, where $a > \gamma$. The absolute value of the entire integrand of the repeated infinite integral here is less than

$$e^{-(a-\gamma)t} \frac{2M}{(\gamma^2 + y^2)^{\frac{1}{2}k}},$$

and when $t \geqq 0$ it follows that the integral in equation (5) with respect to y converges uniformly with respect to t and that the integral with respect to t converges uniformly with respect to y. In the latter case, for instance, we use the fact that the absolute value of the integrand is less than the quantity

$$e^{-(a-\gamma)t} \frac{2M}{|\gamma|^k},$$

obtained by setting $y = 0$ in the expression above.

Finally, the integral

$$\int_0^\infty (u \cos yt - v \sin yt) \int_0^T e^{-(s-\gamma)t}\, dt\, dy$$

is uniformly convergent with respect to T, because the absolute value of the integrand obtained upon integrating with respect to t is less than

$$\frac{2M}{(\gamma^2 + y^2)^{\frac{1}{2}k}} \left| \frac{1 - e^{-(s-\gamma)T}}{s - \gamma} \right| < \frac{4M}{a - \gamma} \frac{1}{(\gamma^2 + y^2)^{\frac{1}{2}k}}.$$

Under these conditions of uniform convergence the interchange of the order of integration in equation (5) is valid.* Upon inverting the order and returning to the complex form for convenience, we can write equation (5) in the form

$$L\{F(t)\} = \frac{1}{2\pi i} \lim_{\beta \to \infty} \int_{\gamma-i\beta}^{\gamma+i\beta} f(z) \int_0^\infty e^{(z-s)t}\, dt\, dz$$

$$= -\frac{1}{2\pi i} \lim_{\beta \to \infty} \int_{\gamma-i\beta}^{\gamma+i\beta} \frac{f(z)}{z - s}\, dz.$$

* See, for instance, Carslaw, *op. cit.*, p. 209.

The last expression represents $f(s)$ since that function satisfies the conditions (Sec. 51) under which the extension of Cauchy's integral formula applies.

When $t = 0$, the inversion integral becomes

$$F(0) = \frac{1}{2\pi i} \lim_{\beta \to \infty} \int_{\gamma - i\beta}^{\gamma + i\beta} f(z)\, dz$$

$$= -\frac{1}{2\pi i} \lim_{\beta \to \infty} \int_{\gamma - i\beta}^{\gamma + i\beta} \frac{(z_0 - z)f(z)}{z - z_0}\, dz,$$

where z_0 is any fixed complex number with $\Re(z_0) > \gamma$. Now the function

$$\phi(z) = (z_0 - z)f(z)$$

is analytic and of the order $O(z^{-k+1})$ where $k > 1$, in the half plane $x \geqq \gamma$. Since the last expression for $F(0)$ is Cauchy's integral formula for the function $\phi(z)$, it follows that its value is $\phi(z_0)$. Therefore

$$F(0) = \phi(z_0) = 0.$$

The proof of Theorem 5 is now complete.

57. Conditions on F(t). Uniqueness of the Inversion. The foregoing conditions under which the inversion integral formula is valid are quite severe. They are not satisfied, for example, by the function $f(s) = 1/s$, since this function is not of the order of $1/s^k$ with $k > 1$. Hence Theorem 5 does not ensure the convergence of the inversion integral in this case to the function $F(t)$. By using a Fourier integral theorem and qualifying the function $F(t)$ instead of $f(s)$, we can relax the conditions so that the inversion integral formula can be seen to be valid in nearly all cases of interest to us. In fact, we shall see that our formula is only a modified form of the Fourier integral.

Let $G(t)$ be a function defined for all real values of t, sectionally continuous over each finite interval of the t-axis, and let it tend to zero when $|t|$ is large in such a manner that the integral

$$\int_{-\infty}^{\infty} G(t)\, dt$$

is absolutely convergent. Also let us agree to define $G(t)$ at each point t_0 where it is discontinuous as the mean value of its limits from the right and left at t_0; that is,

(1) $$G(t_0) = \tfrac{1}{2}[G(t_0 + 0) + G(t_0 - 0)].$$

Any such function can be represented by its Fourier integral:*

(2) $$G(t) = \frac{1}{\pi} \int_0^\infty \int_{-\infty}^\infty G(\tau) \cos y(t - \tau) \, d\tau \, dy.$$

The integral here can be written

$$\frac{1}{2} \lim_{\beta \to \infty} \int_0^\beta \int_{-\infty}^\infty G(\tau)[e^{iy(t-\tau)} + e^{-iy(t-\tau)}] \, d\tau \, dy =$$

$$\frac{1}{2} \lim_{\beta \to \infty} \left[\int_0^\beta e^{iyt} \int_{-\infty}^\infty G(\tau)e^{-iy\tau} \, d\tau \, dy \right.$$

$$\left. + \int_{-\beta}^0 e^{iyt} \int_{-\infty}^\infty G(\tau)e^{-iy\tau} \, d\tau \, dy \right].$$

Hence the Fourier integral formula takes the exponential form

(3) $$G(t) = \frac{1}{2\pi} \lim_{\beta \to \infty} \int_{-\beta}^\beta e^{iyt} \int_{-\infty}^\infty G(\tau)e^{-iy\tau} \, d\tau \, dy.$$

Let $F(t)$ be a function defined for $t \geqq 0$, sectionally continuous and of exponential order $O(e^{x_0 t})$. If we take

$$\begin{aligned} G(t) &= 0 & &\text{when } t < 0, \\ &= e^{-\gamma t}F(t) & &\text{when } t > 0, \end{aligned}$$

where $\gamma > x_0$, then $G(t)$ satisfies the above conditions and it is represented by the Fourier integral formula (3). Hence when $t > 0$,

$$F(t) = \frac{e^{\gamma t}}{2\pi} \lim_{\beta \to \infty} \int_{-\beta}^\beta e^{iyt} \int_0^\infty e^{-(\gamma+iy)\tau}F(\tau) \, d\tau \, dy.$$

Let $z = \gamma + iy$; then this formula can be written

(4) $$F(t) = \frac{1}{2\pi i} \lim_{\beta \to \infty} \int_{\gamma - i\beta}^{\gamma + i\beta} e^{zt}f(z) \, dz = L_i^{-1}\{f(s)\},$$

where $f(s)$ is the Laplace transform of $F(t)$.

According to equation (1), the value of $F(t)$ given by formula (4) at any point t_0 of discontinuity is

(5) $$F(t_0) = \tfrac{1}{2}[F(t_0 + 0) + F(t_0 - 0)].$$

Since $G(t) = 0$ here when $t < 0$, the inversion integral vanishes

---

* See, for instance, "Fourier Series and Boundary Value Problems," pp. 89 ff.

when $t < 0$; also in view of equation (1) the inversion integral (4) must therefore assume the value $\frac{1}{2}[F(+0) + 0]$ at $t = 0$. Our results can be collected in the following form:

Theorem 6. *If $f(s)$ is the transform of any function $F(t)$ which is sectionally continuous and of order $O(e^{x_0 t})(t \geqq 0)$, then the inversion integral of $f(s)$ converges along any line $x = \gamma$ where $\gamma > x_0$ and it represents $F(t)$:*

$$(6) \qquad\qquad F(t) = L_i^{-1}\{f(s)\} \qquad\qquad (t > 0).$$

At any point t_0 of discontinuity, the inversion integral represents the mean value (5), at $t = 0$ it has the value $\frac{1}{2}F(+0)$, and when $t < 0$ it has the value zero.

We can now show that the inverse transform of a given function of s is a unique function $F(t)$. Suppose there were two functions $F_1(t)$ and $F_2(t)$ having the same transform $f(s)$,

$$L\{F_1(t)\} = L\{F_2(t)\} = f(s).$$

We limit our discussion to functions of t that are sectionally continuous and of exponential order and define the functions at points of discontinuity as their mean values (5). The difference of the two functions,

$$\Phi(t) = F_1(t) - F_2(t),$$

is then sectionally continuous and of exponential order. Since

$$L\{\Phi(t)\} = f(s) - f(s) = 0,$$

it follows from Theorem 6 that $\Phi(t) = L_i^{-1}\{0\} = 0$ $(t > 0)$. Therefore

$$F_1(t) = F_2(t) \qquad\qquad (t > 0).$$

In particular, it is not possible to obtain two different functions by using two different values of γ in the inversion integral.

Theorem 7. *There is not more than one function $F(t)$ corresponding to a given transform $f(s)$, where $F(t)$ is sectionally continuous, of exponential order, and defined by equation (5) at each point where the function is discontinuous.*

As an illustration, we know that the function $F(t) = 1$ has the transform $f(s) = 1/s$. There can be no other continuous function of exponential order with the transform $1/s$. As we observed in Sec. 6, a function that differs from $F(t)$ only at discrete points, such as the function

$$F_1(t) = 1 \quad \text{when } t \neq 1 \text{ and } t \neq 2,$$
$$= 0 \quad \text{when } t = 1 \text{ and } t = 2,$$

does have the transform $1/s$. But the mean value (5) of $F_1(t)$ at $t = 1$ and at $t = 2$ is 1 so that $F_1(t)$ is the same as $F(t)$ under the conditions of Theorem 7. According to Theorem 6, the inversion integral of $1/s$ converges to the following values,

$$\frac{1}{2\pi i} \lim_{\beta \to \infty} \int_{\gamma-i\beta}^{\gamma+i\beta} \frac{s^{zt}}{z} \, dz = 1 \quad \text{when } t > 0,$$
$$= \tfrac{1}{2} \quad \text{when } t = 0,$$
$$= 0 \quad \text{when } t < 0.$$

The inverse transform is unique under somewhat broader conditions than those stated above. It is known that any two functions with the same transform can differ at most by a null function, that is, by a function $N(t)$ such that

$$\int_0^t N(\tau) \, d\tau = 0 \quad \text{for every } t \geq 0.$$

The function $N(t)$ cannot differ from zero over any interval of positive length along the t-axis. If the two functions are continuous, they must be identical for all positive t. The proof of these statements, known as Lerch's theorem, can be found in the more theoretical books on the transformation.[*]

58. Derivatives of the Inversion Integral. When the solution of a boundary value problem is found in the form of an inversion integral $L_t^{-1}\{f\}$, it is often possible to verify completely that solution by examining the function f. The two theorems in this section are useful for that purpose. Their proofs follow at once from Theorem 5 and the properties of uniformly convergent infinite integrals.[†]

When the inversion integral is differentiated with respect to t under the integral sign, we obtain $L_t^{-1}\{sf(s)\}$:

$$(1) \quad \frac{1}{2\pi i} \lim_{\beta \to \infty} \int_{\gamma-i\beta}^{\gamma+i\beta} \frac{\partial}{\partial t} [e^{zt} f(z)] \, dz = \frac{1}{2\pi i} \lim_{\beta \to \infty} \int_{\gamma-i\beta}^{\gamma+i\beta} e^{zt} z f(z) \, dz.$$

[*] Doetsch, *op. cit.*, p. 35; Widder, *op. cit.*, p. 63.

[†] Carslaw, *op. cit.*, pp. 198*ff.*; Pierpont, J., "Theory of Functions of Real Variables," Vol. 1, pp. 474*ff.*, 1905.

If the function $sf(s)$ as well as $f(s)$ satisfies the conditions imposed upon the function $f(s)$ in Theorem 5, the integral (1) converges uniformly with respect to t and represents the derivative, with respect to t, of $L_i^{-1}\{f(s)\}$. That derivative satisfies the continuity conditions stated for the function $F(t)$ in Theorem 5. The additional condition needed on $f(s)$ here is that $sf(s) = O(s^{-k})$ where $k > 1$, or that $f(s)$ be of order $O(s^{-k-1})$.

By replacing $f(s)$ in the last paragraph by the function $sf(s)$, it follows that the second derivative with respect to t of $L_i^{-1}\{f(s)\}$ is $L_i^{-1}\{s^2 f(s)\}$, and so on. Thus we have the following theorem:

Theorem 8. *Let $f(s)$ be any function of the complex variable s that is analytic and of order $O(s^{-k-m})$, in some half plane $\Re(s) \geqq x_0$ where $k > 1$ and m is a positive integer. Then the inversion integral along any line $x = \gamma$ where $\gamma \geqq x_0$ converges to the inverse transform $F(t)$ of $f(s)$,*

$$(2) \qquad\qquad L_i^{-1}\{f(s)\} = F(t),$$

and the derivatives of this function are given by the formula

$$(3) \qquad\qquad F^{(n)}(t) = L_i^{-1}\{s^n f(s)\} \quad (n = 1, 2, \cdots, m);$$

furthermore $F(t)$ and each of its derivatives (3) are continuous functions of $t(t \geqq 0)$ of order $O(e^{\gamma t})$, and they vanish at $t = 0$,

$$(4) \qquad\quad F(0) = F'(0) = \cdots = F^{(m)}(0) = 0.$$

It follows from this theorem, for example, that the inverse transform of the function

$$f(s) = \frac{1}{(s^2 + a^2)^{\frac{3}{2}}},$$

which is of the order $O(s^{-3})$ in a right half plane, is the transform of a function $F(t)$ represented by the inversion integral, that $F'(t)$ is continuous $(t \geqq 0)$, and that

$$F(0) = F'(0) = 0.$$

The function $F(t)$ here is given in terms of a Bessel function in Appendix III, No. 57.

It will be recalled that formula (3) cannot hold true without rather severe restrictions on either $F(t)$ or $f(s)$. For according to our basic property of the transformation of derivatives,

$$F^{(n)}(t) = L^{-1}\{s^n f(s) - s^{n-1}F(0) - \cdots - F^{(n-1)}(0)\},$$

when $F^{(n)}(t)$ is sectionally continuous and $F^{(n-1)}(t)$ is continuous and the functions here are of exponential order. If $F^{(n)}(t)$ is to be the inverse transform of $s^n f(s)$, it is essential that $F'(0)$, $F''(0)$, $\cdots$, $F^{(n-1)}(0)$ all vanish.

Of course the function f in the above theorem may involve constants or variables independent of s provided the statements in the theorem are understood to apply for fixed values of those parameters. Concerning differentiation and continuity with respect to such a parameter r, the following theorem can be seen from the properties of uniformly convergent infinite integrals.

Theorem 9. *Let $f(r, s)$ and $\partial/\partial r[f(r, s)]$ be continuous functions of the two variables r, s, analytic with respect to s in some half plane $\Re(s) \geqq x_0$, and let both functions be less in absolute value than $M/|s|^k (k > 1)$, in that half plane, where the constant M is independent of r for all values of r involved. Then the inverse transform of $f(r, s)$ with respect to s is*

$$F(r, t) = L_i^{-1}\{f(r, s)\}$$

where the path of integration is a line $x = \gamma(\gamma \geqq x_0)$, and

$$(5) \qquad \frac{\partial}{\partial r} F(r, t) = L_i^{-1}\left\{\frac{\partial}{\partial r} f(r, s)\right\}.$$

Moreover for each $t \geqq 0$, $F(r, t)$ and its derivative (5) are continuous functions of r. If the parameter r has an infinite range $r \geqq r_0$ and if $f(r, s) \to \phi(s)$ as $r \to \infty$, uniformly with respect to s on the line $x = \gamma$, then

$$(6) \qquad \lim_{r \to \infty} F(r, t) = L_i^{-1}\{\phi(s)\}.$$

The theorem can be applied to the function $\partial/\partial r[f(r, s)]$ to obtain corresponding results for $\partial^2/\partial r^2[F(r, t)]$; the same is true for the higher ordered derivatives.

Illustrations of the use of these theorems will be presented in the next chapter.

59. Representation of the Inverse Transform by a Series. Throughout this section, let $f(s)$ be a function that is analytic in the finite complex plane of the variable s except for a set of poles

$$s_1, s_2, \cdots, s_n, \cdots,$$

confined to some left half plane $\Re(s) < \gamma$. Also left $f(s)$ satisfy conditions under which its inversion integral along the line $x = \gamma$

converges to the inverse transform $F(t)$, say the conditions in either Theorem 5 or 6.   We shall show that $F(t)$ can be represented formally by a series, infinite if there is an infinite number of poles and finite if the number of poles is finite, and we shall establish practical conditions in the following section under which this representation is valid.   When the poles are all simple and $f(s)$ has a fractional form, the series is a generalization of Heaviside's partial fractions expansion (Sec. 16).

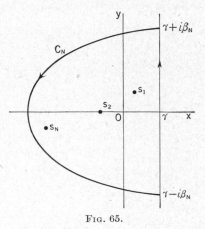

FIG. 65.

Since e^{zt} is analytic and not zero, the singularities of the product $e^{zt}f(z)$ are precisely the poles of $f(z)$.   Let $\rho_n(t)$ denote the residue of that product at s_n, for any fixed t:

(1) $\rho_n(t) =$ the residue of $[e^{zt}f(z)]$ at $z = s_n$.

According to Cauchy's residue theorem the integral of $e^{zt}f(z)$ around a path inclosing the points $s_1, s_2, \cdots, s_N$, has the value

$$2\pi i[\rho_1(t) + \rho_2(t) + \cdots + \rho_N(t)].$$

Let the path be made up of the line segment joining the points $\gamma - i\beta_N$, $\gamma + i\beta_N$, and some curve C_N beginning at the second and ending at the first of these two points and lying in the half plane $x \leqq \gamma$ (Fig. 65).   Then

(2) $\dfrac{1}{2\pi i} \displaystyle\int_{\gamma - i\beta_N}^{\gamma + i\beta_N} e^{zt}f(z)\ dz + \dfrac{1}{2\pi i} \int_{C_N} e^{zt}f(z)\ dz = \sum_{n=1}^{N} \rho_n(t).$

The first of the two integrals here has the same value as the inversion integral $L_i^{-1}\{f(s)\}$ when $\beta_N \to \infty$, since the inversion integral is the limit of the corresponding integral involving β, as $\beta \to \infty$ in any manner.

Let the numbers $\beta_N(N = 1, 2, \cdots)$ be selected so that β_N tends to infinity as N increases, and let the curves C_N and the line $x = \gamma$ enclose the poles $s_1, s_2, \cdots, s_N$, if the number of poles is infinite. If the number is finite, let C_N be such that all the poles are enclosed when N is greater than some fixed number. Then if $f(z)$ satisfies additional conditions under which

$$(3) \qquad \frac{1}{2\pi i} \lim_{N \to \infty} \int_{C_N} e^{zt}f(z)\ dz = 0,$$

it follows, by letting $N \to \infty$ in equation (2), that

$$L_i^{-1}\{f(s)\} = \sum_{n=1}^{\infty} \rho_n(t).$$

The series on the right is necessarily convergent since the limit, as $N \to \infty$, of the left-hand member of equation (2) exists. If the number of poles is finite, there is only a finite number of terms in the series.

Since the inversion integral represents $F(t)$ by hypothesis, the inverse transform of $f(s)$ is represented as the series of residues of $e^{zt}f(z)$:

$$(4) \qquad F(t) = \sum_{n=1}^{\infty} \rho_n(t).$$

It is not essential that the line $x = \gamma$ and the curve C_N enclose exactly N of the poles, of course. For example, if two poles are included in the ring between C_N and C_{N+1}, the residues at these two poles are simply grouped as a single term in the series.

When a pole s_n is a simple pole, the residue can be written, according to Sec. 49, as

$$\rho_n(t) = \lim_{z \to s_n} (z - s_n)e^{zt}f(z),$$

or

$$(5) \qquad \rho_n(t) = e^{s_n t} \lim_{z \to s_n} (z - s_n)f(z).$$

If in particular $f(z)$ has the fractional form

$$(6) \qquad f(z) = \frac{p(z)}{q(z)},$$

where $p(z)$ and $q(z)$ are analytic at $z = s_n$ and $p(s_n) \neq 0$, the residue at the simple pole s_n is

$$(7) \qquad \rho_n(t) = \frac{p(s_n)}{q'(s_n)} e^{s_n t}.$$

Therefore when *all the poles of $f(s)$ are simple* and $f(s)$ has the fractional form (6), the series representation (4) of the inverse transform becomes

$$(8) \qquad F(t) = L^{-1} \left\{ \frac{p(s)}{q(s)} \right\} = \sum_{1}^{\infty} \frac{p(s_n)}{q'(s_n)} e^{s_n t}.$$

When $p(s)$ and $q(s)$ are polynomials, the number of poles is finite and formula (8) becomes the Heaviside expansion formula.

It is often convenient to use the expansion (8) directly and in a formal way, without regard to the conditions under which the inversion integral converges and the integral over C_N tends to zero. The function $F(t)$ so found may be such that its transform can be shown to be the given function $f(s)$, or such that it satisfies a differential equation whose solution was sought by the transformation method. We shall see in the following pages that the conditions under which formula (8) is valid are not severe, so that the formula is usually applicable when the function $p(s)/q(s)$ has only simple poles.

If s_n is a pole of order m, we know that $f(z)$ is represented in some circle about the point s_n by its Laurent series (Sec. 49):

$$(9) \quad f(z) = \frac{A_{-1,n}}{z - s_n} + \frac{A_{-2,n}}{(z - s_n)^2} + \cdots + \frac{A_{-m,n}}{(z - s_n)^m}$$

$$+ \sum_{\nu = 0}^{\infty} A_{\nu,n}(z - s_n)^{\nu}.$$

The function e^{zt} is represented by its Taylor's series about s_n,

$$e^{zt} = e^{s_n t} \left[1 + t(z - s_n) + \frac{t^2}{2!} (z - s_n)^2 + \cdots \right.$$

$$\left. + \frac{t^{m-1}}{(m-1)!} (z - s_n)^{m-1} + \cdots \right].$$

Hence the coefficient of $(z - s_n)^{-1}$ in the product of the two series, or the residue of $e^{zt} f(z)$ at s_n, is

$$(10) \quad \rho_n(t) = e^{s_n t}\left(A_{-1,n} + tA_{-2,n} + \frac{t^2}{2!}A_{-3,n} + \cdots \right.$$
$$\left. + \frac{t^{m-1}}{(m-1)!}A_{-m,n}\right).$$

Note that the residue of $e^{zt}f(z)$ at the pole s_n of order m is therefore the inverse transform of the sum of the terms containing negative powers of $(z - s_n)$ in the Laurent series (9) for $f(z)$. The coefficients in the series (9) can be found, for instance, by writing the Taylor's series for the function

$$\phi_n(z) = (z - s_n)^m f(z);$$

thus it can be seen that

$$(11) \qquad A_{-\nu,n} = \frac{1}{(m-\nu)!}\,\phi^{(m-\nu)}(s_n) \quad (\nu = 1, 2, \cdots, m),$$

where $\phi^{(0)}(s_n)$ denotes $\phi(s_n)$. In particular cases, they can be found by special devices.

Suppose $f(z)$ has two simple poles of the type

$$z = \pm i\omega.$$

The residue of $f(z)$ at $z = i\omega$ can be written

$$r_1 = \lim_{z \to i\omega} (z - i\omega)f(z) = \lim_{z \to -i\omega} (\bar{z} - i\omega)f(\bar{z}).$$

But $(\bar{z} - i\omega)f(\bar{z})$ is the conjugate of $(z + i\omega)f(z)$, since $f(\bar{z})$ is the conjugate of $f(z)$, and the limit as $z \to -i\omega$ of the latter product is the residue r_2 of $f(z)$ at $z = -i\omega$. According to formula (5), the terms in the expansion of $F(t)$ corresponding to those two poles are therefore

$$r_1 e^{i\omega t} + r_2 e^{-i\omega t} = r_1 e^{i\omega t} + \bar{r}_1 e^{-i\omega t},$$

which is twice the real part of $r_1 e^{i\omega t}$. Thus the terms in $F(t)$ are the real simple harmonic terms

$$(12) \qquad 2[\Re(r_1)\cos \omega t - \Im(r_1)\sin \omega t].$$

In case all the poles of $f(z)$ consist of the simple poles

$$z = \pm in\omega \qquad (n = 1, 2, \cdots),$$

then $F(t)$ will be periodic with angular frequency ω.

An examination of formula (10) will show that corresponding to two poles of the *second* order of the type

$$(13) \qquad z = \pm i\omega,$$

$F(t)$ will contain a real term of the type

$$(14) \qquad t(A \sin \omega t + B \cos \omega t),$$

which we call a *resonance type*. If the poles (13) are of the mth order, terms of the resonance type

$$t^\nu(A_\nu \sin \omega t + B_\nu \cos \omega t) \quad (\nu = 1, 2, \cdots, m - 1)$$

in addition to the harmonic term $\nu = 0$ will appear in $F(t)$.

60. Validity of the Series Expansion. In the foregoing section, we found that the expansion of the inverse transform in series of residues,

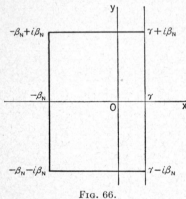

Fig. 66.

$$(1) \qquad F(t) = \sum_{n=1}^{\infty} \rho_n(t),$$

is valid when $f(s)$ contains only poles for its singularities and has a convergent inversion integral, provided the integral of $e^{zt}f(z)$ over the curves C_N satisfies the condition

$$(2) \qquad \lim_{N \to \infty} \int_{C_N} e^{zt}f(z) \, dz = 0.$$

Let us put this last condition in a more practical form.

One of the most convenient curves to use for C_N is an open rectangle with sides along the lines $y = \pm\beta_N$ and $x = -\beta_N$ (Fig. 66). The curve C_N must not pass through any of the poles s_n of course since the integral in equation (2) must converge. We assume $\gamma \geqq 0$ in this discussion since the case $\gamma < 0$ is the simpler of the two; also the value of γ can always be made larger without altering the validity of our results.

Suppose the function $f(z)$ is such that numbers β_N can be selected for which

$$(3) \qquad |f(x \pm i\beta_N)| < \delta_N \qquad (-\beta_N \leqq x \leqq \gamma),$$

where the positive numbers δ_N are independent of x and where

(4) $$\lim_{N \to \infty} \delta_N = 0.$$

This is a requirement that, when the point z is on the upper or lower side of the open rectangle C_N, the function $f(z)$ will approach zero as $N \to \infty$, uniformly with respect to x. When z is on either of those two sides, the integrand of the integral in equation (2) satisfies the inequality

$$|e^{tz}f(z) \, dz| < \delta_N e^{xt} \, dx,$$

so the absolute value of the integral over each of those sides is less than

(5) $$\delta_N \int_{-\beta_N}^{\gamma} e^{xt} \, dx = \frac{\delta_N}{t} (e^{\gamma t} - e^{-\beta_n t}) \qquad (t > 0).$$

Since this quantity tends to zero as $N \to \infty$, when $t > 0$, the integral of $e^{zt}f(z)$ over that part of the path approaches zero.

Suppose also that $f(z)$ is bounded when z is on the left-hand side of the rectangle:

(6) $$|f(-\beta_N + iy)| < M \qquad (-\beta_N \leqq y \leqq \beta_N),$$

where M is independent of the integer N. The absolute value of the integral of $e^{tz}f(z)$ over that side is then less than

$$Me^{-\beta_n t} \int_{-\beta_N}^{\beta_N} dy = 2M\beta_N e^{-\beta_n t},$$

a quantity that approaches zero when N tends to infinity, provided $t > 0$. The condition (2) is therefore satisfied, and we can state sufficient conditions for the validity of the series representation of the inverse transform as follows:

Theorem 10. *Let $f(s)$ be a function for which the inversion integral along a line $x = \gamma$ represents the inverse transform $F(t)$ of $f(s)$, and let $f(s)$ be analytic for all finite s except for poles $s_n(n = 1, 2, \cdots)$ in the half plane $x < \gamma$. Then if positive numbers $\beta_N(N = 1, 2, \cdots)$ can be found where $\beta_N \to \infty$ as $N \to \infty$, such that*

(7) $$|f(x \pm i\beta_N)| < \delta_N, \qquad |f(-\beta_N + iy)| < M$$
$$(-\beta_N \leqq x \leqq \gamma, \, |y| \leqq \beta_N),$$

where δ_N is independent of x and $\delta_N \to 0$ as $N \to \infty$, and the con-

stant M is independent of y and N, the series of the residues of $e^{zt}f(z)$ at the poles s_n converges to $F(t)$ for all positive t:

$$(8) \qquad\qquad F(t) = \sum_1^\infty \rho_n(t) \qquad\qquad (t > 0).$$

Various expressions for $\rho_n(t)$ were given in the last section. In applying the theorem, the numbers β_N can generally be chosen as any convenient numbers such that the sides of the rectangle in Fig. 66 pass between the poles. This will be illustrated in some of the problems of the next two chapters.

The conditions (7) are satisfied if $|f(z)| < B|z|^{-k}$, $(k > 0)$, for all points z on the open rectangle C_N where the constant B is independent of N. When $k > 1$; that is, if

$$(9) \qquad\qquad |f(z)| < \frac{B}{|z|^k} \qquad\qquad (k > 1)$$

on C_N, then the condition (2) is satisfied even when $t = 0$ and

$$(10) \qquad\qquad L_i^{-1}\{f(s)\} \Big]_{t=0} = \sum_1^\infty \rho_n(0).$$

For in view of (9) the absolute value of the integral in condition (2), with $t = 0$, is less than

$$\frac{B}{\beta_N^k} \int_{C_N} |dz| = B\,\frac{2\gamma + 4\beta_N}{\beta_N^k}.$$

This quantity tends to zero as $\beta_N \to \infty$ when $k > 1$.

The open rectangles C_N can of course be replaced by other paths. It can be seen, for example, that the expansion (8) is valid if the conditions (7) are replaced by the condition that $f(z)$ be of the order $O(z^{-k})$ where $k > 0$ at all points z on the arcs of the circles $|z| = \beta_N$ to the left of the line $x = \gamma$. Parabolic arcs, which are convenient when $f(s)$ involves $\sqrt{s}$, can be substituted for the circular arcs.

61. Transformations of the Integral. When the function $f(s)$ has singularities other than poles, it is often possible to reduce the inversion integral to a desirable form of a real integral by transforming the path of integration. We illustrate the procedure here by finding an inverse transformation that was arrived at in another way in Sec. 20.

Consider the function

(1) $$f(s) = \frac{1}{s} e^{-\sqrt{s}},$$

which has a branch point at $s = 0$. Let us write $s = re^{i\theta}$ and

(2) $$\sqrt{s} = \sqrt{r}\, e^{\frac{i\theta}{2}} = \sqrt{r} \left(\cos \frac{\theta}{2} + i \sin \frac{\theta}{2} \right),$$

where $-\pi < \theta < \pi$. With this restriction on θ, the function $\sqrt{s}$ as defined in equation (2) is single valued and analytic at all points in the finite complex plane except on the negative end of the real axis and at the origin. Since $f(s)$ is an analytic function of $\sqrt{s}$, $f(s)$ is analytic in the same region.

Let γ be any positive constant. When s is in the half plane $\Re(s) \geqq \gamma$, then $-\frac{1}{2}\pi < \theta < \frac{1}{2}\pi$ and $\cos \frac{1}{2}\theta > 1/\sqrt{2}$; hence

$$|f(s)| = \frac{1}{|s|} e^{-\sqrt{r} \cos \frac{1}{2}\theta} < \frac{1}{r} e^{-\sqrt{\frac{r}{2}}}.$$

It follows that $r^k |f(s)|$ is bounded in the half plane for $k > 1$, in fact for every constant k, or that $f(s) = O(s^{-k})$. Therefore the inversion integral along the line $x = \gamma$ converges to the inverse transform $F(t)$ of $f(s)$:

(3) $$F(t) = \frac{1}{2\pi i} \lim_{\beta \to \infty} \int_{\gamma - i\beta}^{\gamma + i\beta} e^{tz} \frac{e^{-\sqrt{z}}}{z}\, dz.$$

The integral in this formula plus the integral along the path $ACDD'C'A'$, consisting of the circular arcs and line segments shown in Fig. 67, is zero. For the closed curve so formed lies in a region in which the integrand is analytic. Thus if I_{AC} denotes the integral of $e^{(tz - \sqrt{z})}/z$ over the arc AC, and so on, we can write

(4) $$\frac{1}{2\pi i} \int_{\gamma - i\beta}^{\gamma + i\beta} e^{(tz - \sqrt{z})} \frac{dz}{z} =$$
$$-\frac{1}{2\pi i} (I_{AC} + I_{CD} + I_{DD'} + I_{D'C'} + I_{C'A'}).$$

Let R and r_0 denote the radii of the large and small circular arcs; thus $R^2 = \gamma^2 + \beta^2$ so that $\beta \to \infty$ when $R \to \infty$. Along the arc AC, $z = Re^{i\theta}$, $dz = iRe^{i\theta}\, d\theta$, and $\sqrt{z} = \sqrt{R}\, e^{i\theta/2}$. Hence the integrand of the integral is a continuous function of θ for every $\epsilon \geqq 0$, where ϵ is the angle between DC or $D'C'$ and the negative real axis. For any fixed R, the limit of the integrals I_{AC} and $I_{A'C'}$, as $\epsilon \rightarrow 0$, therefore exists. Likewise for any fixed $r_0 > 0$ the limits of the integrals over the other parts of the path exist. Since formula (4) is true for every positive ϵ and the integral on the left is independent of ϵ, it follows that we can let each of the integrals on the right have their limiting values as $\epsilon \rightarrow 0$, and consider hereafter the path in Fig. 68.

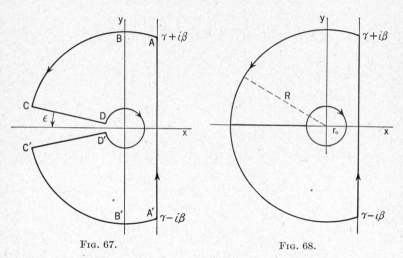

FIG. 67.   FIG. 68.

Let $J_{AC} = \lim\limits_{\epsilon \rightarrow 0} I_{AC}$, and so on, for the integrals over the other arcs and lines. We shall now let $r_0 \rightarrow 0$ and $R \rightarrow \infty$, so that the left-hand member of equation (4), which is incidentally independent of r_0, becomes the inversion integral or $F(t)$.

When z is on the circle $r = r_0$, $z = r_0 e^{i\theta}$, and $\sqrt{z} = \sqrt{r_0}\, e^{i\theta/2}$, so that the integral over that circle can be written

$$J_{DD'} = i \int_{\pi}^{-\pi} e^{(tz - \sqrt{z})}\, d\theta,$$

and the integrand is a continuous function of θ and r_0 when $r_0 \geqq 0$. Therefore

$$\lim_{r_0 \rightarrow 0} J_{DD'} = i \int_{\pi}^{-\pi} d\theta = -2\pi i.$$

On the line CD, $z = re^{i(\pi-\epsilon)}$ and $\sqrt{z} = \sqrt{r}\, e^{i(\pi-\epsilon)/2}$; thus as $\epsilon \to 0$, $z \to -r$ and $\sqrt{z} \to i\sqrt{r}$. On the limiting position of $D'C'$, however, $z = -r$ and $\sqrt{z} = -i\sqrt{r}$. Therefore

$$J_{CD} + J_{D'C'} = \int_R^{r_0} e^{-tr}e^{-i\sqrt{r}}\,\frac{dr}{r} + \int_{r_0}^R e^{-tr}e^{i\sqrt{r}}\,\frac{dr}{r}$$

$$= 2i \int_{r_0}^R e^{-tr}\,\frac{\sin\sqrt{r}}{r}\,dr,$$

and

$$\lim_{r_0\to 0} (J_{CD} + J_{D'C'}) = 2i \int_0^R e^{-tr}\,\frac{\sin\sqrt{r}}{r}\,dr$$

$$= 4i \int_0^{\sqrt{R}} e^{-t\mu^2}\,\frac{\sin\mu}{\mu}\,d\mu.$$

Consequently we can write, in view of formula (4),

$$(5) \quad F(t) = -\frac{1}{2\pi i}\lim_{R\to\infty}(J_{AC} + J_{C'A'}) + 1 - \frac{2}{\pi}\int_0^\infty e^{-t\mu^2}\,\frac{\sin\mu}{\mu}\,d\mu.$$

Now when z is on the arc AB, the real part of the exponent $tz - \sqrt{z}$ is not greater than $t\gamma$. Hence

$$\left|\frac{1}{z}\,e^{tz - \sqrt{z}}\,dz\right| \leqq e^{t\gamma}\,d\theta$$

and, if θ_A is the angle θ at A,

$$|J_{AB}| \leqq e^{t\gamma}\int_{\theta_A}^{\frac{\pi}{2}} d\theta = e^{t\gamma}\left(\frac{\pi}{2} - \theta_A\right).$$

Since $\theta_A \to \pi/2$ when $R \to \infty$, it follows that J_{AB} vanishes as $R \to \infty$. Likewise $J_{B'A'}$ tends to zero as R tends to infinity.

Finally, on the arc BC the real part of the exponent $tz - \sqrt{z}$ is less than $tR\cos\theta$ and

$$|J_{BC}| < \int_{\frac{\pi}{2}}^{\pi} e^{tR\cos\theta}\,d\theta = \int_0^{\frac{\pi}{2}} e^{-tR\sin\phi}\,d\phi,$$

where we have substituted $\phi + \pi/2$ for θ. Since $2\phi/\pi < \sin\phi$ when $0 < \phi < \pi/2$,

$$|J_{BC}| < \int_0^{\frac{\pi}{2}} e^{-\frac{2tR\phi}{\pi}}\,d\phi = \frac{\pi}{2tR}\,(1 - e^{-tR}) \qquad (t > 0),$$

and hence J_{BC} vanishes as R becomes infinite, when $t > 0$. Similarly, the limit of $J_{C'B'}$ is zero.

Therefore the integrals over the large circular arcs AC and $C'A'$ vanish as R becomes infinite, and it follows from equation (5) that

$$F(t) = 1 - \frac{2}{\pi} \int_0^\infty e^{-t\mu^2} \frac{\sin \mu}{\mu} \, d\mu.$$

It is shown in advanced calculus* that

$$\int_0^\infty e^{-t\mu^2} \cos \alpha\mu \, d\mu = \frac{1}{2} \sqrt{\frac{\pi}{t}} \, e^{-\frac{\alpha^2}{4t}},$$

and upon integrating both members of this equation with respect to α from zero to one it follows that

$$\frac{2}{\pi} \int_0^\infty e^{-t\mu^2} \frac{\sin \mu}{\mu} \, d\mu = \frac{1}{\sqrt{\pi t}} \int_0^1 e^{-\frac{\alpha^2}{4t}} \, d\alpha = \frac{2}{\sqrt{\pi}} \int_0^{\frac{1}{2}\sqrt{t}} e^{-\lambda^2} \, d\lambda.$$

Thus we can write our result in the form

$$(6) \qquad F(t) = 1 - \operatorname{erf}\left(\frac{1}{2\sqrt{t}}\right) = \operatorname{erfc}\left(\frac{1}{2\sqrt{t}}\right).$$

* See, for instance, Sokolnikoff, I. S., "Advanced Calculus," p. 359, 1939.

CHAPTER VII

PROBLEMS IN HEAT CONDUCTION

We shall now illustrate the use of the theory just developed in solving further boundary value problems in the conduction of heat in solids. We present examples of problems that cannot be fully treated with the more elementary theory used in solving the problems of Chap. IV.

The formal solution of the problem in the next section is followed by a complete mathematical treatment of that problem. The purpose is to illustrate a means of rigorously establishing the solutions of such problems. Since the procedure is lengthy, the reader is advised to use it sparingly, if at all, in his work on the sets of problems that follow. A clear understanding of the formal method of solution is of primary importance.

62. Temperatures in a Bar with Ends at Fixed Temperatures.
Let $U(x, t)$ denote the tempera-
ture at any point in a bar (Fig.
69) with insulated lateral surface
and with its ends $x = 0$ and
$x = 1$ kept at temperatures zero
and F_0, respectively, when the
initial temperature is zero throughout.

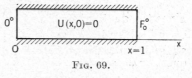

Fig. 69.

In Sec. 40 we obtained a formula for $U(x, t)$ in the form of a series of error functions, a series that converges rapidly when t is small. We shall now obtain another series representation of this temperature function. This series will converge rapidly for large t. Let us proceed formally to the solution here, leaving the full justification of our result to the next section.

We have taken the unit of length as the length of the bar, and we observed earlier that, by a proper choice of the unit of time, we can make $k = 1$ in the heat equation, where k is the diffusivity. The boundary value problem in $U(x, t)$ is then

$$U_t(x, t) = U_{xx}(x, t) \quad (0 < x < 1, t > 0),$$
$$U(x, +0) = 0 \quad\quad (0 < x < 1),$$
$$U(+0, t) = 0, \quad\quad U(1 - 0, t) = F_0 \quad\quad (t > 0),$$

where F_0 is a constant.

179

The problem in the transform of $U(x, t)$ is then

$$su(x, s) = u_{xx}(x, s) \qquad (0 < x < 1),$$

$$u(+0, s) = 0, \qquad u(1 - 0, s) = \frac{F_0}{s}.$$

Since this problem in ordinary differential equations has a solution that is continuous at $x = 0$ and $x = 1$, $u(+0, s) = u(0, s)$ and $u(1 - 0, s) = u(1, s)$. The solution is

$$(1) \qquad u(x, s) = F_0 \frac{\sinh x \sqrt{s}}{s \sinh \sqrt{s}}.$$

As long as we use the same branch of the function $\sqrt{s}$ in both the numerator and denominator, we can define the quotient of hyperbolic sines as follows:

$$(2) \qquad \frac{\sinh x \sqrt{s}}{\sinh \sqrt{s}} = \frac{x \sqrt{s} + \dfrac{(x \sqrt{s})^3}{3!} + \cdots}{\sqrt{s} + \dfrac{(\sqrt{s})^3}{3!} + \cdots} = \frac{x + \dfrac{x^3 s}{3!} + \cdots}{1 + \dfrac{s}{3!} + \cdots}.$$

Since the quotient of two convergent power series in s is analytic except where the denominator vanishes, it follows that $u(x, s)$ is analytic everywhere except at $s = 0$ and the zeros of $\sinh \sqrt{s}$. These singularities,

$$s = 0, \qquad s = -n^2\pi^2 \qquad (n = 1, 2, \cdots),$$

are easily seen to be simple poles. They all lie to the left of the line $\Re(s) = \gamma$ when γ is any positive number.

It follows from equation (2) that the residue of $u(x, s)$ at the pole $s = 0$ can be written

$$\lim_{s \to 0} su(x, s) = F_0 x.$$

Since $u(x, s)$ has the fractional form $p(x, s)/q(s)$, the terms in the series expansion of the inverse transform of $u(x, s)$ that correspond to the remaining poles are

$$\frac{p(x, -n^2\pi^2)}{q'(-n^2\pi^2)} e^{-n^2\pi^2 t} \qquad (n = 1, 2, \cdots),$$

according to Sec. 59. For our function, these terms can be

written

$$F_0 \frac{\sinh x \sqrt{s}\, e^{st}}{\frac{1}{2} \sqrt{s}\, \cosh \sqrt{s} + \sinh \sqrt{s}} \Bigg]_{s=-n^2\pi^2} = 2F_0 \frac{\sin n\pi x}{n\pi \cos n\pi}\, e^{-n^2\pi^2 t}.$$

The inverse transform of $u(x, s)$, or our required temperature function, is therefore determined as

$$(3) \qquad U(x, t) = F_0 \left[x + \frac{2}{\pi} \sum_1^\infty \frac{(-1)^n}{n} e^{-n^2\pi^2 t} \sin n\pi x \right].$$

This formal solution can be verified by showing that the function defined by formula (3) satisfies all the conditions of our boundary value problem. Thus when t approaches zero, the series in brackets must vanish for all $x(0 < x < 1)$. But we shall now see that the theory in the preceding chapter enables us to make the verification in another way which has some advantages over this method.

63. The Solution Established. We have seen that the function

$$u(x, s) = F_0 \frac{\sinh x \sqrt{s}}{s \sinh \sqrt{s}}$$

is analytic with respect to s in any half plane $\Re(s) \geqq \gamma$ where $\gamma > 0$. To examine its order in this half plane, let us write

$$s = re^{i\theta}, \qquad \sqrt{s} = \sqrt{r}\, e^{\frac{i\theta}{2}} \qquad (-\pi < \theta < \pi);$$

then $\Re(\sqrt{s}) = \sqrt{r} \cos(\theta/2) > \sqrt{r/2} \geqq \sqrt{\gamma/2}$. Thus

$$\left| \frac{\sinh x \sqrt{s}}{\sinh \sqrt{s}} \right| = \left| e^{(x-1)\sqrt{s}} \left(\frac{1 - e^{-2x\sqrt{s}}}{1 - e^{-2\sqrt{s}}} \right) \right|$$

$$< \frac{1 + e^{-2x\sqrt{\frac{r}{2}}}}{1 - e^{-2\sqrt{\frac{\gamma}{2}}}} e^{-(1-x)\sqrt{\frac{r}{2}}} \leqq M e^{-(1-x)\sqrt{\frac{r}{2}}},$$

where $M = 2/(1 - e^{-2\sqrt{\gamma/2}})$. Thus if $x \neq 1$, $r^k u(x, s)$ is bounded throughout the half plane for every fixed k. In fact if $x_1 < 1$ and $0 \leqq x \leqq x_1$, then a constant M', independent of x in that interval, exists such that

$$|u(x, s)| < \frac{M'}{|s|^k} \qquad\qquad (\Re(s) \geqq \gamma).$$

In view of this order condition, it follows from Theorem 8, Sec. 58, that the inversion integral of $u(x, s)$ along the line $\Re(s) = \gamma$ converges to the inverse transform of $u(x, s)$,

$$(1) \qquad\qquad U(x, t) = L_i^{-1}\{u(x, s)\}$$

when $0 \leqq x < 1$; also that the function $U(x, t)$ is continuous with respect to $t(t \geqq 0)$ and satisfies the condition

$$(2) \qquad\qquad U(x, +0) = U(x, 0) = 0 \qquad (0 \leqq x < 1),$$

and that

$$(3) \qquad\qquad U_t(x, t) = L_i^{-1}\{su(x, s)\} \qquad (0 \leqq x < 1).$$

Condition (2) is the initial condition in our boundary value problem.

The derivatives of $u(x, s)$ with respect to x,

$$u_x(x, s) = F_0 \frac{\cosh x \sqrt{s}}{\sqrt{s} \sinh \sqrt{s}}, \qquad u_{xx}(x, s) = su(x, s),$$

are also of the order $O(s^{-k})$ for any constant k in the half plane, uniformly with respect to $x(0 \leqq x \leqq x_1)$ where $x_1 < 1$. This is evident when these functions are compared with $u(x, s)$. Hence Theorem 9, Sec. 58, applies and the second derivative with respect to x of the function (1) can be written

$$U_{xx}(x, t) = L_i^{-1}\{u_{xx}(x, s)\} \qquad (0 < x < 1).$$

Since $u_{xx}(x, s) = su(x, s)$, it follows from equation (3) that the function (1) satisfies the heat equation

$$U_t(x, t) = U_{xx}(x, t) \qquad (0 < x < 1).$$

Furthermore, the inversion integral represents a continuous function of x when $0 \leqq x \leqq x_1$, and therefore

$$U(+0, t) = U(0, t) = L_i^{-1}\{u(0, s)\} = 0,$$

since $u(0, s) = 0$.

We have now shown that the function (1) satisfies all the conditions of our boundary value problem except the end condition

$$(4) \qquad\qquad U(1 - 0, t) = F_0 \qquad (t > 0).$$

Of course it is evident that the function (1) satisfies the condition

$$U(1, t) = L_i^{-1}\{u(1, s)\} = L_i^{-1}\left\{\frac{F_0}{s}\right\}$$

and, since F_0/s is the transform of F_0, that $U(1, t) = F_0$. But this does not assure us that our function approaches F_0 as x approaches 1, which is the condition that the temperature function should satisfy.

Let us write

$$\frac{\sinh x\sqrt{s}}{\sinh \sqrt{s}} = e^{(x-1)\sqrt{s}}\left(\frac{1 - e^{-2x\sqrt{s}}}{1 - e^{-2\sqrt{s}}}\right) =$$

$$e^{-(1-x)\sqrt{s}}\left(1 + \frac{e^{-2\sqrt{s}} - e^{-2x\sqrt{s}}}{1 - e^{-2\sqrt{s}}}\right).$$

Thus

(5) $$\frac{1}{F_0} u(x, s) = \frac{1}{s} e^{-(1-x)\sqrt{s}} + g(x, s),$$

where

$$g(x, s) = \frac{1}{s} e^{-(1-x)\sqrt{s}}\left(\frac{e^{-2\sqrt{s}} - e^{-2x\sqrt{s}}}{1 - e^{-2\sqrt{s}}}\right).$$

The first term on the right of equation (5) is the transform of a known function (Sec. 20):

$$L\left\{\operatorname{erfc}\left(\frac{1 - x}{2\sqrt{t}}\right)\right\} = \frac{1}{s} e^{-(1-x)\sqrt{s}} \quad (0 \leqq x \leqq 1).$$

The complementary error function here is continuous and bounded with respect to t, for each fixed x, so that it is represented by the inversion integral (Theorem 6, Sec. 57) along the line $\Re(s) = \gamma$:

(6) $$L_i^{-1}\left\{\frac{1}{s} e^{-(1-x)\sqrt{s}}\right\} = \operatorname{erfc}\left(\frac{1 - x}{2\sqrt{t}}\right) \quad (0 \leqq x \leqq 1).$$

If we note that

$$g(x, s) = \frac{1}{s} e^{-(1+x)\sqrt{s}}\left(\frac{e^{-2(1-x)\sqrt{s}} - 1}{1 - e^{-2\sqrt{s}}}\right),$$

it follows, when $\Re(s) \geqq \gamma$ so that $\Re(\sqrt{s}) > \sqrt{r/2}$, that

$$|g(x, s)| \leqq \frac{1}{r} e^{-\sqrt{\frac{r}{2}}}\left(\frac{2}{1 - e^{-\sqrt{2\gamma}}}\right) \quad (0 \leqq x \leqq 1).$$

That is, $g(x, s)$ is of the order $O(s^{-k})$ in the half plane, where k is any constant, uniformly with respect to x. Consequently the inversion integral of $g(x, s)$ represents a function $G(x, t)$ that is continuous with respect to x, and thus

$$G(1 - 0, t) = G(1, t) = L_i^{-1}\{g(1, s)\} = 0,$$

since $g(1, s) = 0$.

In view of formulas (5) and (6), therefore,

(7) $$U(x, t) = F_0\left[\operatorname{erfc}\left(\frac{1 - x}{2\sqrt{t}}\right) + G(x, t) \right]$$

and, when $t > 0$,

$$U(1 - 0, t) = F_0[\operatorname{erfc}(0) + G(1, t)] = F_0.$$

Our function (1) thus satisfies the end condition (4), and it is therefore completely established as a solution of our boundary value problem. Moreover we have shown that the transform of our temperature function is the function $u(x, s)$ from which we obtained $U(x, t)$. We shall see that some interesting properties of $U(x, t)$ follow from the order properties of $u(x, s)$.

We still have to prove that the series obtained in the last section represents our solution (1).

64. The Series Form Established. We have seen that the function

$$u(x, s) = F_0 \frac{\sinh x \sqrt{s}}{s \sinh \sqrt{s}}$$

is analytic except for the poles $s = 0$ and

$$s = -n^2\pi^2 \qquad (n = 1, 2, \cdots)$$

and that its inversion integral converges to a function $U(x, t)$ that is a solution of our boundary value problem. The series representation of $U(x, t)$ given in Sec. 62 is valid provided the integral

$$\int_{C_n} e^{zt}u(x, z)\, dz,$$

taken along a curve C_n of a family of curves $(n = 1, 2, \cdots)$ between the poles, tends to zero as n tends to infinity (Sec. 59).

Owing to the presence of the hyperbolic function of $\sqrt{s}$ here a very convenient selection of the curve C_n is that of the arc of a parabola with focus at the origin and axis along the real axis (Fig. 70). The equation of C_n is then

$$r = \frac{2a_n^2}{1 - \cos \theta} = a_n^2 \csc^2 \frac{\theta}{2}.$$

We take

$$a_n = (n - \tfrac{1}{2})\pi$$

so that the vertices of the parabolas lie between the poles. The intersections $\gamma \pm i\beta_n$ of the parabola and the line $\Re(z) = \gamma$ are such that $\beta_n \to \infty$ when $n \to \infty$.

When the point $z = re^{i\theta}$ lies on C_n, we can now write

$$\sqrt{z} = a_n \left| \csc \frac{\theta}{2} \right| \left(\cos \frac{\theta}{2} + i \sin \frac{\theta}{2} \right) = a_n(c \pm i) \quad (-\pi < \theta \leq \pi),$$

where $c = |\cot \theta/2|$ since $\cos \theta/2 \geq 0$. Now when $a + ib$ is any complex number, it follows, by noting the real and imaginary parts of $\sinh (a + ib)$, that

$$|\sinh (a + ib)|^2 = \sinh^2 a + \sin^2 b.$$

Consequently,

$$\left| \frac{z}{F_0} u(x, z) \right|^2 = \frac{\sinh^2 (xa_nc) + \sin^2 (xa_n)}{\sinh^2 (a_nc) + \sin^2 a_n};$$

but $\sin^2 a_n = 1$, and $0 \leq x \leq 1$, so that the numerator here is not greater than the denominator. Thus our function satisfies the order property

$$|zu(x, z)| \leq F_0$$

on the parabolas C_m.

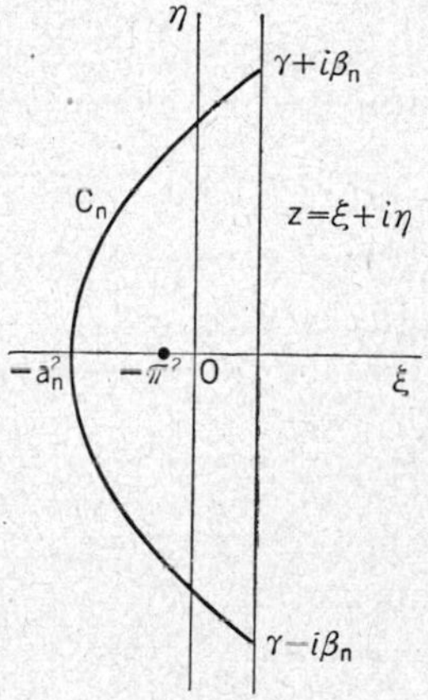

Fig. 70.

We noted at the end of Sec. 60 that when $u(x, z)$ satisfies this order condition the series of residues of $e^{zt}u(x, z)$ converges to the inversion integral for all positive values of t. Hence the series found in Sec. 62 does converge to the solution of our problem; that is, our solution can be written

$$U(x, t) = F_0 \left[x + \frac{2}{\pi} \sum_{1}^{\infty} \frac{(-1)^n}{n} e^{-n^2\pi^2t} \sin n\pi x \right] \quad (t > 0).$$

It is possible to relax the order condition on $u(x, s)$ so as to show that the series here converges to $U(x, 0)$ when $t = 0$ and, hence, that

$$x = -\frac{2}{\pi} \sum_{1}^{\infty} \frac{(-1)^n}{n} \sin n\pi x \qquad (0 \leqq x < 1).$$

This is the Fourier sine series representation of the function $\phi(x) = x$ on the interval $0 \leqq x < 1$. We shall use just this procedure in a later chapter to establish a generalization of the Fourier series representation of an arbitrary function.

65. Properties of the Temperature Function. It was shown in Sec. 63 that for any constant k the transform $u(x, s)$ of our temperature function $U(x, t)$ is of the order of $|s|^{-k}$ in the right half plane of s, uniformly for all x in any interval $0 \leqq x \leqq x_1$ where $x_1 < 1$. The derivatives of $u(x, s)$ with respect to x also satisfy this order property. As a consequence, our temperature function possesses the following properties, according to Theorems 5, 8, and 9 of the last chapter.

The function $U(x, t)$ is a continuous function of both x and t when $t \geqq 0$ and $0 \leqq x < 1$, and each of its derivatives with respect to x or t has this continuity property.

At any interior point of the bar, the temperature begins to change very slowly at the time $t = 0$, since

(1)　$U_t(x, 0) = U_{tt}(x, 0) = U_{ttt}(x, 0) = \cdots = 0$

$$(0 \leqq x < 1).$$

The temperature at each interior point does begin to change at time $t = 0$, however. For if the function $U(x, t)$ were zero during any time interval $0 < t < t_0$, for some fixed x, we know that its transform would have the form

$$u(x, s) = e^{-st_0}\psi(x, s),$$

where $\psi(x, s)$ is the transform of a translation of $U(x, t)$. In view of the known form of $u(x, s)$, it follows that

$$\psi(x, s) = e^{st_0} \frac{\sinh x \sqrt{s}}{s \sinh \sqrt{s}} = \frac{1}{s} \frac{1 - e^{-2x\sqrt{s}}}{1 - e^{-2\sqrt{s}}} \exp\left[st_0 - (1 - x)\sqrt{s}\right].$$

Thus $\psi(x, s)$ becomes infinite as s tends to infinity through real values, when $t_0 > 0$ and $0 < x < 1$, which is contradictory to the statement that $\psi(x, s)$ is a transform.

It was found in Sec. 40 that

$$(2) \quad U(x, t) = F_0 \sum_0^\infty \left[\operatorname{erf}\left(\frac{2n + 1 + x}{2\sqrt{t}}\right) - \operatorname{erf}\left(\frac{2n + 1 - x}{2\sqrt{t}}\right) \right].$$

Since the quantity in the brackets is positive when $t > 0$ and $0 < x < 1$, this temperature formula also shows that the temperature immediately after the time $t = 0$ is not zero. In fact if $F_0 > 0$, then

$$(3) \quad U(x, t) > 0 \quad \text{when } t > 0 \quad (0 < x < 1).$$

The flux of heat through any section $x = x_0$ is

$$\Phi(x_0, t) = -K U_x(x_0, t),$$

where K is the thermal conductivity. Its transform is

$$\phi(x_0, s) = -KF_0 \frac{\cosh x_0 \sqrt{s}}{\sqrt{s} \sinh \sqrt{s}},$$

and we can see by the usual argument that

$$(4) \quad \Phi(x_0, 0) = \Phi_t(x_0, 0) = \Phi_{tt}(x_0, 0) = \cdots = 0 \quad (0 \leqq x_0 < 1);$$

also that the flux through every section begins to change at the time $t = 0$. In fact from formula (2) it can be seen that, if $F_0 > 0$,

$$(5) \quad \Phi(x, t) < 0 \quad \text{when } t > 0 \quad (0 \leqq x_0 \leqq 1).$$

In Sec. 63 we found that

$$U(x, t) = F_0 \left[\operatorname{erfc}\left(\frac{1 - x}{2\sqrt{t}}\right) + G(x, t) \right],$$

where the function $G(x, t)$ and each of its derivatives vanish as t approaches zero, when $0 \leqq x \leqq 1$. Therefore the flux through the right-hand face of the bar is

$$\Phi(1, t) = -KF_0 \left[\frac{1}{\sqrt{\pi t}} + G_x(1, t) \right],$$

and

$$(6) \quad \lim_{t \to 0} \left[\Phi(1, t) + \frac{KF_0}{\sqrt{\pi t}} \right] = 0.$$

188 OPERATIONAL MATHEMATICS IN ENGINEERING [Sec. 66

That is, the flux of heat at that face becomes infinite like

$$\frac{KF_0}{\sqrt{\pi t}},$$

or it is of the order of $1/\sqrt{t}$, as $t \to 0$.

This infinite flux is the result of the discontinuity in the temperature of that face at $t = 0$, a discontinuity we have introduced in our idealization of the problem of temperatures in a bar when the temperature of one face is quickly raised or lowered.

The total quantity of heat that has passed through a unit area of any section up to the time t is

$$Q(x_0, t) = \int_0^t \Phi(x_0, \tau) \, d\tau.$$

Consequently its transform is

$$q(x_0, s) = \frac{1}{s} \, \phi(x_0, s) = -KF_0 \frac{\cosh x_0 \sqrt{s}}{s \sqrt{s} \sinh \sqrt{s}}.$$

It follows from the order of $q(1, s)$ that

(7) $$\lim_{t \to 0} Q(1, t) = 0,$$

a condition that would not be satisfied if there were an instantaneous source of heat over the surface $x = 1$ at $t = 0$. Such a source is an idealization of an actual situation in which a large quantity of heat is generated over a surface in a very short time interval, by combustion, for instance.

66. Uniqueness of the Solution. Our treatment of the boundary value problem is not strictly complete until we have shown that our solution is the only one possible. The physical problem of the temperatures in a bar with prescribed initial temperature and prescribed thermal conditions at the boundary must have just one solution. If we have completely stated the problem as one in mathematics, that problem must also have a unique solution.

The conditions we have imposed on $U(x, t)$, namely,

(1) $$U_t(x, t) = U_{xx}(x, t) \quad (0 < x < 1, t > 0),$$
(2) $$U(x, +0) = 0 \quad\quad\quad\quad (0 < x < 1),$$
(3) $$U(+0, t) = 0, \quad U(1 - 0, t) = F_0 \quad\quad (t > 0),$$

are not sufficient to ensure just one solution. They do not exclude the possibility of instantaneous sources of heat at the ends of the bar at $t = 0$. The equation of conduction (1) is the statement that heat distributes itself interior to the bar after the time $t = 0$, by conduction. In the derivation of that equation, it is assumed that the functions U, U_t, U_x, and U_{xx} are continuous with respect to the two variables x and t, interior to the solid and after conduction starts. We shall therefore require that our solution have these properties of continuity. Physically, the presence of heat sources interior to the bar after $t = 0$ is then prohibited.

Let the required temperature function satisfy the conditions (1), (2), and (3) and the following continuity and order conditions.

(a) $U(x, t)$ is continuous in x and t when $t \geqq 0$ and $0 \leqq x < 1$, and when $t > 0$ and $0 \leqq x \leqq 1$. Also, $|U(x, t)| < Me^{\alpha t}$ for all $t \geqq 0$ and all x $(0 \leqq x \leqq 1)$, where M and α are constants.

(b) The derivatives $U_x(x, t)$ and $U_t(x, t)$ are continuous functions of x and t whose absolute values are less than $Ne^{\beta t}$ when $t \geqq 0$ and $0 \leqq x \leqq x_1$, where N, β, and x_1 are constants and $x_1 < 1$.

Of course, U_{xx} satisfies the conditions imposed on U_t since the two functions are required to be identical.

We have seen that the function

$$(4) \qquad U(x, t) = L_t^{-1} \left\{ F_0 \frac{\sinh x \sqrt{s}}{s \sinh \sqrt{s}} \right\}$$

satisfies the conditions (1), (2), and (3) and that it is continuous, together with each of its partial derivatives, when $0 \leqq x < 1$ and $t \geqq 0$. When $0 \leqq x \leqq x_1 < 1$, the transform of this function, or that of any of its derivatives, is of the order of s^{-k} in any right half plane $\Re(s) \geqq \gamma > 0$, uniformly with respect to x, where k is any constant. Hence the derivatives of the function (4) satisfy the conditions (b).

In Sec. 63 it was found that the function (4) can be written

$$U(x, t) = F_0 \left[\operatorname{erfc} \left(\frac{1 - x}{2 \sqrt{t}} \right) + G(x, t) \right].$$

The function $G(x, t)$ is continuous in x and t and less in absolute value than $Me^{\gamma t}$ when $t \geqq 0$ and $0 \leqq x \leqq 1$, for any $\gamma > 0$.

This follows from the character of $g(x, s)$. Although the error function here is not a continuous function of x and t when $x = 1$ and $t = 0$, it is bounded for all x and t and continuous with respect to x and t when $t > 0$. Consequently the function (4) satisfies the conditions (a).

Suppose there is another function $V(x, t)$ that satisfies the conditions (1), (2), (3), and (a) and (b). Then the function

$$(5) \qquad\qquad W(x, t) = U(x, t) - V(x, t),$$

where $U(x, t)$ is the function (4), also satisfies the continuity and order conditions (a) and (b). Since both U and V satisfy the heat equation and boundary conditions, W must satisfy the homogeneous conditions

$$(6) \qquad\qquad W_t(x, t) = W_{xx}(x, t) \quad (0 < x < 1, t > 0),$$
$$(7) \qquad\qquad W(x, 0) = 0 \qquad\qquad\qquad (0 < x < 1),$$
$$(8) \qquad W(0, t) = 0, \quad \lim_{x \to 1} W(x, t) = 0 \qquad (t > 0).$$

Since W and W_t are continuous functions of x and t ($t \geqq 0$, $0 \leqq x \leqq x_1$) which are of exponential order in t, uniformly with respect to x, we know that their transforms exist, also, in view of condition (7), that

$$L\{W_t(x, t)\} = sw(x, s), \qquad L\{W_{xx}(x, s)\} = w_{xx}(x, s).$$

Moreover, the transform $w(x, s)$ and its derivatives with respect to x are continuous functions of x and analytic functions of s when $0 \leqq x < 1$. According to equation (6) then

$$(9) \qquad\qquad sw(x, s) = w_{xx}(x, s) \qquad (0 < x < 1),$$

when s is in some right half plane. According to conditions (8) it also follows that

$$(10) \qquad\qquad w(0, s) = 0,$$

and that

$$L\{\lim_{x \to 1} W(x, t)\} = 0.$$

Let us show that the last condition can be written

$$(11) \qquad\qquad w(1, s) = 0.$$

If δ and t_0 are any small positive numbers, then

$$L\{W(1 - \delta, t)\} = \int_0^{t_0} e^{-st} W(1 - \delta, t) \, dt + \int_{t_0}^{\infty} e^{-st} W(1 - \delta, t) \, dt.$$

According to conditions (a), the last integral represents a continuous function of $1 - \delta$, $(\delta \geqq 0)$, when $\mathcal{R}(s) > \alpha$, and, since $W(1, t) = 0$, the limit of that integral as $\delta \to 0$ must be zero. Consequently, for each fixed t_0 we can make the absolute value of that integral less than any given small positive number ϵ by taking δ sufficiently small. Since $W(x, t)$ is of exponential order with respect to t, uniformly for all x, the integrand of the first integral on the right is bounded, and

$$\left| \int_0^{t_0} e^{-st} W(1 - \delta, t) \, dt \right| < \int_0^{t_0} M \, dt \qquad [\mathcal{R}(s) > \alpha],$$

where M is a constant. Hence this is less than ϵ if t_0 is taken sufficiently small. Therefore

$$\lim_{x \to 1} L\{W(x, t)\} = \lim_{x \to 1} w(x, s) = 0.$$

Since $w(1, s) = L\{W(1, t)\}$ and since $W(1, t) = 0$ for each $t > 0$, the function $w(x, s)$ is continuous with respect to x at $x = 1$ and condition (11) is satisfied.

In the theory of differential equations, it is shown that a linear ordinary differential equation with prescribed end conditions, such as equation (9) with conditions (10) and (11), has just one solution that is continuous with a continuous derivative $w_\tau(x, s)$. In our problem, that solution is clearly

$$(12) \qquad\qquad w(x, s) = 0.$$

Since $w(x, s)$ is the transform of the difference W of the two solutions U and V, then $W(x, t) = 0$ for all t and

$$(13) \qquad\qquad V(x, t) = U(x, t),$$

for all t. We have used the fact that there is not more than one continuous function of t having a given transform.

The proof that the problem consisting of the conditions (1), (2), (3), and (a) and (b) has just one solution is now complete. The conditions (a) and (b) could have been relaxed somewhat. It is necessary to do so, for instance, when there are discontinuities in either the initial temperature distribution or in the prescribed surface temperatures.

67. Arbitrary End Temperatures. Let the temperature of the

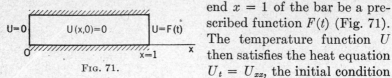

FIG. 71.

end $x = 1$ of the bar be a prescribed function $F(t)$ (Fig. 71). The temperature function U then satisfies the heat equation $U_t = U_{xx}$, the initial condition $U(x, +0) = 0$, and the end conditions

$$U(+0, t) = 0, \qquad U(1 - 0, t) = F(t) \qquad (t > 0).$$

As noted in Sec. 40, the solution of the transformed problem is then

(1)
$$u(x, s) = f(s) \frac{\sinh x \sqrt{s}}{\sinh \sqrt{s}}.$$

Let $V(x, t)$ denote the temperature function found in the preceding sections when $F(t) = 1$. Then

(2)
$$u(x, s) = sf(s)v(x, s)$$

since

$$v(x, s) = \frac{\sinh x \sqrt{s}}{s \sinh \sqrt{s}}.$$

Now $sv(x, s)$ is the transform of $V_t(x, t)$ when $0 \leqq x < 1$. In view of the convolution property, it follows from equation (2) that

(3)
$$U(x, t) = \int_0^t F(t - \tau) V_t(x, \tau) \, d\tau.$$

It was shown that $V(x, t)$ is represented by a series:

$$V(x, t) = x + \frac{2}{\pi} \sum_1^\infty \frac{(-1)^n}{n} e^{-n^2\pi^2 t} \sin n\pi x.$$

The series obtained by differentiating this series term by term with respect to t does not converge when $t = 0$; but it was shown that the function $V_t(x, t)$ is continuous when $t \geqq 0$ and $0 \leqq x < 1$ and that

$$V_t(x, 0) = 0 \qquad\qquad (0 \leqq x < 1).$$

The differentiated series simply fails to represent $V_t(x, t)$ at $t = 0$.

To arrive at another form of the temperature function U, we assume that $F(t)$ is continuous, that $F'(t)$ is sectionally continuous, and that these functions are of exponential order.   Then

$$L\{F'(t)\} = sf(s) - F(+0),$$

and

$$u(x, s) = F(+0)v(x, s) + L\{F''(t)\}v(x, s).$$

Consequently we have the formula

$$(4) \quad U(x, t) = F(+0)V(x, t) + \int_0^t F'(t - \tau)V(x, \tau)\, d\tau.$$

The two formulas (3) and (4) give the temperature $U(x, t)$ in terms of the temperature $V(x, t)$ corresponding to a fixed surface temperature.   They are two forms of Duhamel's formula.   The above series for $V(x, t)$ can be substituted into formula (4), and it can be shown that the temperature function can be written

$$(5) \quad U(x, t) = xF(t) + \frac{2F(+0)}{\pi} \sum_1^\infty \frac{(-1)^n}{n} e^{-n^2\pi^2 t} \sin n\pi x$$

$$+ \frac{2}{\pi} \sum_1^\infty \frac{(-1)^n}{n} \sin n\pi x \int^t F'(t - \tau)e^{-n^2\pi^2\tau}\, d\tau.$$

Other forms in series can be found by using formula (3), or by substituting the series of error functions found in Sec. 40 for $V(x, t)$ into either formula (3) or (4).

Our formulas (3) and (4) can be established as solutions either from the series forms directly, or from the order properties of $u(x, s)$ and $f(s)$, showing that the inversion integral is the solution and finally that the convolution integral represents that solution.

68. Special End Temperatures.   When the end temperature $F(t)$ is a known function, a convenient formula for $U(x, t)$ may be found directly.

For example, let

$$(1) \qquad\qquad F(t) = At$$

in the problem of the last section, where A is a constant.   Then

$$u(x, s) = A\, \frac{\sinh x\, \sqrt{s}}{s^2 \sinh \sqrt{s}},$$

a function with a pole of the second order at $s = 0$. We noted in Sec. 62 that

$$\frac{\sinh x \sqrt{s}}{\sinh \sqrt{s}} = \frac{x + \dfrac{x^3 s}{3!} + \dfrac{x^5 s^2}{5!} + \cdots}{1 + \dfrac{s}{3!} + \dfrac{s^2}{5!} + \cdots}.$$

By carrying out the indicated division here, the first two terms are found to be $x + x(x^2 - 1)s/3!$; hence $u(x, s)$ has the following representation in the neighborhood of $s = 0$:

$$u(x, s) = A \left[\frac{x}{s^2} + \frac{x(x^2 - 1)}{3!s} + \sum_0^\infty a_n(x)s^n \right].$$

The residue of $e^{zt}u(x, z)$ at $z = 0$ is therefore (Sec. 59)

$$A \left[xt + \frac{x(x^2 - 1)}{3!} \right].$$

The residue of $e^{zt}u(x, z)$ at the simple pole $z = -n^2\pi^2$ is

$$2A \frac{e^{zt} \sinh x \sqrt{z}}{z \sqrt{z} \cosh \sqrt{z}} \bigg]_{z = -n^2\pi^2} = \frac{2A(-1)^{n-1}}{\pi^3 n^3} \sin (n\pi x)e^{-n^2\pi^2 t}.$$

Consequently the formula for the temperatures can be written

$$(2) \quad U(x, t) = A \left[\frac{x^3 - x}{6} + xt + \frac{2}{\pi^3} \sum_1^\infty \frac{(-1)^{n-1}}{n^3} e^{-n^2 n^2 t} \sin n\pi x \right].$$

This function can be completely verified as a solution of the boundary value problem by just the same procedure that was used in Secs. 63 and 64. But the procedure can be simplified in this case in view of the fact that $u(x, s)$ is of the order $O(s^{-2})$ in a right half plane and on the parabolas C_n, uniformly with respect to x when $0 \leqq x \leqq 1$. Consequently $U(x, t)$ is a continuous function of its two variables for all x and t ($0 \leqq x \leqq 1$, $t \geqq 0$); also the series representation (2) is valid at $t = 0$. Since $U(x, 0) = 0$, it follows from equation (2) that

$$x - x^3 = \frac{12}{\pi^3} \sum_1^\infty \frac{(-1)^{n-1}}{n^3} \sin n\pi x \quad (0 \leqq x \leqq 1),$$

which is the Fourier sine series expansion of the function $x - x^3$ on the interval $0 \leqq x \leqq 1$.

As a second example, let the face $x = 1$ of the bar be kept at a fixed temperature A from $t = 0$ to $t = t_0$ and thereafter at temperature zero (Fig. 72):

(3) $$\begin{aligned} F(t) &= A \qquad \text{when } 0 < t < t_0, \\ &= 0 \qquad \text{when } t > t_0. \end{aligned}$$

Then

$$f(s) = A \frac{1 - e^{-t_0 s}}{s}$$

and

$$u(x, s) = A \frac{\sinh x \sqrt{s}}{s \sinh \sqrt{s}} (1 - e^{-t_0 s}).$$

Again let $V(x, t)$ denote the temperature function when $F(t) = 1$, obtained in the foregoing sections; also let $V(x, t) = 0$ when $t < 0$. Then

(4) $U(x, t) = A[V(x, t) - V(x, t - t_0)]$.

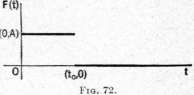

FIG. 72.

The total quantity of heat conducted across any section $x = x_0$, per unit area, from time $t = 0$ on, is

$$\lim_{t \to \infty} Q(x_0, t) = -K \int_0^\infty U_x(x_0, \tau)\, d\tau.$$

The integral on the right is the transform of $U_x(x_0, t)$ with $s = 0$, provided the integral converges; that is,

(5) $$\lim_{t \to \infty} Q(x_0, t) = -K u_x(x_0, 0).$$

In our second example, where $F(t)$ has the form (3),

$$u_x(x_0, s) = A \cosh x_0 \sqrt{s} \frac{\sqrt{s}}{\sinh \sqrt{s}} \frac{1 - e^{-t_0 s}}{s},$$

and the limit of this function as $s \to 0$ is $A t_0$.   Therefore

(6) $$\lim_{t \to \infty} Q(x_0, t) = -K A t_0.$$

The reader can show that, in the general case,

$$(7) \qquad \lim_{t \to \infty} Q(x_0, t) = -K \int_0^\infty F(\tau) \, d\tau$$

when the end temperature $F(t)$ is such that $L\{F(t)\}$ exists when $s \geqq 0$. That is, the total quantity of heat per unit area that is conducted through the bar, or through a wall, is proportional to the integrated temperature of the face whose temperature varies.

PROBLEMS

1. Derive formula (7) above.

2. If the length of the bar is l, show that

$$\lim_{t \to \infty} Q(x_0, t) = -\frac{K}{l} \int_0^\infty F(\tau) \, d\tau$$

when the temperature $F(t)$ of the surface $x = l$ is such that $L\{F(t)\}$ exists when $s \geqq 0$.

3. Derive the formula

$$U(x, t) = 1 - \frac{4}{\pi} \sum_{n=1}^\infty \frac{(-1)^{n-1}}{2n - 1} \cos \frac{(2n - 1)\pi x}{2l} \exp \left[-\frac{(2n - 1)^2 \pi^2 t}{4l^2} \right]$$

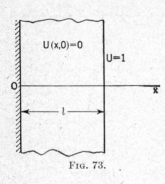

U(x,0)=0

U=1

O

l

Fig. 73.

for the temperatures in a wall with its face $x = 0$ insulated and its face $x = l$ kept at temperature $U = 1$, if the initial temperature is zero (Fig. 73).

4. Obtain the solution of Prob. 3 as a series of error functions (compare Sec. 39).

5. Establish the formula in Prob. 3 as a solution of the boundary value problem.

6. Obtain the solution of the problem in Sec. 39 in the form

$$U(x, t) = \frac{4u_0}{\pi} \sum_1^\infty \frac{(-1)^{n-1}}{2n - 1} \cos \frac{(2n - 1)\pi x}{2l} \exp \left[-\frac{(2n - 1)^2 \pi^2 kt}{4l^2} \right].$$

7. Let the temperature of the face $x = l$ of the wall in Prob. 3 be $F(t)$, where $F(t)$ is continuous, $F'(t)$ is sectionally continuous, and $F(0) = 0$. Derive the temperature formula

$$U(x, t) = F(t) - \frac{4}{\pi} \sum_1^\infty \frac{(-1)^{n-1}}{2n - 1} \cos \frac{(2n - 1)\pi x}{2l} G_n(x, t),$$

where

$$G_n(x, t) = \int_0^t F'(t - \tau) \exp\left[- \frac{(2n - 1)^2\pi^2\tau}{4l^2}\right] d\tau.$$

8. Obtain the solution of the temperature problem

$$U_t(x, t) = U_{xx}(x, t) \qquad (0 < x < 1, t > 0),$$
$$U(x, 0) = 1, \qquad U(0, t) = U(1, t) = 0,$$

in the form

$$U(x, t) = \frac{4}{\pi} \sum_1^\infty \frac{\sin (2n - 1)\pi x}{2n - 1} \exp\left[-(2n - 1)^2\pi^2 t\right].$$

9. Obtain the temperature formula for Prob. 10, Sec. 40, in a new form.

10. At the face $x = 0$ of a wall the loss of heat at each instant is proportional to the temperature of that face, so that

$$U_x(+0, t) = hU(+0, t).$$

If the other conditions on the temperature function are (Fig. 74)

$$U_t(x, t) = U_{xx}(x, t)$$
$$(0 < x < 1, t > 0),$$
$$U(x, +0) = 0 \quad (0 < x < 1),$$
$$U(1 - 0, t) = 1 \quad (t > 0),$$

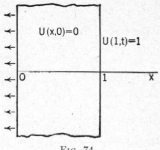

FIG. 74.

show that

$$u(x, s) = \frac{1}{s} \frac{h \sinh x \sqrt{s} + \sqrt{s} \cosh x \sqrt{s}}{h \sinh \sqrt{s} + \sqrt{s} \cosh \sqrt{s}}.$$

Derive the formula

$$U(x, t) = \frac{hx + 1}{h + 1} + 4h \sum_1^\infty \frac{\sin \lfloor \alpha_n(1 - x) \rfloor}{a_n} e^{-\alpha_n^2 t},$$

where

$$a_n = (h^2 + h + \alpha_n^2) \sin 2\alpha_n$$

and $\alpha, \alpha_2, \cdots$ are the positive roots of the equation

$$\tan \alpha = - \frac{\alpha}{h}.$$

Show how those roots can be approximated graphically when the numerical value of h is known; also show that, for any $h > 0$, α_n is only slightly greater than $(n - \frac{1}{2})\pi$ when n is large. To show that the singularities of $u(x, s)$ are all real and negative, and hence that they are the points $s = -\alpha_n^2$, let $\sqrt{s} = \lambda + i\mu$ and show that $(h \sinh \sqrt{s} + \sqrt{s} \cosh \sqrt{s})$ cannot vanish unless $\lambda = 0$. The singularities are all simple poles.

11. If heat is extracted from each unit area of the face $x = 1$ of a slab at a constant rate ϕ_0, while the face $x = 0$ is kept at the initial temperature zero, the boundary value problem can be written

$$U_t(x, t) = U_{xx}(x, t) \qquad (0 < x < 1, t > 0),$$
$$U(x, 0) = U(0, t) = 0, \qquad -KU_x(1, t) = \phi_0,$$

where K is the thermal conductivity of the material. Derive the solution

$$U(x, t) = -\frac{\phi_0}{K} \left\{ x - \frac{8}{\pi^2} \sum_1^\infty \frac{(-1)^{n-1}}{(2n-1)^2} \sin \frac{(2n-1)\pi x}{2} \right.$$

$$\left. \exp\left[-\frac{(2n-1)^2\pi^2 t}{4} \right] \right\}.$$

12. Derive the solution of Prob. 11 in the form of a series involving error functions.

13. If heat is extracted from each unit area of the face $x = 1$ of the slab in Prob. 11 at the constant rate ϕ_0 from time $t = 0$ to time $t = t_0$ and if that face is insulated thereafter, show that the temperature $V(x, t)$ can be written

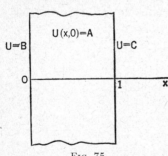

$$V(x, t) = U(x, t) - U(x, t - t_0),$$

where $U(x, t)$ is the temperature function given in Prob. 11 when $t > 0$, and $U(x, t) = 0$ when $t < 0$.

FIG. 75.

14. Derive the formula

$$U(x, t) = B + (C - B)x$$

$$+ \sum_1^\infty \frac{C(-1)^n - B}{n} \sin(n\pi x) \exp(-n^2\pi^2 kt)$$

$$+ \frac{4A}{\pi} \sum_1^\infty \frac{\sin(2n-1)\pi x}{2n-1} \exp[-(2n-1)^2\pi^2 kt],$$

for the temperatures in a slab with initial temperature A and surface temperatures B and C at $x = 0$ and $x = 1$, respectively (Fig. 75), where k is the thermal diffusivity of the material.

69. Arbitrary Initial Temperature. Let the initial temperature of the bar or slab be any prescribed function $g(x)$ of the distance from one face. Selecting the units of length and time in the usual way, the boundary value problem in the temperature $U(x, t)$ in the bar can be written as follows, when the lateral surface is insulated and the ends are kept at temperature zero (Fig. 76).

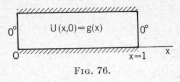

FIG. 76.

$$U_t(x, t) = U_{xx}(x, t) \qquad (0 < x < 1, t > 0),$$
$$U(x, +0) = g(x) \qquad (0 < x < 1),$$
$$U(+0, t) = U(1 - 0, t) = 0 \qquad (t > 0).$$

The transformed problem becomes

(1) $$su(x, s) - g(x) = u_{xx}(x, s),$$
(2) $$u(0, s) = u(1, s) = 0.$$

We may solve this problem by transforming with respect to the variable x. The differential equation (1) has a solution that is defined for all positive x. Let $\bar{u}(z, s)$ denote the transform, with respect to x, of any solution $u(x, s)$; that is,

$$\bar{u}(z, s) = \int_0^\infty e^{-zx} u(x, s) \, dx.$$

Let the function $g(x)$ be defined in some arbitrary manner when $x > 1$, say $g(x) = 0$ when $x > 1$, and let $\bar{g}(z)$ denote the transform of that function with respect to x. Then since $u(0, s) = 0$ the transform of equation (1) can be written

$$s\bar{u}(z, s) - \bar{g}(z) = z^2\bar{u}(z, s) - u_x(0, s)$$

The solution of this algebraic equation is

$$\bar{u}(z, s) = u_x(0, s) \frac{1}{z^2 - s} - \bar{g}(z) \frac{1}{z^2 - s}.$$

Making the inverse transformation with respect to z, with the aid of the convolution, we find that

(3) $$\sqrt{s} \, u(x, s) = u_x(0, s) \sinh x \sqrt{s}$$
$$- \int_0^x g(\xi) \sinh (x - \xi) \sqrt{s} \, d\xi.$$

In view of the condition $u(1, s) = 0$, it follows that

$$u_x(0, s) = \frac{1}{\sinh \sqrt{s}} \int_0^1 g(\xi) \sinh (1 - \xi) \sqrt{s}\, d\xi.$$

Let the last integral be written as the sum of the integrals from $\xi = 0$ to $\xi = x$ and from $\xi = x$ to $\xi = 1$. Then upon substituting $u_x(0, s)$ into equation (3) and making elementary simplifications, we can write the result in the form

$$(4) \qquad u(x, s) = \int_0^1 g(\xi) R(x, \xi, s)\, d\xi,$$

where

$$(5) \quad R(x, \xi, s) = \frac{\sinh (1 - x) \sqrt{s} \sinh \xi \sqrt{s}}{\sqrt{s} \sinh \sqrt{s}} \qquad \text{when } 0 \leq \xi \leq x,$$

$$= \frac{\sinh x \sqrt{s} \sinh (1 - \xi) \sqrt{s}}{\sqrt{s} \sinh \sqrt{s}} \qquad \text{when } x \leq \xi \leq 1.$$

This is the solution of equation (1) and conditions (2), in a convenient form. The function R is called the Green's function for the system of equations (1) and (2).

Now R is an analytic function of s except for the simple poles

$$s = -n^2\pi^2 \qquad\qquad (n = 1, 2, \cdots).$$

If the function $g(x)$ is continuous or sectionally continuous, it follows that $u(x, s)$ is also analytic except for those simple poles.

For the sake of brevity, we assume here that $g(x)$ is a continuous function $(0 \leq x \leq 1)$. According to our extension of the partial fractions expansion (Sec. 59), the residue of $e^{zt}u(x, z)$ at any pole $z = -n^2\pi^2$ is then

$$\left[-\int_0^x g(\xi) \frac{\sin n\pi(1 - x) \sin n\pi\xi}{\frac{1}{2} \cos n\pi}\, d\xi \right.$$

$$\left. -\int_x^1 g(\xi) \frac{\sin n\pi x \sin n\pi(1 - \xi)}{\frac{1}{2} \cos n\pi}\, d\xi \right] e^{-n^2\pi^2 t}.$$

Since $\sin n\pi(1 - x) = -\cos n\pi \sin x$ the residue can be written

$$2 \sin n\pi x \int_0^1 g(\xi) \sin n\pi\xi\, d\xi e^{-n^2\pi^2 t}.$$

Therefore if $u(x, s)$ satisfies the required order properties in a right half plane and on the parabolic arcs C_n passing between the poles, our temperature function has the following series representation:

$$(6) \qquad U(x, t) = 2 \sum_{1}^{\infty} \sin n\pi x \int_0^1 g(\xi) \sin n\pi\xi \, d\xi e^{-n^2\pi^2 t}.$$

When $t = 0$, the series here becomes the Fourier sine series for the function $g(x)$ on the interval $0 < x < 1$. In fact, the boundary value problem in $U(x, t)$ here is one that is somewhat better adapted to the classical method of solution, by using separation of variables and Fourier series, than to the transformation method. We shall discuss the classical method briefly in Chap. IX.

Assuming that the derivative of $g(x)$ is a sectionally continuous function, a careful study of the series will show that the function defined by equation (6) satisfies the heat equation and the boundary conditions. Let us outline here, however, the method of establishing our solution from the order properties of the transform, a method that does not rest on the theory of Fourier series.

The function $R(x, \xi, s)$ is of the order of $\dfrac{1}{\sqrt{s}} e^{-|x-\xi|\sqrt{s}}$ in any right half plane $\Re(s) \geqq \gamma$ where $\gamma > 0$. A direct use of this fact along with the boundedness of $g(x)$ shows that $u(x, s)$ is of the order of $1/s$, which is not sufficient to show that the inversion integral converges. If we let $R_1(x, \xi, s)$ denote the function R when $0 < \xi < x$ and $R_2(x, \xi, s)$ denote the function R when $x < \xi < 1$, equation (4) becomes

$$u(x, s) = \int_0^x g(\xi) R_1(x, \xi, s) \, d\xi + \int_x^1 g(\xi) R_2(x, \xi, s) \, d\xi.$$

Integrating both of these integrals by parts and simplifying, we find that

$$(7) \quad u(x, s) = \frac{g(x)}{s} - g(0)P(x, 0, s) + g(1)P(x, 1, s)$$

$$- \int_0^1 g'(\xi)P(x, \xi, s) \, d\xi,$$

where P is the following integral of R, with respect to ξ:

$$(8) \; P(x, \xi, s) = \frac{\sinh (1 - x) \sqrt{s} \cosh \xi \sqrt{s}}{s \sinh \sqrt{s}} \quad \text{when } 0 \leqq \xi < x,$$

$$= - \frac{\sinh x \sqrt{s} \cosh (1 - \xi) \sqrt{s}}{s \sinh \sqrt{s}} \quad \text{when } x < \xi \leqq 1.$$

The integral in equation (7) is a function of s of the order of $s^{-\frac{3}{2}}$, so that its inversion integral converges for all x and t. We found earlier in this chapter that the inversion integral of the function $P(x, 1, s)$ converges for all x and t. Also,

$$-P(x, 0, s) = P(1 - x, 1, s),$$

and $L_i^{-1}\{g(x)/s\} = g(x)$. Hence the inversion integral of $u(x, s)$ converges to a function $U(x, t)$ having $u(x, s)$ for its transform. It also follows that $U(x, +0) - g(x) = 0$ and that the end conditions are satisfied when $t > 0$.

Assuming $g'(x)$ and $g''(x)$ continuous, two further integrations of the integral in equation (7) by parts can be performed to show that $U(x, t)$ satisfies the heat equation and, hence, that

$$(9) \qquad U(x, t) = L_i^{-1}\{u(x, s)\}$$

is a solution of the problem.

From equations (4) and (5) it can be seen that $u(x, s)$ is of the order of $1/s$ when s is on the parabolic arcs

$$r = \left(n - \frac{1}{2}\right)^2 \pi^2 \csc^2 \frac{\theta}{2}.$$

Therefore the series (6) represents the solution (9) when $t > 0$.

In addition to this, we can see from equation (7) that the inversion integral of the function $u(x, s) - g(x)/s$ converges to zero when $t = 0$ and that it is represented by its series of residues when $t = 0$, provided $0 < x < 1$. It follows that

$$2 \sum_{1}^{\infty} \sin n\pi x \int_0^1 g(\xi) \sin n\pi\xi \, d\xi - g(x) = 0 \qquad (0 < x < 1),$$

which is the Fourier series expansion.

The results hold true if $g(x)$ or its derivatives are sectionally continuous, instead of continuous. The proof is longer, since it involves the writing of each integral as the sum of integrals over intervals on which the functions are continuous.

70. Temperatures in a Cylinder. Let us derive formally the temperature function $U(r, t)$ for a solid circular cylinder of infinite length whose initial temperature is zero and whose surface is kept at unit temperature (Fig. 77). Selecting the unit of length as the radius and making the usual choice of the unit of time, the heat equation becomes

$$(1) \qquad U_t(r, t) = U_{rr}(r, t) + \frac{1}{r} U_r(r, t) \quad (0 \leqq r < 1, t > 0),$$

where r is the distance from the axis of the cylinder. The boundary conditions are

$$U(r, +0) = 0 \quad (0 \leqq r < 1), \qquad U(1 - 0, t) = 1 \quad (t > 0).$$

In addition, the function $U(r, t)$ must, of course, be continuous at $r = 0$.

The transformed problem is therefore

$$(2) \qquad su(r, s) = u_{rr}(r, s) + \frac{1}{r} u_r(r, s),$$

$$u(1, s) = \frac{1}{s}.$$

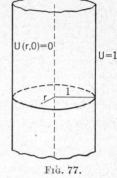

FIG. 77.

Also $u(0, s)$ must at least be finite. A solution of Bessel's equation (2) that is finite at $r = 0$ is

$$u(r, s) = C I_0(r \sqrt{s}),$$

where $I_0(x)$ is Bessel's function of the first kind corresponding to an imaginary argument:

$$I_0(x) - J_0(ix) = 1 + \frac{x^2}{2^2} + \frac{x^4}{2^2 \cdot 4^2} + \frac{x^6}{2^2 \cdot 4^2 \cdot 6^2} + \cdots.$$

In view of the condition $u(1, s) = 1/s$, it follows that

$$(3) \qquad u(r, s) = \frac{1}{s} \frac{I_0(r \sqrt{s})}{I_0(\sqrt{s})}.$$

The roots of the equation $J_0(z) = 0$ are all real and form an infinite sequence. Their values are tabulated. Let $\pm \alpha_1, \pm \alpha_2, \cdots$ denote their values:

$$J_0(\pm \alpha_n) = 0.$$

Then $u(r, s)$ has singularities when $i \sqrt{s} = \pm \alpha_n$, or

$$s = -\alpha_n^2.$$

These singularities are simple poles of $u(r, s)$, and $s = 0$ is another simple pole.   The residue of $u(r, z)e^{zt}$ at $z = 0$ is 1, and the residue at $z = -\alpha_n^2$ is

$$\frac{I_0(r\sqrt{z})}{z\dfrac{d}{dz}I_0(\sqrt{z})}e^{zt}\Bigg]_{z=-\alpha_n^2} = \frac{2}{i\alpha_n}\frac{J_0(\alpha_n r)}{I_0'(i\alpha_n)}e^{-\alpha_n^2 t}.$$

Since $I_0'(x) = iJ_0'(ix)$ and $J_0'(z) = -J_1(z) = J_1(-z)$, this residue can be written

$$-\frac{2}{\alpha_n}\frac{J_0(\alpha_n r)}{J_1(\alpha_n)}e^{-\alpha_n^2 t}.$$

The formula for the temperatures in the cylinder is therefore

$$(4) \qquad U(r, t) = 1 - 2\sum_1^\infty \frac{J_0(\alpha_n r)}{\alpha_n J_1(\alpha_n)}e^{-\alpha_n^2 t}.$$

To write this formula in terms of standard units of length and time, centimeters and seconds, for example, let ρ denote the radial distance and τ the time in such units.   If the radius of the cylinder is ρ_0 and the thermal diffusivity of the material is k, then to transform the heat equation (1) into $U_\tau = k(U_{\rho\rho} + U_\rho/\rho)$ $(0 \leqq \rho < \rho_0)$ we put

$$r = \frac{\rho}{\rho_0}, \qquad t = \frac{k\tau}{\rho_0^2},$$

where r and t are the variables used in formula (4).   Also let $V(\rho, \tau) = AU(r, t)$ so that the constant surface temperature is arbitrary:

$$V(\rho_0, \tau) = A.$$

Our temperature formula then takes the form

$$(5) \qquad V(\rho, \tau) = A\left[1 - 2\sum_1^\infty \frac{J_0\left(\dfrac{\alpha_n \rho}{\rho_0}\right)}{\alpha_n J_1(\alpha_n)}e^{-\frac{\alpha_n^2 k\tau}{\rho_0^2}}\right],$$

where $\alpha_1, \alpha_2, \cdots$ are the positive roots of the equation $J_0(\alpha) = 0$; in particular,

$$\alpha_1 = 2.405, \qquad \alpha_2 = 5.520, \qquad \alpha_3 = 8.654, \qquad \alpha_4 = 11.79.$$

PROBLEMS

1. The initial temperature of a slab is $U(x, 0) = Ax$. If the faces $x = 0$ and $x = l$ are kept at temperature zero, derive the temperature formula

$$U(x, t) = \frac{2Al}{\pi} \sum_1^\infty \frac{(-1)^{n-1}}{n} e^{-\frac{n^2\pi^2kt}{l^2}} \sin \frac{n\pi x}{l}.$$

2. Derive the following formula for the temperature function in Prob. 1:

$$U(x, t) = Ax - Al \sum_0^\infty \left\{ \operatorname{erf}\left[\frac{(2n+1)l + x}{2\sqrt{kt}} \right] - \operatorname{erf}\left[\frac{(2n+1)l - x}{2\sqrt{kt}} \right] \right\}.$$

3. If the slab in Prob. 1 is 20 cm. thick and is made of iron with $k = 0.15$ c.g.s. unit, and if the initial temperature varies uniformly through the slab from $0°$ to $100°$C., find to the nearest degree the temperature at the center after the faces have been kept at $0°$C. (*a*) for 1 min., (*b*) for 100 min.

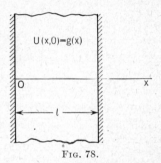

$\quad$ *Ans.* (*a*) $48°$C.; (*b*) $0°$C.

4. Solve Prob. 3 if the slab is made of concrete with $k = 0.005$ c.g.s. unit.

5. If the faces $x = 0$ and $x = l$ of a slab are insulated (Fig. 78) and the initial temperature is $U(x, 0) = g(x)$, set up the boundary value problem for the temperature $U(x, t)$ and derive the formula

Fig. 78.

$$U(x, t) = \frac{1}{l} \int_0^l g(\xi)\, d\xi$$

$$+ \frac{2}{l} \sum_1^\infty \cos \frac{n\pi x}{l} \int_0^l g(\xi) \cos \frac{n\pi \xi}{l}\, d\xi \exp\left(-\frac{n^2\pi^2kt}{l^2} \right).$$

6. In Prob. 5, let the initial temperature distribution be

$$g(x) = A \qquad \text{when } 0 < x < \tfrac{1}{2}l,$$
$$\quad\;\; = 0 \qquad \text{when } \tfrac{1}{2}l < x < l.$$

Show that

$$U(x, t) = \frac{A}{2} + \frac{2A}{\pi} \sum_1^\infty \frac{(-1)^{n-1}}{2n-1} \cos \frac{(2n-1)\pi x}{l} \exp\left[-\frac{(2n-1)^2\pi^2kt}{l^2} \right].$$

7. Two slabs of iron ($k = 0.15$ c.g.s. unit) each 10 cm. thick, one at 100°C. throughout and the other at 0°C. throughout, are pressed into contact and their outer faces are insulated. Find the temperature at the plane of contact 4 min. later.

8. The face $x = 0$ of a slab is kept at temperature zero while the face $x = 1$ is insulated. If the initial temperature is $U = g(x)$, derive a formula for the temperature $U(x, t)$, taking $k = 1$.

9. The initial temperature of a cylinder of infinite length is zero. If the surface $r = 1$ is kept at temperature A from $t = 0$ to $t = t_0$ and at temperature zero thereafter, derive the following formula for the temperatures in the cylinder:

$$W(r, t) = A[U(r, t) - U(r, t - t_0)],$$

where $U(r, t)$ is the function defined by formula (4), Sec. 70, when $t \geqq 0$ and $U(r, t) = 0$ when $t < 0$.

10. The flux of heat into an infinite cylinder through its surface $r = 1$ is a constant, so that $U_r(1, t) = A$. If the initial temperature is zero, derive the formula

$$U(r, t) = 2A \left[\frac{r^2}{4} - \frac{1}{8} + t - \sum_{n=0}^{\infty} \frac{J_0(\beta_n r)}{\beta_n^2 J_1'(\beta_n)} \right],$$

where $\beta_1, \beta_2, \cdots$ are the positive roots of the equation $J_1(\beta) = 0$. It can be seen from Bessel's equation that $-J_0''(x) = J_0(x) - J_1(x)/x$, and since $-J_0''(x) = J_1'(x)$ the denominators in the series can be found from tables.

71. Radiation at the Face of a Semi-infinite Solid. In the following problem, the transform has an essential singularity so that a transformation of the path of the inversion integral will be used to obtain the temperature function in the form of a real integral. Unless an extension of the Fourier integral is first developed, this problem cannot be solved by the method of separation of variables. We give only a formal solution here. Otherwise the analytical details that would be involved become quite lengthy.

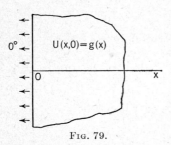

Fig. 79.

Let $U(x, t)$ denote the temperature in a semi-infinite solid $x \geqq 0$ whose initial temperature is a prescribed function $g(x)$ of the distance from the face (Fig. 79).   Let transfer of heat take place at the face into a medium at temperature zero, in accordance with Newton's law of transfer:

$$-KU_x(0, t) = -E[U(0, t) - 0],$$

where K is the thermal conductivity of the material of the solid and E is the external conductivity of the face.

The boundary value problem can be written as follows:

$$U_t(x, t) = U_{xx}(x, t) \qquad (x > 0, t > 0),$$
$$U(x, 0) = g(x), \qquad U_x(0, t) = hU(0, t),$$

where h is the relative emissivity, $h = E/K$.   In addition, some order condition must be imposed on $U(x, t)$ when x tends to infinity, a condition that takes the place of a condition at the right-hand boundary.   It will be convenient to require that $g(x)$ be bounded for all x and then impose the condition that, for some constant M and all x and t,

$$|U(x, t)| < M.$$

The transform $u(x, s)$ then satisfies the conditions

(1) $\qquad u_{xx}(x, s) - su(x, s) = -g(x),$

(2) $\qquad u_x(0, s) = hu(0, s), \qquad |u(x, s)| < N.$

By transforming here with respect to x the reader will find that the solution of equation (1) satisfying the first of conditions (2) is

(3) $\quad u(x, s) = \dfrac{u(0, s)}{2\sqrt{s}} [(\sqrt{s} + h)e^{x\sqrt{s}} + (\sqrt{s} - h)e^{-x\sqrt{s}}]$

$$- \frac{1}{\sqrt{s}} \int_0^x g(\xi) \sinh(x - \xi)\sqrt{s}\, d\xi.$$

The coefficient of $e^{x\sqrt{s}}$ here is

$$u(0, s) \frac{\sqrt{s} + h}{2\sqrt{s}} - \frac{1}{2\sqrt{s}} \int_0^x g(\xi)e^{-\xi\sqrt{s}}\, d\xi.$$

In view of the condition $|u(x, s)| < N$, it is necessary that this coefficient vanish as x tends to infinity; that is,

$$u(0, s) = \frac{1}{\sqrt{s} + h} \int_0^\infty g(\xi)e^{-\xi\sqrt{s}}\, d\xi.$$

When this value of $u(0, s)$ is substituted into equation (3), the result can be reduced to the form

$$(4) \qquad u(x, s) = \int_0^\infty g(\xi) R(x, \xi, s) \, d\xi,$$

where the Green's function R is defined as follows:

$$(5) \quad R(x, \xi, s) = \frac{h \sinh \xi \sqrt{s} + \sqrt{s} \cosh \xi \sqrt{s}}{\sqrt{s} \, (\sqrt{s} + h)} e^{-x\sqrt{s}}$$

$$(0 \leqq \xi \leqq x),$$

$$= \frac{h \sinh x \sqrt{s} + \sqrt{s} \cosh x \sqrt{s}}{\sqrt{s} \, (\sqrt{s} + h)} e^{-\xi\sqrt{s}} \quad (\xi \geqq x).$$

Let $s = re^{i\theta}$ where $-\pi < \theta < \pi$, and $\sqrt{s} = re^{i\theta/2}$. Then $\sqrt{s}$ has a positive real part and $\sqrt{s} + h$ never vanishes since $h > 0$.

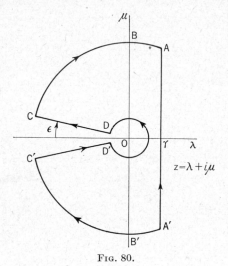

FIG. 80.

Since $\sinh (a \sqrt{s})/\sqrt{s}$ can be defined as an analytic function for all finite s, the function R is analytic except for the branch point $s = 0$ of the factor $e^{-x\sqrt{s}}$ or $e^{-\xi\sqrt{s}}$. When the function $g(x)$ satisfies appropriate order and continuity conditions, the function $u(x, s)$ is analytic except at the origin, since $-\pi < \theta < \pi$, and it is of the proper order in a right half plane $\Re(s) \geqq \gamma > 0$ so that

$$U(x, t) = L_i^{-1}\{u(x, s)\}.$$

Moreover the integral of $e^{zt}u(x, z)$ over the circular arcs ABC and $A'B'C'$ (Fig. 80) tends to zero as the radius becomes infinite. Let r_0 be the radius of the small circle about the origin. We find that

$$\lim_{r_0 \to 0} R(x, \xi, r_0 e^{i\theta}) = \frac{h\xi + 1}{h} \qquad (0 \leqq \xi \leqq x),$$

$$= \frac{hx + 1}{h} \qquad (\xi \geqq x).$$

When z is on this circle, $dz = ir_0 e^{i\theta}\, d\theta$. When $g(x)$ satisfies appropriate conditions then the integral of $e^{zt}u(x, z)\, dz$ over the small circle vanishes as $r_0 \to 0$, since $r_0 R(x, \xi, z)$ has this property.

The limiting values of the integrals along the lines $C'D'$ and DC, as ϵ and r_0 tend to zero and the radius of the large circle becomes infinite, can be seen by setting $z = re^{-i\pi}$ and $z = re^{i\pi}$ and writing $\sqrt{z} = \sqrt{r}\, e^{-i\pi/2} = -\sqrt{r}$ in the first case and $\sqrt{z} = \sqrt{r}\, e^{i\pi/2} = \sqrt{r}$ in the second. The sum of these integrals is equal to the inversion integral:

$$(6) \quad L_t^{-1}\{u(x, s)\} = \frac{1}{2\pi i}\left[\int^{\infty} e^{-rt} u(x, re^{-i\pi})\, dr \right.$$

$$\left. - \int_0^{\infty} e^{-rt} u(x, re^{i\pi})\, dr \right]$$

$$- \frac{1}{2\pi i}\int_0^{\infty} e^{-rt}\, dr \int^{\infty} g(\xi)[R(x, \xi, re^{-i\pi})$$

$$- R(x, \xi, re^{i\pi})]\, d\xi.$$

When $\xi > x$

$$R(x, \xi, re^{-i\pi}) = \frac{h \sin x\, \sqrt{r} + \sqrt{r}\, \cos x\, \sqrt{r}}{\sqrt{r}\, (h - i\, \sqrt{r})} e^{i\xi\sqrt{r}}$$

and

$$R(x, \xi, re^{i\pi}) = \frac{h \sin x\, \sqrt{r} + \sqrt{r}\, \cos x\, \sqrt{r}}{\sqrt{r}\, (h + i\, \sqrt{r})} e^{-i\xi\, \sqrt{r}}.$$

The difference of these functions becomes, after simplifying,

$$(7) \quad \frac{2i}{\sqrt{r}\, (h^2 + r)}\, (h \sin x\, \sqrt{r} + \sqrt{r}\, \cos x\, \sqrt{r})(h \sin \xi\, \sqrt{r}$$

$$+ \sqrt{r}\, \cos \xi\, \sqrt{r}).$$

This function is symmetric with respect to x and ξ, as is the function R; that is, $R(x, \xi, s) = R(\xi, x, s)$, for all x and ξ. Therefore the function (7) is also the difference of the limits of R at the upper and lower sides of the negative real axis when $0 < \xi < x$.

The formula (6) can thus be written

$$U(x, t) = \frac{1}{\pi} \int^{\infty} e^{-rt} \frac{h \sin x \sqrt{r} + \sqrt{r} \cos x \sqrt{r}}{\sqrt{r}\,(h^2 + r)}$$

$$dr \int^{\infty} g(\xi)(h \sin \xi \sqrt{r} + \sqrt{r} \cos \xi \sqrt{r})\, d\xi.$$

Introducing the new variable of integration $\alpha = \sqrt{r}$, our temperature formula becomes

$$(8) \qquad u(x, t) = \frac{2}{\pi} \int^{\infty} e^{-\alpha^2 t} \phi(\alpha, x)\, d\alpha \int^{\infty} g(\xi)\phi(\alpha, \xi)\, d\xi,$$

where

$$(9) \qquad \phi(\alpha, x) = \frac{h \sin \alpha x + \alpha \cos \alpha x}{\sqrt{h^2 + \alpha^2}}.$$

When $t = 0$ here, we have the following generalization of the Fourier integral representation of the arbitrary function $g(x)$:

$$(10) \qquad g(x) = \frac{2}{\pi} \int_0^{\infty} \phi(\alpha, x)\, d\alpha \int^{\infty} g(\xi)\phi(\alpha, \xi)\, d\xi. \qquad (x > 0).$$

When $h = 0$, this becomes the Fourier cosine integral formula for the function $g(x)$.

72. The Use of Iterated Transformations. Let $U(x, y, t)$ be the temperature function for a semi-infinite slab $x \geq 0, 0 \leq y \leq 1$ with initial temperature zero, when $U = 0$ on the faces $x = 0$ and $y = 0$ and $U = 1$ on $y = 1$ (Fig. 81). The boundary value problem in $U(x, y, t)$ can be written

$$U_{xx} + U_{yy} = U_t \qquad (t > 0, x > 0, 0 < y < 1),$$
$$U(x, y, 0) = 0 \qquad (x > 0, 0 < y < 1),$$
$$U(0, y, t) = 0 \qquad (t > 0, 0 < y < 1),\ |U(x, y, t)| < M,$$
$$U(x, 0, t) = 0, \qquad U(x, 1, t) = 1, \quad (t > 0, x > 0).$$

The problem in the transform of U with respect to t is still one in partial differential equations, namely,

$$u_{xx}(x, y, s) + u_{yy}(x, y, s) = su(x, y, s),$$
$$u(0, y, s) = 0 \quad (0 < y < 1), \ |u(x, y, s)| < M',$$
$$u(x, 0, s) = 0, \qquad u(x, 1, s) = \frac{1}{s}, \qquad (x > 0).$$

Let $\bar{u}(z, y, s)$ be the Laplace transform of $u(x, y, s)$ with respect to x, and let

$$\phi(y, s) = u_x(0, y, s),$$

a function that is not prescribed directly by the boundary conditions.   Then

(1) $\qquad z^2\bar{u}(z, y, s) - \phi(y, s) + \bar{u}_{yy}(z, y, s) = s\bar{u}(z, y, s),$

(2) $\qquad\qquad \bar{u}(z, 0, s) = 0, \qquad \bar{u}(z, 1, s) = \frac{1}{sz};$

also, $|\bar{u}(z, y, s)| < M''$.

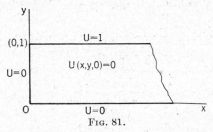

FIG. 81.

The solution of the ordinary differential equation (1) satisfying the conditions (2) can be written

(3) $\quad \bar{u}(z, y, s) = \dfrac{1}{\sin p}\left[\dfrac{\sin py}{sz} - \dfrac{\sin py}{p}\int_0^1 \phi(\eta, s)\sin p(1 - \eta)\, d\eta \right.$

$$\left. - \frac{\sin p(1 - y)}{p}\int_0^y \phi(\eta, s)\sin p\eta\, d\eta \right],$$

where

$$p^2 = z^2 - s.$$

Now the function $\bar{u}(z, y, s)$ is to be bounded for all values of its arguments when the complex variables z and s lie in some right half planes.   But the function $\sin p$ is zero when $p = \pm n\pi$, that is, when

$$z = \pm \sqrt{s + n^2\pi^2} \qquad (n = 0, 1, 2 \cdots).$$

Therefore it is necessary that the function in the brackets in equation (3) be zero when $z = \sqrt{s + n^2\pi^2}$; otherwise for each fixed real s there can be no right half plane of z throughout which $\bar{u}(z, y, s)$ is bounded. Setting the function in the brackets to zero when z has those values, we obtain the following conditions on the unknown function $\phi(y, s)$:

(4) $$\frac{1}{s \sqrt{s + n^2\pi^2}} + \frac{\cos n\pi}{n\pi} \int_0^1 \phi(\eta, s) \sin n\pi\eta \, d\eta = 0$$

$$(n = 1, 2, \cdots).$$

The points $z = 0$ and $z = -\sqrt{s + n^2\pi^2}$ are left as singularities of the function $\bar{u}(z, y, s)$ for each fixed s and y. They are simple poles. The singularities of this function of z that arise from the branch points of p are removable since we can set

$$\frac{\sin py}{\sin p} = \frac{y - \dfrac{p^2 y^3}{3!} + \cdots}{1 - \dfrac{p^2}{3!} + \cdots} = \frac{y - \dfrac{(z^2 - s)y^3}{3!} + \cdots}{1 - \dfrac{(z^2 - s)}{3!} + \cdots},$$

and similarly for $\sin (cp)/p$ where c is independent of z.

The residue of $e^{zx}\bar{u}(z, y, s)$ at $z = 0$ is

$$\frac{\sinh y \sqrt{s}}{s \sinh \sqrt{s}}.$$

The residue at $z = -\sqrt{s + n^2\pi^2}$ is

$$-\frac{n\pi \sin n\pi y}{\sqrt{s + n^2\pi^2} \cos n\pi} \left[\frac{-1}{s \sqrt{s + n^2\pi^2}} \right.$$
$$\left. + \frac{\cos n\pi}{n\pi} \int_0^1 \phi(\eta, s) \sin n\pi\eta \, d\eta \right] e^{-x\sqrt{s+n^2\pi^2}}.$$

In view of condition (4), this residue reduces to

$$2(-1)^n \frac{n\pi \sin n\pi y}{s(s + n^2\pi^2)} e^{-x\sqrt{s+n^2\pi^2}}.$$

Therefore

(5) $$u(x, y, s) = \frac{\sinh y \sqrt{s}}{s \sinh \sqrt{s}} + \frac{2\pi}{s} \sum_1^\infty \frac{n(-1)^n}{s + n^2\pi^2} e^{-x\sqrt{s+n^2\pi^2}} \sin n\pi y.$$

The inverse transform of the first term on the right, with respect to s, was found earlier in two different forms (Sec. 40 and Sec. 62). Let it be denoted by $V(y, t)$; then

(6) $\displaystyle V(y, t) = L^{-1} \left\{ \frac{\sinh y \sqrt{s}}{s \sinh \sqrt{s}} \right\}$

$$= \sum_0^\infty \left[\operatorname{erf} \left(\frac{2n+1+y}{2 \sqrt{t}} \right) - \operatorname{erf} \left(\frac{2n+1-y}{2 \sqrt{t}} \right) \right]$$

$$= y + \frac{2}{\pi} \sum_1^\infty \frac{(-1)^n}{n} e^{-n^2 \pi^2 t} \sin n\pi y.$$

The function $V(y, t)$ represents the temperature in a slab $0 < y < 1$ initially at zero, when $V = 0$ on the face $y = 0$ and $V = 1$ on $y = 1$. It is one of the theta functions.

To obtain the inverse transforms of the terms of the series in formula (5) in a convenient form, we write

$$\frac{1}{s(s + n^2 \pi^2)} e^{-x \sqrt{s+n^2\pi^2}} = \frac{1}{n^2 \pi^2} \left(\frac{1}{s} - \frac{1}{s + n^2 \pi^2} \right) e^{-x \sqrt{s+n^2\pi^2}}.$$

Since the inverse transform of $e^{-x \sqrt{s}}/s$ is erfc $(\frac{1}{2} x / \sqrt{t})$, it follows that

(7) $\displaystyle L^{-1} \left\{ \frac{e^{-x \sqrt{s+n^2\pi^2}}}{s + n^2 \pi^2} \right\} = e^{-n^2 \pi^2 t} \operatorname{erfc} \left(\frac{x}{2 \sqrt{t}} \right).$

From formulas (2) and (5) of Sec. 41 it follows that

(8) $\displaystyle 2L^{-1} \left\{ \frac{1}{s} e^{-x \sqrt{s+n^2\pi^2}} \right\} = e^{n\pi x} \operatorname{erfc} \left(\frac{x}{2 \sqrt{t}} + n\pi \sqrt{t} \right)$

$$+ e^{-n\pi x} \operatorname{erfc} \left(\frac{x}{2 \sqrt{t}} - n\pi \sqrt{t} \right).$$

Let $E_n(x, t)$ denote the difference of the two inverse transforms just found:

(9) $\displaystyle E_n(x, t) = \frac{1}{2} \left[e^{n\pi x} \operatorname{erfc} \left(\frac{x}{2 \sqrt{t}} + n\pi \sqrt{t} \right) \right.$

$$\left. + e^{-n\pi x} \operatorname{erfc} \left(\frac{x}{2 \sqrt{t}} - n\pi \sqrt{t} \right) \right] - e^{-n^2 \pi^2 t} \operatorname{erfc} \left(\frac{x}{2 \sqrt{t}} \right).$$

Then our temperature function can be written formally from equation (5) as

(10) $\displaystyle U(x, y, t) = V(y, t) + \frac{2}{\pi} \sum_1^\infty \frac{(-1)^n}{n} E_n(x, t) \sin n\pi y,$

where the function $V(y, t)$ is defined by equation (6).

Since the values of the terms of the series in formula (10) can be found from tables, and since the functions $E_n(x, t)$ tends to zero quite rapidly as n increases, it can be seen that our formula is not an inconvenient one for the computation of temperatures.

In verifying the function (10) as the solution, it should be noted that

$$\frac{2}{\pi} \sum_1^\infty \frac{(-1)^n}{n} \sin n\pi y = -y \qquad (0 \leqq y < 1),$$

for this series arises when we put $x = 0$. The function $V(y, t)$ satisfies the original heat equation for $U(x, y, t)$. Also note that each term of the remaining series on the right of formula (10) will satisfy that heat equation if it is shown that the functions E_n satisfy the equation

$$\frac{\partial^2 E_n}{\partial x^2} - n^2 \pi^2 E_n = \frac{\partial E_n}{\partial t} \qquad (n = 1, 2, \cdots).$$

The verification is left as a problem.

73. Duhamel's Formula in Heat Conduction. In Sec. 67 we obtained a formula for the temperatures in a bar with variable end temperature, in terms of the temperature function when the end temperature is constant. Let us now obtain a more general formula that simplifies heat-conduction problems in the same way.

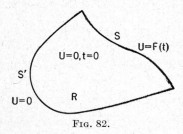

FIG. 82.

Let $U(x, y, z, t)$ be the temperatures in any solid, filling a region R, that is initially at temperature zero throughout. Let the temperature at every point of some part S of the boundary be a prescribed function $F(t)$ of time, and let the remainder S' of the boundary be kept at temperature zero (Fig. 82).

If $\lambda(U)$ represents the linear differential form or operation

$$(1) \quad \lambda(U) = \frac{1}{c\delta} \left[\frac{\partial}{\partial x} \left(K \frac{\partial U}{\partial x} \right) + \frac{\partial}{\partial y} \left(K \frac{\partial U}{\partial y} \right) + \frac{\partial}{\partial z} \left(K \frac{\partial U}{\partial z} \right) \right],$$

the equation of conduction can be written

$$(2) \qquad\qquad U_t = \lambda(U) \qquad (x, y, z \text{ in } R, t > 0).$$

We assume that the thermal coefficients K, c, and δ, representing conductivity, specific heat, and density, are either constant or vary with x, y, and z, but not with time. The boundary value problem in U consists of equation (2) and the conditions

(3) $$U(x, y, z, 0) = 0 \qquad \text{interior to } R,$$
(4) $$U = 0 \quad \text{on } S', \qquad U = F(t) \quad \text{on } S.$$

The transform $u(x, y, z, s)$ then satisfies the conditions

(5) $$su = \lambda(u) \qquad \text{in } R,$$
(6) $$u = 0 \quad \text{on } S', \qquad u = f(s) \quad \text{on } S.$$

Let $V(x, y, z, t)$ be the temperature function U when $F(t) = 1$; that is, V satisfies the heat equation (2), the initial condition (3), and the surface condition

(7) $$V = 0 \quad \text{on } S', \qquad V = 1 \quad \text{on } S.$$

Then the transform $v(x, y, z, s)$ satisfies the differential equation (5) and the conditions

(8) $$v = 0 \quad \text{on } S', \qquad v = \frac{1}{s} \quad \text{on } S.$$

Since s is a parameter in the linear homogeneous differential equation (5), the product of $sf(s)$ by the solution v is also a solution. But according to conditions (8),

$$sf(s)v = 0 \quad \text{on } S', \qquad sf(s)v = f(s) \quad \text{on } S;$$

thus the function $sf(s)v$ satisfies all the conditions (5) and (6), and it is therefore the same as the function u:

(9) $$u(x, y, z, s) = sf(s)v(x, y, z, s).$$

Since sv is the transform of V_t, it follows from equation (9) with the aid of the convolution that

(10) $$U(x, y, z, t) = \int_0^t F(t - \tau)V_t(x, y, z, \tau) \, d\tau.$$

This is the formula of Duhamel, giving the temperature U corresponding to a variable surface temperature in terms of the temperature V corresponding to a constant surface temperature. If the function $F(t)$ is continuous $(t \geqq 0)$ and $F(0) = 0$, then $sf(s)$ is the transform of $F'(t)$ and it follows from equation (9) that

(11) $$U(x, y, z, t) = \int_0^t F'(t - \tau)V(x, y, z, \tau) \, d\tau.$$

When $F(0) \neq 0$, then $sf(s) = L\{F'(t)\} + F(0)$ and an additional term appears in the form (11) of Duhamel's formula. Another form is the following:

$$(12) \qquad U(x, y, z, t) = \frac{\partial}{\partial t} \int_0^t F(t - \tau) V(x, y, z, \tau) \, d\tau.$$

These forms can be verified directly under broad conditions on the function $F(t)$ as solutions of the boundary value problem in U.

The differential operator λ could clearly be replaced by any linear differential operator in space coordinates with coefficients that are not functions of t.*

PROBLEMS

1. The face $x = 0$ of a semi-infinite solid (Fig. 83) is exposed to a medium at constant temperature A. Heat is transferred from that medium to the face of the solid according to Newton's law; that is, the flux of heat is $E[A - U(0, t)]$ where $U(x, t)$ is the temperature in the solid. Thus the boundary condition at the face becomes

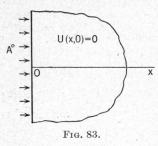

$U(x,0)=0$

FIG. 83.

$$U_x(0, t) = h[U(0, t) - A],$$

where $h = E/K$. If the initial temperature is zero, derive the following formula with the aid of the tables in Appendix III:

$$U(x, t) = A \left[\operatorname{erfc}\left(\frac{x}{2\sqrt{kt}}\right) - e^{hx}e^{h^2kt} \operatorname{erfc}\left(h\sqrt{kt} + \frac{x}{2\sqrt{kt}}\right)\right].$$

Examine the variation of the temperature $U(0, t)$ of the face.

2. Let $V(x, t)$ be the temperature function for the solid in Prob. 1 when $A = 1$. Let $W(x, t)$ be the temperature of the solid when the constant A is replaced by a function $\Phi(t)$, so that the medium to which the face is exposed has a variable temperature. Derive the formula

$$W(x, t) = \int_0^t \Phi(t - \tau) V_t(x, \tau) \, d\tau.$$

3. The temperature of the face of a semi-infinite solid $x \geqq 0$ varies in the following manner:

$$U(0, t) = A \sin \omega t.$$

---

* A similar derivation of more general forms of Duhamel's formula will be found in a paper by R. C. F. Bartels and R. V. Churchill, Resolution of Boundary Problems by the Use of a Generalized Convolution, *Bulletin of the American Mathematical Society*, Vol. 48, pp. 276–282, 1942.

Taking the initial temperature as zero, for convenience, show that when t is large the temperature at each point is approximately

$$U(x, t) = A \sin\left(\omega t - x\sqrt{\frac{\omega}{2k}}\right) \exp\left(-x\sqrt{\frac{\omega}{2k}}\right),$$

a simple periodic function of time. Note that the closed contour in Fig. 80 will enclose two simple poles $s = \pm i\omega$ of $u(x, s)$ in this case. Also note that the above formula could be obtained without the use of the transform by assuming that $U(x, t)$ has the form

$$f(x) \sin \omega t + g(x) \cos \omega t$$

and solving for $f(x)$ and $g(x)$.

4. The diffusivity of the earth's soil in a certain locality is $k = 0.0049$ c.g.s. unit. The temperature of the surface of the soil has an annual variation from -8 to $22°C$. Assuming the variation is approximately sinusoidal (Prob. 3), show that the freezing temperature will penetrate to a depth of less than 170 cm. (considerably less, because of the latent heat of freezing).

5. Use Duhamel's formula to write a formula for the temperatures in the semi-infinite slab of Sec. 72 when the condition on the surface $y = 1$ is replaced by the condition

$$U(x, 1, t) = F(t),$$

the other conditions remaining unchanged.

6. Show that Duhamel's formula applies if the surface S' in Sec. 73 is insulated, instead of being kept at temperature zero. Problem 7 of Sec. 68 is a special case.

7. Let the functions $V(x, t)$ and $W(y, t)$ satisfy the heat equations $V_t = kV_{xx}$ and $W_t = kW_{yy}$, respectively. Prove by direct substitution that the product of those functions,

$$U(x, y, t) = V(x, t)W(y, t),$$

satisfies the heat equation

$$U_t = k(U_{xx} + U_{yy}).$$

If in addition $V(0, t) = V(a, t) = 0$ and $W(0, t) = W(b, t) = 0$, and if $V(x, 0) = f(x)$ and $W(y, 0) = g(y)$, then show that $U(x, t)$ represents the temperatures in a rectangular plate (Fig. 84) with insulated faces, if the edges are at temperature zero and the initial temperature is

$$U(x, y, 0) = f(x)g(y).$$

8. Use the product of solutions (Prob. 7) to obtain the following formula for the temperatures in an infinite prism with a square cross section, if the initial temperature is A and the surface temperature is zero, taking the unit of length as the side of the square and $k = 1$:

$$V(x, y, t) = AU(x, t)U(y, t),$$

where U is the temperature function found in Prob. 8 of Sec. 68.

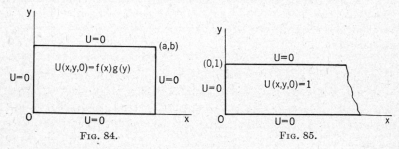

Fig. 84.　　　　　　　Fig. 85.

9. With the aid of Prob. 7, derive the formula

$$U(x, y, t) = \frac{4}{\pi} \operatorname{erf}\left(\frac{x}{2\sqrt{t}}\right) \sum_{1}^{\infty} \frac{\sin (2n-1)y}{2n-1} e^{-(2n-1)^2\pi^2 t}$$

for the temperatures in the semi-infinite slab $x \geqq 0$, $0 \leqq y \leqq 1$ with its boundary at temperature zero and $U(x, y, 0) = 1$ (Fig. 85), taking $k = 1$.

10. Generalize the method of Prob. 7 to the case of three dimensions, and give an illustration of its use in finding the temperatures in a cube.

CHAPTER VIII

PROBLEMS IN MECHANICAL VIBRATIONS

This chapter contains further illustrations of the uses of those properties of the Laplace transformation that involve complex variables. The problems taken as illustrations deal with vibrations and resonance in continuous mechanical systems—systems in which the mass and elastic characteristics are distributed over the system. Consequently these problems are boundary value problems in partial differential equations, of the type treated in Chap. IV.

It is the intention here to present fairly simple physical problems in their mathematical form, even though the same mathematical problem has a more important physical interpretation. In particular, it may be advisable to examine the telegraph equation [Sec. 33, equation (2)] and to note that, when certain electrical coefficients in a transmission line can be assumed to have the value zero, the equation is the same as the equations of the second order involved in this or the preceding chapter. Interpretations of the problems in terms of potential or current in a transmission line are then possible and frequently of interest.

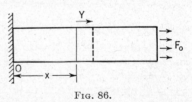

FIG. 86.

74. A Bar with a Constant Force on One End. In Sec. 35 we derived a formula for the longitudinal displacements in an elastic bar in the form of a prism, when one end of the bar is fixed and a constant force F_0 per unit area acts parallel to the bar on the other end (Fig. 86). Let all parts of the bar be initially at rest and unstrained. The displacements $Y(x, t)$ then satisfy the conditions in the boundary value problem

$$Y_{tt}(x, t) = a^2 Y_{xx}(x, t) \quad (0 < x < c, t > 0),$$
$$Y(x, 0) = Y_t(x, 0) = 0,$$
$$Y(0, t) = 0, \qquad E Y_x(c, t) = F_0,$$

219

where $a^2 = E/\delta$, E is Young's modulus of elasticity, and δ is the mass per unit volume of the material.

Let us obtain another formula for $Y(x, t)$ here.

By transforming the above problem, we found that the transform of $Y(x, t)$ is

$$y(x, s) = \frac{aF_0}{E} \frac{\sinh \dfrac{sx}{a}}{s^2 \cosh \dfrac{sc}{a}}.$$

We can write

$$\frac{1}{s} \sinh \frac{sx}{a} = \frac{x}{a} + \frac{s^2 x^3}{3!a^3} + \frac{s^4 x^5}{5!a^5} + \cdots,$$

a function that is analytic at $s = 0$. The function $y(x, s)$ then has a simple pole at $s = 0$. The residue at that pole is

$$\frac{aF_0}{E} \frac{x}{a} = \frac{F_0}{E} x.$$

The remaining singularities of $y(x, s)$ are the zeros of the function $\cosh (sc/a)$; that is, $s = s_n$ where

$$s_n = \frac{a}{c} (2n - 1) \frac{\pi}{2} i \quad (n = 0, \pm 1, \pm 2, \cdots).$$

By expanding the function $\cosh (sc/a)$ by Taylor's series in powers of $(s - s_n)$, it will be seen that the product $(s - s_n)y(x, s)$ is analytic at $s = s_n$. Hence the singularities s_n are all simple poles. The residues of $e^{zt}y(x, z)$ at these poles, according to Sec. 59, are

$$\rho_n = \frac{aF_0}{E} \frac{\sinh \dfrac{s_n x}{a}}{s_n^2 \dfrac{c}{a} \sinh \dfrac{s_n c}{a}} e^{s_n t} = -\frac{F_0 c}{E\pi^2} \frac{\sin \dfrac{(2n-1)\pi x}{2c}}{\left(n - \dfrac{1}{2}\right)^2 \sin \left(n - \dfrac{1}{2}\right) \pi} e^{s_n t}$$

$$= \frac{4cF_0(-1)^n}{\pi^2 E(2n - 1)^2} \sin \frac{(2n-1)\pi x}{2c} \exp \left[\frac{(2n-1)\pi at}{2c} i\right].$$

The poles s_n consist of a set of points on the positive imaginary axis and their complex conjugates. Let us add the residues ρ_1 and ρ_0, corresponding to the poles $\pm \pi ai/(2c)$:

$$\rho_1 + \rho_0 = -\frac{4cF_0}{\pi^2 E} \sin \frac{\pi x}{2c} \left[\exp \left(\frac{\pi ati}{2c}\right) + \exp \left(-\frac{\pi ati}{2c}\right)\right]$$

$$= -\frac{8cF_0}{\pi^2 E} \sin \frac{\pi x}{2c} \cos \frac{\pi at}{2c}.$$

Adding the residues corresponding to any pole and its conjugate we find, in just the same way,

$$\rho_n + \rho_{-(n-1)} = \frac{8cF_0}{\pi^2 E} \frac{(-1)^n}{(2n-1)^2} \sin \frac{(2n-1)\pi x}{2c} \cos \frac{(2n-1)\pi a t}{2c}.$$

Formally, then, the inverse transform of $y(x, s)$ is

(1) $Y(x, t) =$

$$\frac{F}{E} \left[x + \frac{8c}{\pi^2} \sum_{1}^{\infty} \frac{(-1)^n}{(2n-1)^2} \sin \frac{(2n-1)\pi x}{2c} \cos \frac{(2n-1)\pi a t}{2c} \right].$$

Every term in this series is a periodic function of t with the period

(2) $$T_0 = \frac{4c}{a} = 4c \sqrt{\frac{\delta}{E}}.$$

Hence every point of the bar vibrates with this period.

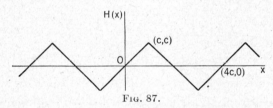

FIG. 87.

75. Another Form of the Solution. Since $Y(x, 0) - 0$, our formula (1) of the foregoing section indicates that

$$x - -\frac{8c}{\pi^2} \sum_{1}^{\infty} \frac{(-1)^n}{(2n-1)^2} \sin \frac{(2n-1)\pi x}{2c} \qquad (0 < x < c).$$

Moreover the values of the terms of this series remain the same after x is replaced by $2c - x$, and the terms are antiperiodic with respect to x with the period $2c$. Hence if the range of the variable x is unlimited, this series should represent the triangular wave function $H(x)$ shown in Fig. 87 and defined as follows:

(1) $$\begin{aligned} H(x) &= x & \text{when } 0 < x < c \\ &= 2c - x & \text{when } c < x < 2c, \\ &= -H(-x); \\ H(x + 4c) &= H(x) & \text{for all } x. \end{aligned}$$

Incidentally, this function can be described easily in terms of the function $H(2c, x)$ of Sec. 19. Thus, for all real x, we should have

$$(2) \qquad H(x) = \frac{8c}{\pi^2} \sum_1^\infty \frac{(-1)^{n-1}}{(2n-1)^2} \sin \frac{(2n-1)\pi x}{2c}.$$

The series here is actually the Fourier series representation of the periodic function $H(x)$, and therefore formula (2) is valid.

In our formula for the displacement $Y(x, t)$, let $m = 2n - 1$ and write

$$2 \sin \frac{m\pi x}{2c} \cos \frac{m\pi a t}{2c} = \sin \frac{m\pi(x + at)}{2c} + \sin \frac{m\pi(x - at)}{2c}.$$

Then

$$Y(x, t) = \frac{F_0}{E} \left\{ x - \frac{4c}{\pi^2} \sum_{n=1}^\infty \frac{(-1)^{n-1}}{m^2} \left[\sin \frac{m\pi(x + at)}{2c} \right. \right.$$
$$\left. \left. + \sin \frac{m\pi(x - at)}{2c} \right] \right\},$$

and, in view of formula (2) above, our formula can be written

$$(3) \qquad Y(x, t) = \frac{F_0}{E} \left[x - \frac{1}{2} H(x + at) - \frac{1}{2} H(x - at) \right].$$

This formula is simple enough that it can easily be verified as the solution of our problem. In showing that it satisfies the end condition $EY_x(c, t) = F_0$, it is necessary to observe that the derivative of the function $H(x)$ is the following square wave function:

$$H'(x) = 1 \qquad \text{when } -c < x < c,$$
$$= -1 \qquad \text{when } c < x < 3c;$$
$$H'(x + 4c) = H'(x) \quad \text{for all } x.$$

Incidentally we have obtained the following useful inverse transformation here:

$$(4) \qquad L^{-1} \left\{ \frac{2a \sinh \dfrac{sx}{a}}{s^2 \cosh \dfrac{sc}{a}} \right\} = 2x - H(x + at) - H(x - at),$$

a formula that can be verified by transforming the periodic function of t on the right.

Formula (3) is well adapted to graphical descriptions of the variation of $Y(x, t)$ with either x or t. The graph of $H(x + at)$

for a fixed t, for example, is obtained by translating the graph of $H(x)$ to the left through a distance at.

The displacement of the end $x = c$ is

$$Y(c, t) = \frac{F_0}{E} \left[c - \frac{1}{2} H(at + c) + \frac{1}{2} H(at - c) \right].$$

But $H(x + 2c) = -H(x)$ and hence $H(at + c) = -H(at - c)$; therefore

(5) $$Y(c, t) = \frac{F_0}{E} [c + H(at - c)].$$

This function is shown graphically in Fig. 32.

The reader can examine the force at the fixed end $x = 0$ and show that it assumes the values $2F_0$ and zero periodically.

76. Resonance in the Bar with a Fixed End.   Let a simple periodic force per unit area,

$$F(t) = A \sin \omega t,$$

act at the end $x = c$ of the bar.   If the end $x = 0$ is fixed and the initial displacement and velocity are zero, we need to change only the end condition at $x = c$ in the problem of Sec. 74 to read

$$EY_x(c, t) = A \sin \omega t.$$

The transform of the displacement now becomes

$$y(x, s) = \frac{B}{s^2 + \omega^2} \frac{\sinh \dfrac{sx}{a}}{s \cosh \dfrac{sc}{a}},$$

where $B = aA\omega/E$.

Now $y(x, s)$ is an analytic function of s except at the points $s = \pm i\omega$ and $s = s_n$, where

$$s_n = \frac{(2n - 1)\pi a}{2c} i \quad (n = 0, \pm 1, \pm 2, \cdots).$$

If $i\omega$ is not equal to any one of the numbers s_n, that is, if

$$\omega \neq \frac{(2n - 1)\pi a}{2c} \quad (n = 1, 2, \cdots),$$

the singularities are all simple poles.   They fall along the imaginary axis and are distributed symmetrically with respect to the origin. It follows from Sec. 59 that the function $Y(x, t)$ can be written formally as a series of the type

(1) $Y(x, t) = \alpha_0(x) \sin \omega t + \beta_0(x) \cos \omega t$

$$+ \sum_1^\infty [\alpha_n(x) \sin \omega_n t + \beta_n(x) \cos \omega_n t],$$

where

(2) $$\omega_n = \frac{(2n - 1)\pi a}{2c} \qquad (n = 1, 2, \cdots).$$

At this time we shall not obtain the residues of $e^{zt}y(x, z)$. This would be the way to find the functions $\alpha_n(x)$ and $\beta_n(x)$. We can see from formula (1) that the motion of each point of the bar is the superposition of two periodic motions, one with frequency ω and the other with frequency $\omega_1 = \frac{1}{2}\pi a/c$.

But if the frequency ω of the external force coincides with one of the frequencies ω_n,

$$\omega = \omega_r = \frac{(2r - 1)\pi a}{2c},$$

where r is some positive integer, then $y(x, s)$ has poles of the second order at $s = \pm i\omega_r$. Corresponding to these poles, $Y(x, t)$ will contain a term of the resonance type (Sec. 59)

$$t[C_r(x) \sin \omega_r t + D_r(x) \cos \omega_r t],$$

which can be written in the form

(3) $$tM_r(x) \sin [\omega_r t + \epsilon_r(x)].$$

Thus one component of the displacement will be an oscillating motion with an amplitude that grows indefinitely as t increases. The remaining components consist of a periodic motion with frequency ω_1.

This type of vibration of the bar is called resonance, for the idealized case in which there is no damping. The external force is in resonance with the bar when its frequency ω coincides with any of the frequencies

(4) $$\omega_r = \frac{(2r - 1)\pi a}{2c} \qquad (r = 1, 2, \cdots),$$

which can now be called resonance frequencies.

We shall see that the set of resonance frequencies depends upon
the manner in which the bar is supported, as well as upon the
physical properties of the bar.   For example, if the end $x = 0$ is
free, the resonance frequencies are not the same as the frequencies
(4).

For any prescribed force $F(t)$ at the end $x = c$, the transform
of $Y(x, t)$ is

$$y(x, s) = \frac{a}{E} f(s) \frac{\sinh \dfrac{sx}{a}}{s \cosh \dfrac{sc}{a}}.$$

Consequently, if the function $F(t)$ contains a term of the type
$A_1 \sin \omega_1 t$ or $B_1 \cos \omega_1 t$, then $y(x, s)$ will contain a term with the
product $(s^2 + \omega_1^2) \cosh (sc/a)$ in the denominator, and $Y(x, t)$
will contain a resonance term (3) with $r = 1$.   Similarly, if the
force has a simple periodic component with the frequency ω_r,
resonance will occur.   Thus to cause resonance it is not necessary
that $F(t)$ be limited to the simple form $F(t) = A \sin \omega_r t$.

In fact, whenever $F(t)$ is any periodic function with frequency
ω_1, resonance will occur.   This can be seen either from the
Fourier series representation of $F(t)$ or from the form in Sec. 19
of the transform of a periodic function.   The frequency ω_1, may
be replaced by any other frequency ω_r given by equation (4).

77. Resonance When Damping Is Present.   In actual mechanical systems, some damping of vibrations is always present, at

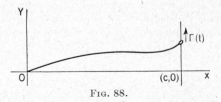

Fig. 88.

least in the form of internal resistance to the motion.   Let us
consider a case in which the damping force is proportional to the
velocity.

We shift to another physical interpretation of the problem
considered up to this point, namely, that of the transverse
displacements $Y(x, t)$ in a string stretched from the origin and

looped around a smooth support $x = c$ (Fig. 88). In view of the damping, the equation of motion can be written

$$Y_{tt}(x, t) = a^2 Y_{xx}(x, t) - 2b Y_t(x, t) \quad (0 < x < c, t > 0),$$

where a^2 is the tension divided by the mass per unit length and b is a damping coefficient $(b > 0)$.

If the applied vertical force on the loop is proportional to sin ωt and the string is initially at rest along the x-axis, the boundary conditions are

$$Y(x, 0) = Y_t(x, 0) = 0, \qquad Y(0, t) = 0, \qquad Y_x(c, t) = A \sin \omega t.$$

The transformed problem

$$a^2 y_{xx}(x, s) - (s^2 + 2bs) y(x, s) = 0,$$

$$y(0, s) = 0, \qquad y_x(c, s) = \frac{A\omega}{s^2 + \omega^2},$$

has the solution

$$y(x, s) = \frac{A\omega}{s^2 + \omega^2} \frac{\sinh px}{p \cosh pc},$$

where

$$p = \frac{\sqrt{s^2 + 2bs}}{a}.$$

The function $y(x, s)$ has singularities at $s = \pm i\omega$ and at the zeros of the function cosh pc, which are the roots of the quadratic equation

$$s^2 + 2bs = -\frac{(2n - 1)^2 \pi^2 a^2}{4c^2}.$$

When $2b < \pi a/c$, these roots can be written

(1) $$s = -b \pm i\beta_n$$

where

$$\beta_n = \left[\frac{(2n - 1)^2 \pi^2 a^2}{4c^2} - b^2 \right]^{\frac{1}{2}}.$$

Since their real parts are $-b$, these roots cannot coincide with $\pm i\omega$. Regardless of the value of ω, the singularities of $y(x, s)$ are all simple poles.

Corresponding to the poles $s = \pm i\omega$, $Y(x, t)$ will have a term of the type

(2) $$Y_1(x, t) = M_\omega(x) \sin [\omega t + \epsilon_\omega(x)],$$

and corresponding to the poles (1) it will have a series of terms of the type

$$(3) \qquad Y_2(x,\, t) = e^{-bt} \sum_1^\infty \alpha_n(x) \sin [\beta_n t + \epsilon_n(x)].$$

That is, $Y(x,\, t)$ is composed of two components:

$$(4) \qquad Y(x,\, t) = Y_1(x,\, t) + Y_2(x,\, t).$$

The component $Y_1(x,\, t)$ is called the forced vibration. The component $Y_2(x,\, t)$ is the transient vibration, one that is negligible for large t. In fact, by transforming the problem in the case of an arbitrary initial displacement and velocity, an examination of $y(x,\, s)$ will show that the component $Y_2(x,\, t)$ disappears under the proper choice of those initial conditions.

The resonance frequencies are now those frequencies for which the amplitude $M_\omega(x)$ of $Y_1(x,\, t)$ is greatest. The determination of $M_\omega(x)$ from $y(x,\, s)$ is a straightforward matter, but rather lengthy. When b is small, the resonance frequencies are close to those found when damping is not present.

Thus resonance with damping consists of a sustained periodic motion with maximum amplitude. The amplitude may be great enough to cause the mechanical system to fail.

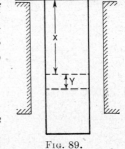

FIG. 89.

PROBLEMS

1. An elastic bar is clamped along its length c so as to prevent longitudinal displacements and then hung from its end $x = 0$. At the instant $t = 0$, the clamp is removed and the bar vibrates longitudinally due to its own weight (Fig. 89). Thus

$$Y_{tt}(x,\, t) = a^2 Y_{xx}(x,\, t) + g \quad (0 < x < c,\, t > 0), \; Y_x(c,\, t) = 0,$$

where g is the acceleration of gravity. Complete the boundary value problem, and derive the formula

$$Y(x,\, t) = \frac{gx}{2a^2}(2c - x) - \frac{16gc^2}{\pi^3 a^2} \sum_1^\infty \frac{1}{(2n-1)^3} \sin \frac{(2n-1)\pi x}{2c}$$
$$\cos \frac{(2n-1)\pi at}{2c}.$$

2. Derive the following formula for the angular displacements in the spinning shaft of Prob. 4, Sec. 36, whose ends $x = \pm c$ are clamped at the instant $t = 0$:

$$\Theta(x, t) = \frac{8c\omega}{\pi^2 a} \sum_{1}^{\infty} \frac{(-1)^{n-1}}{(2n-1)^2} \cos \frac{(2n-1)\pi x}{2c} \sin \frac{(2n-1)\pi a t}{2c}.$$

3. Derive another formula for the displacements in the bar of Prob. 7, Sec. 35.

4. A simple periodic force acts on all points of a bar with the end $x = 0$ fixed and the end $x = c$ free. If the initial displacement and velocity are zero, the displacements satisfy the conditions

$$Y_{tt}(x, t) = a^2 Y_{xx}(x, t) + B \sin \omega t,$$
$$Y(x, 0) = Y_t(x, 0) = Y(0, t) = Y_x(c, t) = 0,$$

where ω is the frequency of the applied force. Show that the frequencies at which resonance will occur are

$$\omega = \frac{(2n-1)\pi a}{2c} \qquad (n = 1, 2, \cdots).$$

5. The end $x = 0$ of a bar is fixed and the end $x = c$ is forced to move in the manner $Y(c, t) = A \sin \omega t$. Show that the resonance frequencies are

$$\omega_n = \frac{n\pi a}{c} \qquad (n = 1, 2, \cdots).$$

6. A simple periodic transverse force acts on all points of a stretched string of length c with fixed ends, so that the equation of motion has the same form as the equation in Prob. 4. Show that the resonance frequencies are

$$\omega_n = \frac{(2n-1)\pi a}{c} \qquad (n = 1, 2, \cdots).$$

7. Determine the resonance frequencies when simple periodic forces act on both ends of a bar. Show that when both forces have the same frequency the set of frequencies is different from what it is when the frequencies are distinct.

8. Show that the values of the resonance frequencies are independent of the initial conditions, using the problem of Sec. 76 to demonstrate this.

9. Determine the nature of the vibrations of the bar considered in this section when the damping is such that $2b \geqq \pi a/c$.

78. Verification of Solutions. When the formal solution of a problem can be written in terms of a finite number of simple functions, it is of course generally desirable to use that form to verify the result as the solution of the boundary value problem. This was illustrated in Sec. 75. But if a verification is required when the result is expressed only as an infinite series or an infinite integral, the procedure illustrated below may be useful. This procedure is based on the properties of the transform. It was illustrated for problems in heat conduction in Chap. VII.

Consider again the problem of the displacements in a bar with the end $x = 0$ fixed and with a force $A \sin \omega t$ per unit area on the end $x = c$. In Sec. 76, we found that the transform of the displacement is

$$y(x, s) = \frac{B}{s^2 + \omega^2} \frac{\sinh \dfrac{sx}{a}}{s \cosh \dfrac{sc}{a}}.$$

When $\Re(s) \geqq \gamma$, where $\gamma > 0$,

$$\left| \frac{\sinh \dfrac{sx}{a}}{\cosh \dfrac{sc}{a}} \right| = \left| e^{-\frac{(c-x)s}{a}} \frac{1 - e^{-\frac{2sx}{a}}}{1 + e^{-\frac{2sc}{a}}} \right| < \frac{2}{1 - e^{-\frac{2\gamma c}{a}}}.$$

Consequently, for some constant M independent of x,

$$|y(x, s)| < \frac{M}{|s|^3},$$

for all s in the half plane $\Re(s) \geqq \gamma$. Since $y(x, s)$ is an analytic function of s in that half plane, it follows from Sec. 58 that the inversion integral $L_i^{-1}\{y(x, s)\}$ converges to a continuous function $Y(x, t)$ of x and t and that $Y(x, 0) = Y(0, t) = 0$. Also

$$Y_t(x, t) = L_i^{-1}\{sy(x, s)\}, \qquad Y_x(x, t) = L_i^{-1}\{y_x(x, s)\}.$$

These functions are continuous. Moreover $Y_t(x, 0) = 0$ and

$$Y_x(c, t) = L_i^{-1}\{y_x(c, s)\} = L_i^{-1}\left\{\frac{B}{a(s^2 + \omega^2)}\right\} = \frac{B}{\omega a} \sin \omega t.$$

Hence the inversion integral is a function $Y(x, t)$ that satisfies all the boundary conditions in the problem.

To show that it satisfies the differential equation, we first write

$$\frac{1}{s^2 + \omega^2} = \frac{1}{s^2} - \frac{\omega^2}{s^2(s^2 + \omega^2)},$$

so that the transform of $Y_t(x, t)$ can be written

$$sy(x, s) = u(x, s) + v(x, \cdot s)$$

where

$$u(x, s) = B \frac{\sinh \dfrac{sx}{a}}{s^2 \cosh \dfrac{sc}{a}}, \qquad v(x, s) = \frac{-B\omega^2}{s^2(s^2 + \omega^2)} \frac{\sinh \dfrac{sx}{a}}{\cosh \dfrac{sc}{a}}.$$

Now $v(x, s)$ is of the order of s^{-4} in the right half plane, and therefore $L_i^{-1}\{sv\} = V_t(x, t)$, where $V(x, t)$ represents the inversion integral of $v(x, s)$.

The function $u(x, s)$ is of the weaker order $O(s^{-2})$. But we found in Sec. 75 that it is the transform of the periodic function

$$U(x, t) = \frac{B}{2a} [2x - H(x + at) - H(x - at)].$$

Since $U_t(x, t)$ is sectionally continuous with respect to t, we know that $su(x, s)$ is the transform of the periodic function $U_t(x, t)$. According to Theorem 6 of Sec. 57 then, $L_i^{-1}\{su\} = U_t(x, t)$. Consequently,

$$L_i^{-1}\{s^2y\} = U_t(x, t) + V_t(x, t) = Y_{tt}(x, t),$$

where $Y(x, t)$ is the inversion integral of $y(x, s)$.

Since the differentiation of $y(x, s)$ with respect to x introduces a factor s as the essential change, it can be seen in the same way that

$$L_i^{-1}\{y_{xx}(x, s)\} = Y_{xx}(x, t).$$

Then

$$Y_{tt}(x, t) - a^2 Y_{xx}(x, t) = L_i^{-1}\{s^2y(x, s) - a^2 y_{xx}(x, s)\} = 0,$$

since $y(x, s)$ satisfies the transformed equation. The inversion integral is therefore established as a solution of the boundary value problem. Note that if $y(x, s)$ had been of the order $O(s^{-4})$ the separation of sy into the components u and v would not have been necessary.

Next we shall show that the series consisting of the sum of the residues of the function $e^{st}y(x, s)$ converges to the inversion integral, so that we can conclude that this series represents the solution. We do this by showing that $y(x, s)$ satisfies the conditions of Theorem 10, Sec. 60.

The poles of $y(x, s)$ are the points

$$s = \pm\omega i, \ \pm\frac{\pi a}{2c} i, \ \pm\frac{3\pi a}{2c} i, \ \pm\frac{5\pi a}{2c} i, \cdots .$$

Let $s = \xi + i\eta$. Then in Fig. 66 the lines $\eta = \pm\beta_N$ will pass between the poles when N is sufficiently large if we take

$$\beta_N = \frac{N\pi a}{c} \qquad (N = 1, 2, \cdots).$$

Since

$$y(x, s) = \frac{B}{s(s^2 + \omega^2)} e^{\frac{(c-x)s}{a}} \frac{e^{\frac{2sx}{a}} - 1}{e^{\frac{2sc}{a}} + 1},$$

it is easy to see that $|y(x, s)|$ is bounded in the half plane $\xi \leqq -\gamma$ uniformly with respect to x. Therefore $|y(x, -\beta_N + i\eta)|$ is bounded.

Now since

$$|\sinh (\lambda + i\mu)|^2 = \sinh^2 \lambda + \sin^2 \mu,$$
$$|\cosh (\lambda + i\mu)|^2 = \sinh^2 \lambda + \cos^2 \mu,$$

it follows that, when $s = \xi \pm i\beta_N$,

$$\left|\frac{\sinh \dfrac{sx}{a}}{\cosh \dfrac{sc}{a}}\right|^2 = \frac{\sinh^2 \dfrac{\xi x}{a} + \sin^2 \dfrac{\beta_N x}{a}}{\sinh^2 \dfrac{\xi c}{a} + 1} \leqq 1.$$

Therefore $|y(x, s)| \leqq |B/(s^3 + \omega^2 s)|$ when $s = \xi \pm i\beta_N$, and the conditions of Theorem 10, Sec. 60, are satisfied. In fact, since $y(x, s)$ is of the order $O(s^{-3})$ on the rectangular path, the series of residues converges to the inversion integral for all $t \geqq 0$.

The series form of the solution is now rigorously established for any value of the frequency ω. When ω does not coincide with any of the resonance frequencies, the explicit form of our solution becomes

$$Y(x, t) = \frac{B}{\omega^2} \frac{\sin \dfrac{\omega x}{a}}{\cos \dfrac{\omega c}{a}} \sin \omega t + \frac{2B}{c} \sum_{n=1}^{\infty} \frac{(-1)^{n-1}}{m_n} \frac{\sin m_n x}{\omega^2 - m_n^2 a^2} \sin m_n at,$$

where $m_n = (n - \frac{1}{2})\pi/c$. This is found by computing the residues in the usual manner.

The solution found has continuous derivatives of the first order. Its derivatives of the second order are sectionally continuous functions of either x or t, and the function and its derivatives are of exponential order for large t. By following the method in Sec. 66, it can be seen that there is no other solution of this type. In this case the procedure is quite simple as a result of the favorable continuity conditions.

79. Free Vibrations of a String. A string, stretched between the origin and the point $(c, 0)$, is given a prescribed initial displacement $Y = g(x)$ and released from rest in that position. To find the transverse displacements $Y(x, t)$, we must solve the problem,

$$Y_{tt}(x, t) = a^2 Y_{xx}(x, t) \quad (0 < x < c, t > 0),$$
$$Y(x, 0) = g(x), \qquad Y_t(x, 0) = Y(0, t) = Y(c, t) = 0.$$

The transformed problem,

$$a^2 y_{xx}(x, s) - s^2 y(x, s) = -sg(x),$$
$$y(0, s) = y(c, s) = 0,$$

can be solved easily by transforming with respect to x. Its solution can be written

$$y(x, s) = \frac{\phi(x, s)}{a \sinh \dfrac{sc}{a}},$$

where

$$\phi(x, s) = \sinh \frac{(c - x)s}{a} \int_0^x g(\xi) \sinh \frac{\xi s}{a} \, d\xi$$
$$+ \sinh \frac{xs}{a} \int_x^c g(\xi) \sinh \frac{(c - \xi)s}{a} \, d\xi.$$

The function $g(x)$ must naturally be continuous and vanish at $x = 0$ and $x = c$. If its derivative is at least sectionally continuous, the function $\phi(x, s)$ is analytic for all finite s, and, except for $s = 0$, the zeros of sinh sc/a are simple poles of $y(x, s)$. These poles are $s = \pm s_n$ where

$$s_n = \frac{n\pi a}{c} i \qquad (n = 1, 2, \cdots).$$

Since

$$\phi(x, s_n) = \cos n\pi \sin \frac{n\pi x}{c} \int_0^c g(\xi) \sin \frac{n\pi \xi}{c} d\xi =$$
$$\frac{c}{2} b_n \cos n\pi \sin \frac{n\pi x}{c},$$

where

(1) $$b_n = \frac{2}{c} \int_0^c g(\xi) \sin \frac{n\pi \xi}{c} d\xi,$$

the sum of the residues of $e^{ts}y(x, s)$ at $s = \pm s_n$ is

$$\frac{1}{2} \sum_1^\infty b_n \sin \frac{n\pi x}{c} \left[\exp \left(\frac{in\pi at}{c} \right) + \exp \left(-\frac{in\pi at}{c} \right) \right].$$

The formal solution of the problem is therefore

(2) $$Y(x, t) = \sum_1^\infty b_n \sin \frac{n\pi x}{c} \cos \frac{n\pi at}{c},$$

where the coefficients b_n are given by formula (1).

When $t = 0$, the series here becomes the Fourier sine series for the function $g(x)$ on the interval $0 \leqq x \leqq c$. By writing

$$Y(x, t) = \frac{1}{2} \left[\sum_1^\infty b_n \sin \frac{n\pi(x + at)}{c} + \sum_1^\infty b_n \sin \frac{n\pi(x - at)}{c} \right],$$

an examination of the series indicates that

(3) $$Y(x, t) = \tfrac{1}{2}[G(x + at) + G(x - at)],$$

where $G(x)$ is the periodic function defined as follows for all real x:

$$G(x) = -G(-x) = g(x) \quad \text{when } 0 \leqq x \leqq c,$$
$$G(x + 2c) = G(x) \qquad \text{for all } x.$$

The result in the form (3) is easily verified as the solution of the boundary value problem.   It is also a convenient form to use in studying the motion of the string.

80. Resonance in a Bar with a Mass Attached. The end
$x = 0$ of a bar is fixed. To the end $x = c$, a concentrated mass
is attached (Fig. 90). A longitudinal periodic force $B \sin \omega t$ acts
on this mass. Let us find the resonance frequencies. The
elastic displacements in the mass itself are assumed to be negligible, and the bar is assumed to be too heavy to be considered
simply as a coil spring without mass.

Let A be the area of the cross section of the bar and $Y(x, t)$ the
longitudinal displacement in the bar. The force exerted by the

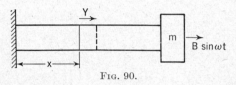

FIG. 90.

bar on the mass m is then $-EAY_x(c, t)$, so that the end conditions
are

$$Y(0, t) = 0, \qquad mY_{tt}(c, t) = -EAY_x(c, t) + B \sin \omega t.$$

If the initial displacement and velocity are zero, the remaining
conditions in the problem are

$$Y_{tt}(x, t) = a^2 Y_{xx}(x, t) \qquad (0 < x < c, t > 0),$$
$$Y(x, 0) = Y_t(x, 0) = 0.$$

This is also the problem of the torsional vibrations in a shaft
with one end fixed and with a flywheel, on which a periodic torque
acts, attached to the other end. Note that one end condition
here involves the second derivative.

The transformed problem is

$$s^2 y(x, s) = a^2 y_{xx}(x, s),$$

$$y(0, s) = 0, \qquad EAy_x(c, s) + ms^2 y(c, s) = \frac{B\omega}{s^2 + \omega^2}.$$

The solution of this problem can be written

$$y(x, s) = \frac{\alpha \sinh \dfrac{sx}{a}}{s(s^2 + \omega^2)\left(s \sinh \dfrac{sc}{a} + \beta \cosh \dfrac{sc}{a}\right)},$$

where

$$\alpha = \frac{B\omega}{m}, \qquad \beta = \frac{AE}{am}.$$

The last factor in the denominator vanishes when s is any root of the equation

$$\tanh \frac{sc}{a} = -\frac{\beta}{s}.$$

It can be shown that the roots of this equation are pure imaginary numbers. They can be written $s = \pm i a \lambda_n/c$ where λ_n are the positive roots of

(1) $$\tan \lambda = \frac{k}{\lambda},$$

and where $k = \beta c/a$. The roots of equation (1) are easily approximated graphically.*

If the factor $s^2 + \omega^2$ also vanishes when s has one of the values $i a \lambda_n/c$, then $y(x, s)$ will have a pole of the second order and $Y(x, t)$ will contain a term of the resonance type. Hence resonance occurs when the frequency of the external force has any one of the values

(2) $$\omega = \frac{a\lambda_n}{c} \qquad (n = 1, 2, \cdots),$$

where the numbers λ_n are the positive roots of equation (1). The frequencies (2) are the required resonance frequencies.

The series form of $Y(x, t)$ can, of course, be written in the usual way by computing the residues of $e^{st}y(x, s)$ at the poles.

81. Transverse Vibrations of Bars. Let $Y(x, t)$ denote the transverse displacement of a point of a bar or beam whose cross-sectional dimensions are small in comparison with the length of the bar, where x is distance along the beam and t is time. The bending moment transmitted by one part of the bar to the other across the section at x is approximately $EIY_{xx}(x, t)$, where the product EI is the flexural rigidity of the bar. When the cross section is uniform, the displacements at points where there is no external force acting satisfy the fourth-order equation

(1) $$\frac{\partial^2 Y}{\partial t^2} + a^2 \frac{\partial^4 Y}{\partial x^4} = 0 \qquad \left(a^2 = \frac{EI}{A\delta}\right),$$

where A is the area of the cross section and δ is the mass per unit volume. Some further assumptions are used in the derivation of

* Compare equation (6) and Fig. 98, Sec. 92.

this equation.* If an external force, such as the weight of the
beam, is to be accounted for, then a term proportional to this
force must appear in the right-hand member of equation (1).

Let the end $x = 0$ be hinged, so that no bending moment is
transmitted across the section at $x = 0$ and the displacement is
zero there. Let the end $x = c$ be hinged on a support which
moves parallel to the Y-axis in a simple harmonic manner (Fig.
91). If the beam is initially at rest along the x-axis, the boundary
conditions that accompany equation (1) are then

$$Y(x, 0) = Y_t(x, 0) = 0,$$
$$Y(0, t) = Y_{xx}(0, t) = 0,$$
$$Y(c, t) = A \sin \omega t, \qquad Y_{xx}(c, t) = 0.$$

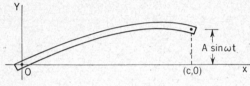

Fig. 91.

Let us find the frequencies ω at which resonance will occur.

The problem in the transform $y(x, s)$ is

$$(2) \qquad a^2 \frac{d^4 y}{dx^4} + s^2 y = 0,$$

$$y(0, s) = y_{xx}(0, s) = y_{xx}(c, s) = 0, \qquad y(c, s) = \frac{A\omega}{s^2 + \omega^2}.$$

It will be convenient to let

$$(3) \qquad q^4 = -\frac{s^2}{a^2}.$$

Then the general solution of equation (2) can be written

$$(4) \quad y(x, s) = C_1 \sin qx + C_2 \cos qx + C_3 \sinh qx + C_4 \cosh qx,$$

where the C's can be functions of the parameter s. When these
constants are determined so that the boundary conditions on
$y(x, s)$ are satisfied, the solution (4) becomes

$$(5) \qquad y(x, s) = \frac{A\omega}{s^2 + \omega^2} \frac{\sin qx \sinh qc + \sinh qx \sin qc}{2 \sin qc \sinh qc}.$$

* See, for instance, Timoshenko, S., "Vibration Problems in Engineering,"
1937; or Den Hartog, J. P., "Mechanical Vibrations," 1940.

Now $\sin qc = 0$ when $qc = \pm n\pi (n = 1, 2, \cdots)$, and $\sinh qc = 0$ when $qc = \pm in\pi$. Hence the function $y(x, s)$ has singularities at the points s for which

$$s = \pm i\omega, \qquad q^2 c^2 = \pm n^2 \pi^2.$$

The last equation can be written $q^4 c^4 = n^4 \pi^4$. In view of the relation (3) between q and s, the singularities are therefore

$$s = \pm i\omega, \qquad s = \pm i \, \frac{n^2 \pi^2 a}{c^2}.$$

It can be seen that all these singularities are simple poles if ω is distinct from all the numbers ω_n, where

$$\omega_n = \frac{n^2 \pi^2 a}{c^2} \qquad (n = 1, 2, \cdots).$$

In this case then the displacement will have the form

$$Y(x, t) = \alpha_0(x) \sin [\omega t + \epsilon_0(x)] + \sum_1^\infty \alpha_n(x) \sin [\omega_n t + \epsilon_n(x)].$$

If ω coincides with any ω_n, there will be poles of the second order at $s = \pm i\omega_n$ and a resonance term will occur in $Y(x, t)$. Hence the resonance frequencies are the frequencies

(6) $$\omega = \omega_n = \frac{n^2 \pi^2 a}{c^2}.$$

In case the hinge at $x = c$ is kept fixed and a simple harmonic torque acts on that end of the beam, the conditions at $x = c$ have the form

$$Y(c, t) = 0, \qquad Y_{xx}(c, t) = B \sin \omega t.$$

The reader can show that $y(x, s)$ then has the same denominator as it does in equation (5). Therefore the resonance frequencies are again those given by formula (6). Other cases are included in the problems at the end of the chapter.

82. Duhamel's Formula for Vibration Problems. As in the case of problems in heat conduction (Sec. 73), the convolution property of the transform displays a relation between the solutions of problems in vibrations with variable boundary conditions and corresponding problems with fixed conditions. Consider, for example, the transverse displacements $Y(x, t)$ in a string. If both damping and an elastic support are present, the equation of motion has the form (Fig. 92)

$$(1) \qquad Y_{tt}(x, t) = a^2 Y_{xx}(x, t) - b Y_t(x, t) - h Y(x, t).$$

To permit the end $x = 0$ to be elastically supported or kept fixed or to slide freely along the Y-axis, we can write the condition

$$(2) \qquad\qquad \lambda_1(Y) = 0 \qquad\qquad \text{at } x = 0,$$

where $\lambda_1(Y) = h_1 Y - k_1 Y_x$. If a prescribed force $F(t)$ acts on the end $x = c$, a fairly general boundary condition is

$$(3) \qquad\qquad \lambda_2(Y) = F(t) \qquad\qquad \text{at } x = c,$$

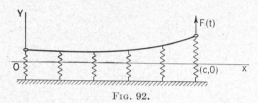

FIG. 92.

where $\lambda_2(Y) = h_2 Y + k_2 Y_x$. Then if

$$(4) \qquad\qquad Y(x, 0) = Y_t(x, 0) = 0,$$

the transform $y(x, s)$ satisfies the conditions

$$(5) \qquad\qquad (s^2 + bs + h)y(x, s) = a^2 y_{xx}(x, s),$$
$$(6) \qquad\qquad \lambda_1[y(0, s)] = 0, \qquad \lambda_2[y(c, s)] = f(s).$$

Let $Z(x, t)$ represent the displacement $Y(x, t)$ in the special case in which $F(t) = 1$.

Then $z(x, s)$ satisfies equation (5) and the boundary conditions

$$\lambda_1[z(0, s)] = 0, \qquad \lambda_2[z(c, s)] = \frac{1}{s}.$$

It follows that the product $sf(s)z(x, s)$ satisfies the conditions (5) and (6), and therefore

$$(7) \qquad\qquad y(x, s) = sf(s)z(x, s).$$

In view of the convolution property then,

$$(8) \qquad\qquad Y(x, t) = \frac{\partial}{\partial t} \int_0^t F(t - \tau) Z(x, \tau) \, d\tau,$$

or

(9) $$Y(x, t) = \int_0^t F(t - \tau) Z_t(x, \tau)\, d\tau.$$

These are two forms of Duhamel's formula for the resolution of the problem in $Y(x, t)$ with a variable end condition into one with a fixed end condition. Another form can be written by recalling that

$$sf(s) = L\{F'(t)\} + F(0);$$

thus,

(10) $$Y(x, t) = F(0)Z(x, t) + \int_0^t F'(t - \tau) Z(x, \tau)\, d\tau.$$

The derivation of these formulas can be extended easily to other problems. In the case of transverse vibrations of bars, for instance, the derivative of the fourth order with respect to x replaces $Y_{xx}(x, t)$, and additional boundary conditions are involved. In the case of transverse displacements in a membrane, the Laplacian of Y replaces Y_{xx} in our problem. In these cases, the steps in the derivation of Duhamel's formula are the same as in the case treated above.

PROBLEMS

1. The end $x = 0$ of a bar is elastically supported (Fig. 93), so that the longitudinal force exerted on that end is proportional to the longitudinal displacement; that is,

$$Y_x(0, t) = hY(0, t).$$

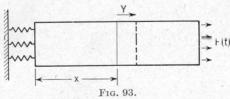

FIG. 93.

If the force on the end $x = c$ is $F(t) = A \sin \omega t$, derive the following formula for the resonance frequencies:

$$\omega_n = \frac{a\alpha_n}{c} \qquad\qquad (n = 1, 2, \cdots),$$

where the numbers α_n are the positive roots of the equation $\tan \alpha = hc/\alpha$.

2. One end of a beam is built in (Fig. 94) so that, if $Y(x, t)$ is the transverse displacement,

$$Y(0, t) = Y_x(0, t) = 0.$$

The unsupported end $x = c$ is forced to vibrate in a simple periodic manner, so that

$$Y(c, t) = B \sin \omega t, \qquad Y_{xx}(c, t) = 0.$$

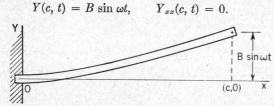

Fig. 94.

Show that resonance occurs when

$$\omega = \frac{a\alpha_n^2}{c^2} \qquad\qquad (n = 1, 2, \cdots),$$

where α_n is any root of the equation* $\tan \alpha = \tanh \alpha$, and where a is the coefficient in the differential equation (1), Sec. 81.

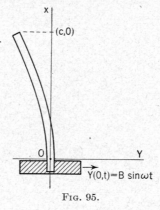

Fig. 95.

3. One end of a bar of length c is free. The other end is built into a support which undergoes a transverse displacement $Y = B \sin \omega t$ (Fig. 95). Show that the transverse vibrations will be in resonance when

$$\omega = \frac{a\alpha_n^2}{c^2} \qquad\qquad (n = 1, 2, \cdots),$$

* Values of the first few roots of this and other similar equations will be found in Timoshenko, *op. cit.*

where α_n is any root of the equation $\cos \alpha = - \operatorname{sech} \alpha$ and a is the coefficient in equation (1) of Sec. 81.

4. Both ends of a beam of length c are built in. A simple periodic force acts perpendicular to the beam at all points, so that the transverse displacements $Y(x, t)$ satisfy the equation

$$\frac{\partial^2 Y}{\partial t^2} + a^2 \frac{\partial^4 Y}{\partial x^4} = B \sin \omega t.$$

Show that resonance occurs when

$$\omega = \frac{a\alpha_n^2}{c^2}$$

where α_n is any root of the equation $\cos \alpha = \operatorname{sech} \alpha$.

5. A membrane is stretched across the fixed circle $r = c$. If a simple periodic force acts perpendicular to the membrane at all points, the transverse displacements $Z(r, t)$ satisfy the equation

$$Z_{tt} = b^2 \left(Z_{rr} + \frac{1}{r} Z_r \right) + A \sin \omega t.$$

Show that the resonance frequencies are

$$\omega = \frac{b\alpha_n}{c},$$

where α_n is any positive root of the equation $J_0(\alpha) = 0$.

6. A string is stretched from the origin to the point $(c, 0)$ and given an initial velocity $Y_t(x, 0) = g(x)$ but no initial displacement. Derive the formula

$$Y(x, t) = \frac{2}{\pi a} \sum_1^\infty \frac{1}{n} \sin \frac{n\pi x}{c} \sin \frac{n\pi a t}{c} \int_0^c g(\xi) \sin \frac{n\pi\xi}{c} \, d\xi.$$

7. The end $x = 0$ of a bar is fixed. If the bar is initially stretched so that its longitudinal displacements are $Y(x, 0) = Ax$ and released from that position at $t = 0$ with no initial velocity, and if the end $x = 0$ is free, derive a formula for the longitudinal displacements $Y(x, t)$.

8. Derive a formula for the longitudinal displacements in the bar of Sec. 74 when the constant force F_0 is replaced by the force

$$F(t) = At^2,$$

and make a complete verification of your solution.

CHAPTER IX

STURM-LIOUVILLE SYSTEMS

83. Introduction. A Sturm-Liouville system is a system of equations consisting of a linear homogeneous ordinary differential equation of the second order and a pair of linear homogeneous boundary conditions. A certain coefficient in the differential equation contains a parameter, denoted here by the letter λ. One boundary condition applies to each end of a prescribed interval.*

We shall develop the theory of the Sturm-Liouville system

$$X''(x) - [\lambda + q(x)]X(x) = 0,$$
$$X(0) = 0, \qquad X(1) = 0,$$

where $q(x)$ is a prescribed continuous function on the interval $0 \leqq x \leqq 1$. The theory for more general systems will be discussed afterward.

It will be found that this system has a solution $X = X_n(x)$ for each value λ_n of a discrete set of values $\lambda_1, \lambda_2, \cdots$ of the parameter λ and that an arbitrary function $F(x)$ on the interval can be expanded in a series of the functions $X_n(x)$. The use of this important result in the solution of boundary value problems in partial differential equations will be illustrated. The expansion theorem is needed to complete the method of combining particular solutions, one of the oldest and most important ways of solving boundary value problems.

The solution of a problem in heat conduction together with our theory of the Laplace transform will be used here to obtain the theory of the above system. The results, however, are useful in problems to which the transformation method is not adapted.

The theory is not simple. This could be expected since it is general enough to include the theory of Fourier series. When $q(x) \equiv 0$ in the above problem, for example, it can be seen that

---

* The first extensive development of the theory of such systems was published by J. C. F. Sturm and J. Liouville in the first three volumes of *Journal de mathématique*, 1836–1838.

$\lambda_n = -n^2\pi^2$ and $X_n(x) = \sin n\pi x$. The series expansion of the arbitrary function is then the Fourier sine series for the interval $0 < x < 1$. The use of the theory in the solution of boundary value problems, however, is not difficult.*

84. A Problem in Heat Conduction. Let $U(x, t)$ be the temperatures in a slender rod or wire in which the rate of loss of heat through the surface at each point is proportional to the temperature at that point. Let the ends of the wire be kept at temperature zero. If the initial temperature is a prescribed

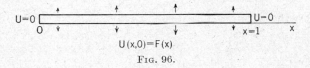

$$U(x,0) = F(x)$$

Fig. 96.

function $F(x)$, then by a proper choice of the units of length and time the boundary value problem can be written (Fig. 96)

$$U_t(x, t) = U_{xx}(x, t) - q(x)U(x, t) \quad (0 < x < 1,\, t > 0)$$
$$U(0, t) = 0, \qquad U(1, t) = 0, \qquad U(x, 0) = F(x).$$

The coefficient $q(x)$, the thermal emissivity, is assumed to be a continuous function of x. To simplify the development here, we shall also assume that $F(x)$ is a continuous function $(0 \leq x \leq 1)$ and that

$$F(0) = F(1) = 0.$$

The transform $u(x, s)$ of the function $U(x, t)$ satisfies the conditions

$$u_{xx}(x, s) - [s + q(x)]u(x, s) = -F(x),$$
$$u(0, s) = 0, \qquad u(1, s) = 0.$$

We cannot expect to solve this problem in ordinary differential equations of the second order since the coefficient $q(x)$ is an arbitrary function. But by writing the solution in terms of solutions of somewhat simpler problems, and by other devices, we can determine several properties of the function $u(x, s)$.

---

* This use is also illustrated in the author's book, "Fourier Series and Boundary Value Problems." Some of the simpler properties of the system are derived there.

Our experience with simpler problems leads us to expect that the function $u(x, s)$ will have a set of poles s_1, s_2, $\cdots$ and, if $\rho_n(x, t)$ is the residue of $e^{st}u(x, s)$ at the pole s_n, that

$$U(x, t) = \sum_1^\infty \rho_n(x, t).$$

When $t = 0$, it should follow that

$$F(x) = \sum_1^\infty \rho_n(x, 0) \qquad (0 \leqq x \leqq 1).$$

This is a series representation of $F(x)$ that turns out to be the Sturm-Liouville series. To establish this result it will not be necessary to complete the solution of the temperature problem. We shall be concerned primarily with the condition

$$U(x, 0) = F(x).$$

85. The Solution of the Transformed Problem. The problem in $u(x, s)$ was found to be

(1) $$u'' - (s + q)u = -F, \qquad u(0, s) = u(1, s) = 0,$$

where the primes denote differentiation with respect to x and q denotes the function $q(x)$. The solution of this problem can be written in terms of two solutions of the corresponding homogeneous differential equation

(2) $$y'' - (s + q)y = 0.$$

Let $y_1(x, s)$ be a function that satisfies this equation and the conditions

$$y_1(0, s) = 0, \qquad y_1'(0, s) = 1,$$

and let $y_2(x, s)$ be another solution of this equation that satisfies the conditions

$$y_2(1, s) = 0, \qquad y_2'(1, s) = 1.$$

It is shown in the theory of differential equations that unique solutions $y = y_1(x, s)$ and $y = y_2(x, s)$ exist which, together with their first derivatives with respect to x, are continuous functions of x and s.* Moreover, these functions are analytic with respect to s for every finite s.

---

* See, for instance, Ince, E. L., "Ordinary Differential Equations," p. 72, 1927.

The solution of problem (1) can now be written

$$(3) \qquad u(x, s) = \int_0^1 G(x, \xi, s) F(\xi) \, d\xi,$$

where G is the Green's function defined as follows:

$$(4) \qquad G(x, \xi, s) = -\frac{y_2(x, s) y_1(\xi, s)}{y_1(1, s)} \qquad \text{if } \xi \leqq x,$$

$$= -\frac{y_1(x, s) y_2(\xi, s)}{y_1(1, s)} \qquad \text{if } \xi \geqq x.$$

The function G is continuous with respect to ξ at $\xi = x$; but its derivative $G_\xi(x, \xi, s)$ has a jump at $\xi = x$.

The reader can verify the above solution directly by writing equation (3) in the form

$$u(x, s) y_1(1, s) = -y_2(x, s) \int_0^x y_1(\xi, s) F(\xi) \, d\xi$$
$$- y_1(x, s) \int_x^1 y_2(\xi, s) F(\xi) \, d\xi.$$

It must be kept in mind that y_1 and y_2 satisfy the homogeneous differential equation (2) and the conditions specified at $x = 0$ and at $x = 1$.

The solution (3) can be derived by the method of variation of parameters. That is, the functions $\alpha(x, s)$ and $\beta(x, s)$ can be found so that the function

$$u = \alpha y_1 + \beta y_2$$

satisfies the conditions of problem (1). If we require that α and β satisfy the condition

$$(5) \qquad \alpha' y_1 + \beta' y_2 = 0,$$

then

$$u' = \alpha y_1' + \beta y_2', \qquad u'' = \alpha y_1'' + \beta y_2'' + \alpha' y_1' + \beta' y_2'.$$

By substituting into the differential equation (1) and noting that y_1 and y_2 satisfy equation (2), we find that

$$(6) \qquad \alpha' y_1' + \beta' y_2' = -F(x).$$

Upon solving equations (5) and (6) we find that $\alpha' = y_2 F / D$ and $\beta' = -y_1 F / D$ provided the determinant

$$D = y_1(x, s) y_2'(x, s) - y_1'(x, s) y_2(x, s)$$

does not vanish. But $y_1'' = (s + q)y_1$ and $y_2'' = (s + q)y_2$, and it follows readily that $D' = 0$; hence D is the same for all x. When $x = 1$,

$$D = y_1(1, s);$$

therefore D has this value for all x. The solution then takes the form

$$u = \frac{y_1 \int y_2 F \, dx - y_2 \int y_1 F \, dx}{y_1(1, s)}.$$

Writing the integrals here as definite integrals with the variable x as one limit in each, the other limits can be determined so that the boundary conditions in problem (1) are satisfied. This gives the solution (3).

In view of the properties of y_1 and y_2 and the continuity of $F(x)$, it can be seen from formula (3) that u, u', and u'' are continuous functions of x and s, analytic with respect to s, except at the roots of the equation

$$y_1(1, s) = 0.$$

86. The Residues of u(x, s). Let s_n be a value of s for which $y_1(1, s) = 0$. Then s_n is a singularity of $u(x, s)$. We found above that

$$y_1(x, s)y_2'(x, s) - y_1'(x, s)y_2(x, s) = y_1(1, s).$$

When $s = s_n$, it follows that $y_1 y_2' - y_2 y_1' = 0$ and hence that y_1/y_2 is a constant:

(1) $$y_2(x, s_n) = Cy_1(x, s_n).$$

Since $y_1(0, s) = 0$ for all s and $y_1(1, s_n) = 0$, the function $y_1(x, s_n)$ satisfies the conditions

$$y_1'' - (s_n + q)y_1 = 0, \qquad y_1(0, s_n) = y_1(1, s_n) = 0.$$

That is, $X = y_1(x, s_n)$ is a solution of the Sturm-Liouville system

(2) $$X''(x) - [\lambda + q(x)]X(x) = 0, \qquad X(0) = X(1) = 1,$$

corresponding to the value $\lambda = s_n$ of the parameter.

The numbers s_n are called the *characteristic numbers* of the system (2), and the functions $y_1(x, s_n)$ are the *characteristic functions*.

Let us now show that none of the roots s_n of the characteristic equation $y_1(1, s) = 0$ are multiple roots. Since $y_1(x, s)$ is analytic at $s = s_n$, it can be represented by its Taylor's series about that point, namely,

$$y_1(x, s) = y_1(x, s_n) + A(x, s_n)(s - s_n) + B(x, s_n)(s - s_n)^2 + \cdots,$$

where the first coefficient has the value

$$A(x, s_n) = \frac{\partial}{\partial s} y_1(x, s)\bigg]_{s=s_n}$$

Since

$$y_1(1, s) = A(1, s_n)(s - s_n) + \cdots,$$

the roots of the equation $y_1(1, s) = 0$ will be multiple roots only if $A(1, s_n) = 0$.

Since $y_1(0, s) = 0$ for all s, the coefficients A, B, $\cdots$ must vanish when $x = 0$. Therefore

$$A(0, s_n) = 0.$$

The differential equation that $y_1(x, s)$ satisfies can be written

$$y'' - (q + s_n)y - (s - s_n)y = 0.$$

If we substitute the series $y_1(x, s_n) + A(x, s_n)(s - s_n) + \cdots$ for y here, the resulting series in powers of $s - s_n$ on the left must be zero for all s. In particular, the coefficient of the first power of $s - s_n$ must vanish; that is,

$$A''(x, s_n) - (q + s_n)A(x, s_n) = y_1(x, s_n).$$

Eliminating the function $q + s_n$ between this equation and the equation

$$y_1''(x, s_n) - (q + s_n)y_1(x, s_n) = 0,$$

we see that $A''y_1 - y_1''A = y_1^2$; that is,

$$\frac{d}{dx}[A'(x, s_n)y_1(x, s_n) - y_1'(x, s_n)A(x, s_n)] = [y_1(x, s_n)]^2.$$

Upon integrating both members here from $x = 0$ to $x = 1$ and recalling that $A(0, s_n) = 0$ and $y_1(0, s_n) = y_1(1, s_n) = 0$, we see that

(3) $$-A(1, s_n)y_1'(1, s_n) = \int_0^1 [y_1(x, s_n)]^2\, dx.$$

We shall show in the following section that the characteristic functions $y_1(x, s_n)$ have real values. The squares of these functions are therefore nonnegative, and the integral in equation (3) is positive; consequently

$$A(1, s_n) \neq 0.$$

We can now see that the function $1/y_1(1, s)$ has a simple pole at $s = s_n$, since the function

(4) $$\frac{s - s_n}{y_1(1, s)} = \frac{1}{A(1, s_n) + B(1, s_n)(s - s_n) + \cdots}$$

is analytic at s_n. The residue of $1/y_1(1, s)$ at $s = s_n$ is the limit of the function (4) as $s \to s_n$; that is, the residue is $1/A(1, s_n)$.

The function $u(x, s)$ was found in the form

$$u(x, s) = \int_0^1 G(x, \xi, s)F(\xi) \, d\xi,$$

where the Green's function G is the quotient of an analytic function and $y_1(1, s)$. Hence $u(x, s)$ has simple poles at $s = s_n$. In view of equation (1) we can write, for the numerators in the expressions for G (Sec. 85),

$$-y_2(x, s_n)y_1(\xi, s_n) = -Cy_1(x, s_n)y_1(\xi, s_n),$$
$$-y_1(x, s_n)y_2(\xi, s_n) = -Cy_1(x, s_n)y_1(\xi, s_n).$$

Consequently the residue of $u(x, s)$ at $s = s_n$ is

(5) $$-\frac{Cy_1(x, s_n)}{A(1, s_n)} \int_0^1 y_1(\xi, s_n)F(\xi) \, d\xi.$$

It follows from equation (1) that

$$Cy_1'(1, s_n) = y_2'(1, s_n) = 1,$$

and from equation (3) that

$$\frac{1}{A(1, s_n)} = -\frac{y_1'(1, s_n)}{\int_0^1 [y_1(x, s_n)]^2 \, dx}.$$

The expression (5) for the residue of $u(x, s)$ can therefore be written

(6) $$\frac{y_1(x, s_n) \int_0^1 y_1(\xi, s_n)F(\xi) \, d\xi}{\int_0^1 [y_1(x, s_n)]^2 \, dx}.$$

Let $\phi_n(x)$ denote a function that is proportional to $y_1(x, s_n)$ and such that $\int_0^1 [\phi_n(x)]^2 \, dx = 1$. The functions $\phi_n(x)$, called the *normalized characteristic functions* of our Sturm-Liouville system, are thus

$$(7) \qquad \phi_n(x) = y_1(x, s_n) \left\{ \int_0^1 [y_1(x, s_n)]^2 \, dx \right\}^{-\frac{1}{2}}.$$

In terms of these functions, the residue (6) of $u(x, s)$ at $s = s_n$ can be written

$$(8) \qquad \rho_n(x) = \phi_n(x) \int_0^1 \phi_n(\xi) F(\xi) \, d\xi.$$

87. The Characteristic Numbers and Functions. We have seen that $X = y_1(x, s_n)$ is a solution of the Sturm-Liouville system

$$(1) \qquad X''(x) - [s + q(x)]X(x) = 0, \qquad X(0) = X(1) = 0,$$

when the parameter s has the value s_n. Suppose there is a complex characteristic number

$$s = \alpha + i\beta,$$

and let

$$X(x) = u(x) + iv(x)$$

be the corresponding characteristic function, where u and v are real. Substituting these expressions into problem (1) and separating the real and imaginary parts, we obtain the equations

$$
\begin{aligned}
u'' - (\alpha + q)u + \beta v &= 0, \\
v'' - (\alpha + q)v - \beta u &= 0,
\end{aligned}
$$
$$(2) \qquad u(0) - u(1) - v(0) - v(1) = 0.$$

Multiplying the first equation by v and the second by u and subtracting, we find that

$$(3) \qquad u''v - v''u = -\beta(u^2 + v^2).$$

Since the expression on the left is the derivative of $u'v - v'u$, it follows upon integrating and applying the conditions (2) that

$$-\beta \int_0^1 (u^2 + v^2) \, dx = u'v - v'u \Big]_0^1 = 0.$$

The integral here is positive. Therefore $\beta = 0$.

Thus every characteristic number s_n of the system (1) is real.
Since $\beta = 0$, it also follows from equation (3) that $u'v - v'u$ is
a constant.   In view of the conditions (2), this constant is zero;
hence v/u is a constant: $v = ku$.   The original solution therefore
has the form

$$X = (1 + ik)u.$$

But if any constant times u is a solution of the homogeneous
system (1), then u itself is a solution.   Hence if a characteristic
function exists, it can be made real by multiplying by the proper
constant.   Thus we can assume without loss of generality that
the functions $y_1(x, s_n)$ are real.

Let $X_m(x)$ and $X_n(x)$ be characteristic functions of the system
(1) corresponding to the distinct characteristic numbers s_m and
s_n, respectively.   Then

$$X_m'' = (s_m + q)X_m, \qquad X_n'' = (s_n + q)X_n,$$

and, eliminating the function q between these equations,

$$X_m''X_n - X_n''X_m = (s_m - s_n)X_mX_n.$$

Therefore

$$(s_m - s_n) \int_0^1 X_mX_n \, dx = X_m'X_n - X_mX_n' \Big]_0^1.$$

The last expression vanishes since

$$X_m(0) = X_m(1) = X_n(0) = X_n(1) = 0.$$

Thus the characteristic functions of the Sturm-Liouville
system (1) are *orthogonal* on the interval $0 < x < 1$; that is,

$$(4) \qquad \int_0^1 X_m(x)X_n(x) \, dx = 0.$$

We collect the principal results found so far in this chapter
as follows:

Theorem 1.   *The solution $u(x, s)$ of our transformed temperature
problem is analytic for all finite s except at the zeros s_n of the function
$y_1(1, s)$.   The numbers s_n are the characteristic numbers of the
Sturm-Liouville system (1).   They are all real, and the corresponding normalized characteristic functions $\phi_n(x)$ form an orthogonal
set on the interval $0 < x < 1$.   The points $s = s_n$ are simple poles
of $u(x, s)$, and the residue of $u(x, s)$ at s_n is $c_n\phi_n(x)$, where*

$$c_n = \int_0^1 F(x)\phi_n(x) \, dx.$$

The numbers c_1, c_2, $\cdots$ are called the *Fourier constants* of $F(x)$ corresponding to the orthonormal set of functions $\phi_1(x)$, $\phi_2(x)$, $\cdots$. Thus far, the function $F(x)$ is only assumed to be continuous. It could equally well have been assumed sectionally continuous.

88. Other Properties of the Characteristic Numbers and Functions. Our functions $y_1(x, s)$ and $y_2(x, s)$ are solutions of the equation

(1) $$y''(x, s) - sy(x, s) = q(x)y(x, s).$$

Proceeding as if the function on the right were not unknown, we add the general solution of the equation $y'' - sy = 0$ to a particular solution of equation (1) to obtain the general solution of the latter. A particular solution of $u'' - (s + q)u = -F$ was written in terms of a Green's function in Sec. 85. With the aid of that result, it follows that the general solution of (1) can be written in the form

(2) $$y(x, s) = C_1 \sinh x \sqrt{s} + C_2 \sinh (1 - x) \sqrt{s} + \int_0^1 g(x, \xi, s)q(\xi)y(\xi, s)\, d\xi,$$

where the Green's function here is

$$g(x, \xi, s) = -\frac{\sinh (1 - x) \sqrt{s} \sinh \xi \sqrt{s}}{\sqrt{s} \sinh \sqrt{s}} \quad \text{if } \xi < x,$$

$$= -\frac{\sinh x \sqrt{s} \sinh (1 - \xi) \sqrt{s}}{\sqrt{s} \sinh \sqrt{s}} \quad \text{if } \xi > x.$$

Equation (2) can be written

(3) $$y(x, s) =$$
$$\sinh x \sqrt{s} \left[C_1 - \int_x^1 \frac{\sinh (1 - \xi) \sqrt{s}}{\sqrt{s} \sinh \sqrt{s}} q(\xi)y(\xi, s)\, d\xi \right]$$
$$+ \sinh (1 - x) \sqrt{s} \left[C_2 - \int_0^x \frac{\sinh \xi \sqrt{s}}{\sqrt{s} \sinh \sqrt{s}} q(\xi)y(\xi, s)\, d\xi \right].$$

Solutions of the differential equation (1) therefore satisfy the integral equation (3).

The particular solution $y = y_1(x, s)$ satisfies the conditions $y_1(0, s) = 0$, $y_1'(0, s) = 1$. In this case, equation (3) reduces to the equation

(4) $$\sqrt{s}\, y_1(x, s) = \sinh x \sqrt{s} + \int_0^x y_1(\xi, s)q(\xi) \sinh (x - \xi) \sqrt{s}\, d\xi.$$

Likewise for the solution $y = y_2$, which satisfies corresponding conditions at $x = 1$, equation (3) becomes

$$(5) \quad \sqrt{s}\, y_2(x, s) = -\sinh{(1 - x)}\sqrt{s}$$
$$+ \int_x^1 y_2(\xi, s)q(\xi) \sinh{(\xi - x)}\sqrt{s}\, d\xi.$$

Since y_1 and y_2 are analytic functions of s for all finite s, we need be consistent only in our choice of the branch of $\sqrt{s}$. Let $-\pi < \theta \leqq \pi$ when $s = re^{i\theta}$. Then the real part of $\sqrt{s}$ is never negative.

For a fixed s, let $M(s)$ be the maximum value of the function $|\sqrt{s}\, y_1(x, s)e^{-x\sqrt{s}}|$, where $0 \leqq x \leqq 1$. Since that function is continuous with respect to x, it has the value $M(s)$ at some point $x = x_0$; that is,

$$M(s) = |\sqrt{s}\, y_1(x_0, s)e^{-x_0 s}|.$$

Now $|e^{-x_0\sqrt{s}} \sinh{x_0}\sqrt{s}| \leqq 1$, and in view of equation (4) it follows that

$$M(s) \leqq 1$$
$$+ \frac{1}{|\sqrt{s}|} \int_0^{x_0} |\sqrt{s}\, y_1 e^{-\xi\sqrt{s}} q e^{-(x_0 - \xi)\sqrt{s}} \sinh{(x_0 - \xi)}\sqrt{s}|\, d\xi$$
$$\leqq 1 + \frac{M(s)Q}{\sqrt{r}},$$

where $r = |s|$ and $Q = \int_0^1 |q(\xi)|\, d\xi$. It follows that

$$(6) \qquad\qquad M(s) \leqq \left(1 - \frac{Q}{\sqrt{r}}\right)^{-1} < 2 \quad \text{when } r \geqq r_0,$$

where $r_0 > 4Q^2$.

A similar result can be obtained for the function y_2 using equation (5). Consequently a fixed number r_0 exists such that for all s with $r \geqq r_0$,

$$(7) \quad |\sqrt{s}\, y_1(x, s)e^{-x\sqrt{s}}| < 2, \qquad |\sqrt{s}\, y_2(x, s)e^{-(1-x)\sqrt{s}}| < 2.$$

It follows now from equation (4) that, when $r \geqq r_0$,

$$(8) \qquad 2\sqrt{s}\, y_1(1, s)e^{-\sqrt{s}} = 1 - e^{-2\sqrt{s}} + O\left(\frac{1}{\sqrt{r}}\right),$$

where the last symbol denotes a function of s of the order of $r^{-\frac{1}{2}}$, that is, a function whose absolute value never exceeds $Cr^{-\frac{1}{2}}$ where C is some constant. We have seen that the zeros s_n of $y_1(1, s)$ are all real. When s is sufficiently large and positive, the right-hand member of equation (8) cannot vanish. Hence the zeros s_n are all less than some fixed number γ; also, our function $u(x, s)$ is analytic in the half plane $\Re(s) \geqq \gamma$.

When $s = -\mu^2$, where μ is real, it follows from equation (8) that the equation $y_1(1, s) = 0$ has the form

$$\sin \mu + O\left(\frac{1}{\mu}\right) = 0.$$

The large roots of this equation are approximately $n\pi$, and the following conclusions can be drawn.

An infinite set of characteristic numbers $s_1, s_2, \cdots$ *exist. They are all real, and only a finite number of them can be positive. When* n *is large, the numbers* $\sqrt{-s_n}$ *are approximately equal to* $n\pi$; *that is,*

$$(9) \qquad \lim_{n \to \infty} (\sqrt{-s_n} - n\pi) = 0.$$

It can be seen from equations (4) and (7) that the functions $|\sqrt{s_n}\, y_1(x, s_n)|$ and $|y_1'(x, s_n)|$ are bounded uniformly for all n and x. A direct estimation from these same equations shows that the square of the normalizing factor for the characteristic functions $y_1(x, s_n)$ has the property

$$\lim_{n \to \infty} |s_n| \int_0^1 [y_1(x, s_n)]^2\, dx = \tfrac{1}{2}.$$

Hence the normalized characteristic functions $\psi_n(x)$ of the Sturm-Liouville system have the following property.

A fixed number K exists such that, for all n and x,

$$(10) \qquad |\phi_n(x)| < K, \qquad \left|\frac{\phi_n'(x)}{\sqrt{s_n}}\right| < K.$$

89. The Inversion Integral. The Green's function $G(x, \xi, s)$ is a function of ξ that satisfies the homogeneous differential equation of which $y_1(\xi)$ and $y_2(\xi)$ are solutions. Therefore

$$G(x, \xi, s) = \frac{1}{s}G_{\xi\xi} - \frac{q(\xi)}{s}G(x, \xi, s).$$

When we substitute this expression for G into the formula

$$u(x, s) = \int_0^1 G(x, \xi, s)F(\xi) \, d\xi,$$

we find, after an integration by parts, that

(1) $\quad su(x, s) = F(x) - \int_0^1 G_\xi(x, \xi, s)F'(\xi) \, d\xi$

$$- \int_0^1 G(x, \xi, s)q(\xi)F(\xi) \, d\xi.$$

This step is valid if $F(x)$ is continuous with a sectionally continuous derivative $F'(x)$ and if

(2) $$F(0) = F(1) = 0.$$

If conditions (2) are not satisfied, or if $F(x)$ has finite discontinuities, additional terms occur in equation (1); but our principal results can still be derived. It is necessary, however, to break up those additional terms into functions whose transforms are known and functions of an appropriate order with respect to s.

From the definition of G and the formulas of the last section, it can be seen that constants r_0 and M_0 exist such that when $r \geq r_0$

(3) $$|G_\xi(x, \xi, s)| < \frac{M_0|e^{-|x-\xi|\sqrt{s}|}}{|1 - e^{-2\sqrt{s}} + O(r^{-\frac{1}{2}})|},$$

(4) $$|\sqrt{s}\, G(x, \xi, s)| < \frac{M_0|e^{-|x-\xi|\sqrt{s}|}}{|1 - e^{-2\sqrt{s}} + O(r^{-\frac{1}{2}})|}.$$

Consequently, when $\Re(s) \geq \gamma$, these functions are of the order of $|e^{-|x-\xi|\sqrt{s}|}$, and, if $\psi(\xi)$ is any continuous function, it follows that

$$\int_0^1 |G(x, \xi, s)\psi(\xi)| \, d\xi = O(r^{-1}),$$

$$\int_0^1 |G_\xi(x, \xi, s)\psi(\xi)| \, d\xi = O(r^{-\frac{1}{2}}),$$

in the half plane, uniformly with respect to x.

According to equation (1) then, when $\Re(s) \geq \gamma$,

$$u(x, s) - \frac{F(x)}{s} = O\left(\frac{1}{r^{\frac{3}{2}}}\right).$$

It follows from Theorem 5, Sec. 56, that the inversion integral of this function converges to a continuous function of $t(t \geqq 0)$ and that

$$(5) \qquad L_i^{-1} \left\{ u(x, s) - \frac{F(x)}{s} \right\} = 0 \qquad \text{when } t = 0.$$

We shall show next that this inversion integral can be represented by the series of residues when $t = 0$. The residue of $F(x)/s$ at the pole $s = 0$ is $F(x)$. The residue of $e^{st} u(x, s)$ with $t = 0$ is the residue of $u(x, s)$ itself.

90. The Sturm-Liouville Expansion. We have seen that the poles $s = s_n$ of $u(x, s)$ lie on the real axis and that $\sqrt{-s_n}$ approaches $n\pi$ as n increases. When n is sufficiently large, the parabolas P_n with the equations

$$(1) \qquad r = \left(n + \frac{1}{2} \right)^2 \pi^2 \csc^2 \frac{\theta}{2} \qquad (n = 1, 2, \cdots),$$

therefore pass between the poles.

When s is on the parabola P_n, then

$$\sqrt{s} = \left(n + \frac{1}{2} \right) \pi \left(\left| \cot \frac{\theta}{2} \right| \pm i \right),$$

and

$$1 - e^{-2\sqrt{s}} = 1 + \exp \left[-(2n + 1)\pi \left| \cot \frac{\theta}{2} \right| \right] > 1.$$

It follows from equations (3) and (4) of the last section that, when s is on P_n,

$$\int^1 |G_\xi(x, \xi, s)\psi(\xi)| \, d\xi = O\left(\frac{1}{\sqrt{s}} \right),$$

and the corresponding integral with G_ξ replaced by G is of the order of $1/s$. In view of equation (1) of the last section, therefore,

$$(2) \qquad u(x, s) - \frac{F(x)}{s} = O\left(\frac{1}{s^{\frac{3}{2}}} \right) \qquad \text{when } s \text{ is on } P_n.$$

It was pointed out in Sec. 60 that when $u(x, s)$ is of the order of s^{-k} with $k > 1$, on the paths between the poles, the series of residues converges to the inversion integral when $t = 0$ as well as for $t > 0$. Since $L_i^{-1}\{u - F/s\} = 0$ when $t = 0$, it follows that

$$\sum_1^\infty c_n\phi_n(x) - F(x) = 0$$

where

(3) $$c_n = \int_0^1 F(x)\phi_n(x)\ dx.$$

It can be seen in fact, from the uniformity of our order properties, that the series here is uniformly convergent with respect to x. We have now established the following expansion theorem.

Theorem 2. *Let $\phi_n(x)$ be the normalized characteristic functions of the Sturm-Liouville system*

(4) $$X'' - (\lambda + q)X = 0, \qquad X(0) = X(1) = 0,$$

where q is a continuous function of x on the interval $0 \leqq x \leqq 1$. If $F(x)$ is any continuous function on that interval, with a sectionally continuous first derivative, and if $F(0) = F(1) = 0$, the series

$$\sum_1^\infty c_n\phi_n(x) \text{ converges uniformly to } F(x); \text{ that is,}$$

(5) $$F(x) = \sum_1^\infty c_n\phi_n(x) \qquad\qquad (0 \leqq x \leqq 1),$$

where c_n are the Fourier constants (3).

In case the function $F(x)$ is sectionally continuous, together with its derivative $F'(x)$, the representation (5) is still valid when $0 < x < 1$ except at the points of discontinuity. In fact the series is uniformly convergent in any interval that does not include a point of discontinuity of $F(x)$, or either of the points $x = 0$ or $x = 1$, in its interior or at one of its end points.

PROBLEMS

1. Continue the treatment of the problem in heat conduction begun in Sec. 84, and thus derive the temperature formula

$$U(x, t) = \sum_1^\infty c_n\phi_n(x)e^{s_n t},$$

proceeding formally. (This formula can be rigorously established as the solution.)[*]

[*] The details are included in a paper in the *American Journal of Mathematics*, Vol. 61, pp. 651–664, 1939.

2. Show that the characteristic numbers of the system

$$X''(x) - (\lambda + h)X(x) = 0, \qquad X(0) = X(1) = 0,$$

where h is any real constant, are $\lambda = -h - n^2\pi^2 (n = 1, 2, \cdots)$ and that the normalized characteristic functions are $\phi_n(x) = \sqrt{2} \sin n\pi x$, hence that any function $F(x)$ satisfying the conditions of Theorem 2 is represented by its Fourier sine series

$$F(x) = 2 \sum_{1}^{\infty} \sin n\pi x \int_{0}^{1} F(\xi) \sin n\pi\xi \, d\xi \qquad (0 \leqq x \leqq 1).$$

3. As a special case of the expansion in Prob. 2, show that

$$x - x^2 = \frac{8}{\pi^3} \sum_{1}^{\infty} \frac{\sin (2n - 1)\pi x}{(2n - 1)^3} \qquad (0 \leqq x \leqq 1).$$

4. Let P_n denote the parabolas of Sec. 90, and let $u(x, s)$ be the transform of the temperature function when $F(x)$ is only required to be sectionally continuous, together with its derivative $F'(x)$. For any fixed x between $x = 0$ and $x = 1$ at which $F(x)$ is continuous, let $v(x, s)$ denote the function $u(x, s) - F(x)/s$. Show that for each positive angle $\theta_0 (\theta_0 < \pi)$, a constant M_0 exists for which

$$|v(x, s)| < M_0|s|^{-\frac{3}{2}}$$

when $-\theta_0 \leqq \theta \leqq \theta_0$ and $|s| \geqq r_0$, where r_0 is any positive number. Also show that $|sv(x, s)|$ is bounded when s is on P_n. Under these conditions, show that the integrals of $v(x, s)$ over the arcs of the parabolas P_n in the half plane $\Re(s) \leqq \gamma$ tend to zero as $n \to \infty$ and, hence, that

$$F(x) = \sum_{1}^{\infty} c_n\phi_n(x).$$

5. By writing the Sturm-Liouville equation in the form

$$X'' - qX = \lambda X,$$

$X(0) = X(1) = 0$, show that every characteristic function $X = y_1(x, s_n)$ is a solution of the homogeneous integral equation

$$X(x) = -\lambda \int_{0}^{1} G(x, \xi, 0)X(\xi) \, d\xi$$

with $\lambda = s_n$, provided $s = 0$ is not one of the characteristic numbers s_n.

91. Other Sturm-Liouville Systems. The development above can be modified without difficulty to permit the boundary conditions to have the more general form

(1) $\quad A_1 X(a) + A_2 X'(a) = 0, \qquad B_1 X(b) + B_2 X'(b) = 0,$

where the interval is now $a \leqq x \leqq b$. The principal results are the same. When $a = 0$ and $b = 1$, the numbers $\sqrt{-s_n}$ approach $(n + \frac{1}{2})\pi$ as n increases in case just one of the constants A_2 or B_2 is zero; otherwise $\sqrt{-s_n}$ approaches $n\pi$.

Consider the general Sturm-Liouville equation

(2) $\qquad \dfrac{d}{dx}[r(x)X(x)] - [q(x) + \lambda p(x)]X(x) = 0.$

Let p, q, r, r', and $(rp)''$ be continuous functions of x, and let r and p be different from zero, throughout the interval $a \leqq x \leqq b$. By introducing the new variables y and Y, where

(3) $\qquad y = \dfrac{1}{C}\int_a^x \sqrt{\dfrac{p(\xi)}{r(\xi)}}\, d\xi, \qquad Y = (pr)^{\frac{1}{4}}X,$

and writing $\mu = C^2 \lambda$ where

$$C = \int_a^b \sqrt{\dfrac{p(\xi)}{r(\xi)}}\, d\xi,$$

we find that equation (2) takes the form

(4) $\qquad \dfrac{d^2 Y}{dy^2} - [\mu + q_1(y)]Y = 0.$

The interval $0 \leqq y \leqq 1$ corresponds to the interval $a \leqq x \leqq b$, and the function $q_1(y)$ is continuous in that interval. This is the form we have treated above. Under these changes of variables, the boundary conditions (1) change to new conditions of the same type. Consequently, when the coefficients p, q, and r satisfy the conditions stated above, the system consisting of equation (4) and conditions

(5) $\qquad \alpha_1 Y(0) + \beta_1 Y'(0) = 0, \qquad \alpha_2 Y(1) + \beta_2 Y'(1) = 0,$

is a standard form to which the system consisting of equations (1) and (2) can be reduced.

It can be left as a problem for the reader to show that the characteristic functions $X_n(x)$ of the system of equations (1) and (2) are orthogonal on the interval (a, b) *with respect to the weight function* $p(x)$; that is,

(6) $\qquad \displaystyle\int_a^b p(x)X_m(x)X_n(x)\, dx = 0 \qquad (m \neq n),$

also that, if $p(x)$ does not change sign in the interval, every characteristic number of the system is real.

The above transformations of variables enable us to write the following results for the new system from the results found for the standard one.

Theorem 3.   *Let* p, q, r, r', *and* $(pr)''$ *be continuous functions of* x, *where* p *and* r *are positive, on the interval* $a \leqq x \leqq b$. *Then the Sturm-Liouville system*

(7) $$(rX')' - (q + \lambda p)X = 0,$$
$$A_1X(a) + A_2X'(a) = B_1X(b) + B_2X'(b) = 0,$$

has an infinite set of characteristic numbers λ_1, λ_2, $\cdots$, *only a finite number of which are positive.   Let*

$$\phi_n(x) = X_n(x) \left(\int_a^b pX_n^2 dx \right)^{-\frac{1}{2}}$$

be the normalized characteristic functions.   Then any function $F(x)$ *that is sectionally continuous and has a sectionally continuous derivative* $F'(x)$ *can be represented as follows:*

(8) $$F(x) = \sum_1^\infty c_n\phi_n(x) \qquad (a < x < b),$$

at each point where $F(x)$ *is continuous, where*

$$c_n = \int_a^b F(x)p(x)\phi_n(x) \, dx \quad (n = 1, 2, \cdots).$$

Moreover the functions $|\phi_n(x)|$ *and* $|\sqrt{\lambda_n}\, \phi_n'(x)|$ *are uniformly bounded for all* n *and* x.

Note that if the equation is Bessel's equation,

$$(xX')' - \left(\frac{\nu^2}{x} + x\lambda \right) X = 0,$$

where ν is a constant, and if $a = 0$, then the conditions of the theorem are not satisfied.   Such singular cases can be treated individually by the method we have used, to get corresponding expansion theorems.

Representations of functions defined on infinite intervals in the form of infinite integrals, such as the Fourier double integral, can be obtained in a similar way; but a transformation of the inversion integral takes the place of the residue theory.   This was illustrated formally in Sec. 71.   Extensions to differential equations of higher order can also be made.

92. Steady Temperatures in a Wall.   Let $U(x, y)$ be the steady-state temperatures in a semi-infinite wall bounded by the planes $x = 0$, $x = 1$, and $y = 0$ (Fig. 97).   Let the face $x = 0$ be insulated, and let surface heat transfer take place at the face $x = 1$, while the face $y = 0$ is kept at temperature $F(x)$, so that the boundary value problem becomes

(1) $\qquad U_{xx}(x, y) + U_{yy}(x, y) = 0 \quad (0 < x < 1, y > 0),$

(2) $\qquad U_x(0, y) = 0, \qquad U_x(1, y) = -hU(1, y) \qquad (y > 0),$

(3) $\qquad U(x, 0) = F(x), \qquad \lim_{y \to \infty} U(x, y) = 0 \quad (0 < x < 1),$

where the constant h is positive or zero, and the function $F(x)$ is prescribed.

This problem can also be interpreted as one in the electrostatic potential in a semi-infinite slot.

The Laplace transformation is not well adapted to the solution of this problem.   Although the variable y ranges through all positive values, the transform with respect to y of the derivatives $U_{yy}(x, y)$ involves the function $U_y(x, 0)$, which is not prescribed by the boundary conditions.   The determination of such unknown functions appearing in the transformed problem is often quite difficult.

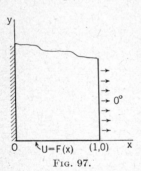

Fig. 97.

Let us use the classical method of separating variables and combining particular solutions.   We obtain all possible functions of the form

$$U = X(x)Y(y)$$

that satisfy the homogeneous differential equation (1) and the homogeneous boundary conditions.   Then we try to determine a linear combination of those functions that will also satisfy the remaining condition $U(x, 0) = F(x)$.

If $U = X(x)Y(y)$ is to satisfy equation (1), then

$$X''(x)Y(y) + X(x)Y''(y) = 0;$$

that is,

$$\frac{X''(x)}{X(x)} = -\frac{Y''(y)}{Y(y)}.$$

Since $X''(x)/X(x)$ is a function of x alone, it does not vary with y. Similarly the function $-Y''(y)/Y(y)$ does not vary with x, and the two functions can be equal only if they have some fixed value λ; that is, if

$$X''(x) - \lambda X(x) = 0, \qquad Y''(y) + \lambda Y(y) = 0.$$

If $U = X(x)Y(y)$ is to satisfy the condition $U_x(0, y) = 0$ for all $y > 0$, then $X'(0)Y(y) = 0$. The solution $Y(y) = 0$ for all y is trivial. Therefore $X'(0) = 0$. Similarly if the second of conditions (2) is to be satisfied, then $X'(1) = -hX(1)$. The function $X(x)$ must therefore be a solution of the Sturm-Liouville system

(4) $X''(x) - \lambda X(x) = 0, \qquad X'(0) = 0, \qquad X'(1) + hX(1) = 0.$

We know that this system has solutions only for a discrete set of real values of the parameter λ. The trivial solution $X(x) \equiv 0$ is of course disregarded.

Since $U(x, y)$ is to vanish as $y \to \infty$, the function $Y(y)$ must be a solution of the system

(5) $\qquad\qquad Y''(y) + \lambda Y(y) = 0, \qquad \lim_{y \to \infty} Y(y) = 0.$

Recalling that the characteristic numbers of the Sturm-Liouville system are negative, except possibly for some finite number of them, we write the function that satisfies the first two of conditions (4) in the form

$$X(x) = C \cos x \sqrt{-\lambda},$$

where C is an arbitrary constant. This function satisfies the condition $X'(1) + hX(1) = 0$ if λ is a root of the equation

$$\sqrt{-\lambda} \sin \sqrt{-\lambda} + h \cos \sqrt{-\lambda} = 0.$$

Thus the characteristic numbers are $\lambda = -\alpha_n^2$ where α_n are the positive roots of the equation

(6) $\qquad\qquad\qquad \tan \alpha = -\dfrac{h}{\alpha}.$

These roots are the abscissas of the points of intersection of the curves $\eta = \tan \alpha$ and $\eta = -h/\alpha$ (Fig. 98). The number α_n is only slightly less than $n\pi$ when n is large.

The characteristic function corresponding to $\lambda = -\alpha_n^2$ is

$$X = C \cos \alpha_n x.$$

To normalize the characteristic functions, let

$$\beta_n = \int_0^1 \cos^2 \alpha_n x \, dx = \frac{1}{2}\left(1 + \frac{\sin \alpha_n \cos \alpha_n}{\alpha_n}\right).$$

Since α_n is a root of equation (6), it follows that

$$(7) \qquad\qquad 2\beta_n = 1 - \frac{h}{h^2 + \alpha_n^2}.$$

The normalized characteristic functions of the system (4) are thus

$$(8) \qquad\qquad \phi_n(x) = \frac{1}{\sqrt{\beta_n}} \cos \alpha_n x.$$

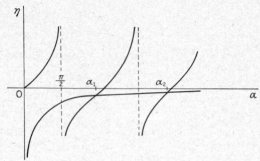

Fig. 98.

When $\lambda = -\alpha_n^2$, the solution of the system (5) is

$$Y(y) = c_n e^{-\alpha_n y},$$

where c_n is any constant. Hence the functions $X(x)Y(y)$ that satisfy all the homogeneous conditions in our boundary value problem are

$$X(x)Y(y) = c_n \frac{\cos \alpha_n x}{\sqrt{\beta_n}} e^{-\alpha_n y} \qquad (n = 1, 2, \cdots).$$

The sum of any number of these functions will also satisfy those conditions; but unless $F(x)$ is a linear combination of a finite number of the functions $\cos \alpha_n x$, no finite sum will satisfy the remaining condition

$$(9) \qquad\qquad U(x, 0) = F(x) \qquad (0 < x < 1).$$

The function represented by the infinite series

$$\sum_1^\infty c_n \frac{\cos \alpha_n x}{\sqrt{\beta_n}} e^{-\alpha_n y}$$

formally satisfies the homogeneous conditions. According to the Sturm-Liouville theory, this function will reduce to the prescribed function $F(x)$ when $y = 0$ provided the numbers c_n are the Fourier constants of $F(x)$ corresponding to the orthogonal functions $\phi_n(x)$; that is, if

$$(10) \qquad c_n = \frac{1}{\sqrt{\beta_n}} \int_0^1 F(x) \cos \alpha_n x \, dx.$$

(Note that the series $\displaystyle\sum_1^\infty c_n \phi_n(x)$ here is not a Fourier series unless $h = 0$.)

The formal solution of our problem is therefore

$$(11) \qquad U(x, y) = \sum_1^\infty \frac{c_n}{\sqrt{\beta_n}} e^{-\alpha_n y} \cos \alpha_n x$$

where the constants c_n and β_n are given by formulas (10) and (7).

In the special case $F(x) = 1$, the temperature formula reduces to

$$U(x, t) = -2h \sum_1^\infty \frac{\cos \alpha_n}{\alpha_n^2 \beta_n} e^{-\alpha_n y} \cos \alpha_n x.$$

93. Verification of the Solution. If $F(x)$ and $F'(x)$ are sectionally continuous functions, we know that the Sturm-Liouville series

$$\sum_1^\infty c_n \frac{\cos \alpha_n x}{\sqrt{\beta_n}} \qquad\qquad (0 < x < 1)$$

converges to $F(x)$. Since the functions $e^{-\alpha_n y}(n = 1, 2, \cdots)$ are bounded for all n and $y(y \geqq 0)$, it follows from Abel's test * that the series

$$(1) \qquad \sum_1^\infty \frac{c_n}{\sqrt{\beta_n}} \cos \alpha_n x e^{-\alpha_n y}$$

is uniformly convergent with respect to $y(y \geqq 0)$. Consequently, the series represents a continuous function of y at $y = 0$ and the temperature function found above satisfies the condition

$$U(x, +0) = U(x, 0) = F(x) \qquad (0 < x < 1).$$

* See the author's "Fourier Series and Boundary Value Problems," Sec. 55.

Let y_0 be any positive number. When $y \geqq y_0$, the absolute values of the terms in the series (1) are all less than a constant times $e^{-\alpha_n y_0}$. Consequently the series is uniformly convergent with respect to x and y when $y \geqq y_0$ and $0 \leqq x \leqq 1$. Similarly the series obtained by differentiating that series term by term are uniformly convergent. The series can therefore be differentiated term by term when $y > 0$. Since the terms of the series (1) satisfy the partial differential equation $U_{xx} + U_{yy} = 0$, it follows that the function represented by the series satisfies that equation when $y > 0$. In view of the uniform convergence, the function represented by the series, together with its derivatives, is a continuous function of x and y ($0 \leqq x \leqq 1, y > 0$). It follows readily that the remaining boundary conditions in the problem are satisfied.

Thus formula (11) of the last section is rigorously established as a solution of the boundary value problem of that section.

PROBLEMS

1. Prove the orthogonality property (6), Sec. 91.

2. If $h = 0$ in the problem of Sec. 92, show that $\lambda = 0$ is a characteristic number and that the solution is

$$U(x, y) = \int_0^1 F(\xi)\, d\xi + 2 \sum_1^\infty e^{-n\pi y} \cos n\pi x \int_0^1 F(\xi) \cos n\pi\xi\, d\xi.$$

3. Derive the temperature formula in Prob. 1, Sec. 90, by the method used in Sec. 92.

4. In the region $0 \leqq x \leqq 1, y \geqq 0$, a function $U(x, y)$ satisfies

$$U_{xx} + U_{yy} = 0, \qquad U_x(0, y) = 0, \qquad U(1, y) = 0, \qquad U(x, 0) = F(x);$$

also $U(x, y)$ is bounded as $y \to \infty$. Give a physical interpretation of this problem, and derive the formula

$$U(x, y) = 2 \sum_{n=1}^\infty e^{-m_n y} \cos m_n x \int_0^1 F(\xi) \cos m_n\xi\, d\xi,$$

where $m_n = (n - \frac{1}{2})\pi$.

5. Let $U(x, y)$ be the steady-state temperatures in a thin plate in the shape of a semi-infinite strip. Let surface heat transfer take place at the faces so that

$$U_{xx} + U_{yy} - bU = 0 \qquad (0 < x < 1, y > 0).$$

If $U(x, y)$ is bounded as $y \rightarrow \infty$ and satisfies the conditions

$$U(0, y) = 0, \qquad U_x(1, y) = -hU(1, y), \qquad U(x, 0) = 1 \quad (0 < x < 1),$$

derive the formula

$$U(x, y) = 2h \sum_{1}^{\infty} \frac{A_n}{\alpha_n} e^{-y\sqrt{b+\alpha_n^2}} \sin \alpha_n x,$$

where $A_n = (1 - \cos \alpha_n)/(h + \cos^2 \alpha_n)$ and $\alpha_1, \alpha_2, \cdots$ are the positive roots of the equation $\tan \alpha = -\alpha/h$.

6. Let $U(x, y)$ be the steady-state temperatures in an infinite prism bounded by the planes $x = 0$, $y = 0$, $x = 1$, and $y = 1$. If $U = 1$ on

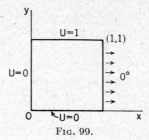

FIG. 99.

the face $y = 1$ and if $U_x = -hU$ at $x = 1$, and $U = 0$ on the other two faces (Fig. 99), derive the formula

$$U(x, y) = 2h \sum_{1}^{\infty} \frac{A_n}{\alpha_n} \frac{\sinh \alpha_n y}{\sinh \alpha_n} \sin \alpha_n x,$$

where the numbers A_n and α_n are those described in Prob. 5.

7. Solve the problem

$$U_{xx}(x, t) = (t + 1)U_t(x, t), \qquad U(0, t) = 0, \qquad U_x(1, t) = 0,$$
$$U(x, 0) = F(x),$$

where $0 \leqq x \leqq 1$, $t \geqq 0$. When $F(x) = 1(0 < x < 1)$, show that the solution becomes

$$U(x, t) = 2 \sum_{n=1}^{\infty} \frac{1}{m_n} (t + 1)^{-m_n^2} \sin m_n x,$$

where $m_n = (n - \frac{1}{2})\pi$.

8. The end $x = 1$ of a stretched string is elastically supported (Fig. 100) so that the transverse displacement $Y(x, t)$ satisfies the condition $Y_x(1, t) = -hY(1, t)$. Let

$$Y(0, t) = 0, \qquad Y(x, 0) = bx, \qquad Y_t(x, 0) = 0.$$

Show that the solution of the equation $Y_{tt}(x, t) = Y_{xx}(x, t)$ is then

$$Y(x, t) = 2bh(h + 1) \sum_{1}^{\infty} \frac{\sin \alpha_n \sin \alpha_n x}{\alpha_n^2(h + \cos^2 \alpha_n)} \cos \alpha_n t,$$

where $\alpha_1, \alpha_2, \cdots$ are the positive roots of the equation $\tan \alpha = -\alpha/h$.

9. The longitudinal displacements $Y(x, t)$ in a certain nonhomogeneous bar satisfy the conditions

$$\frac{\partial}{\partial x}\left(e^x \frac{\partial Y}{\partial x}\right) = e^{-x}\frac{\partial^2 Y}{\partial t^2} \qquad (0 < x < 1, t > 0),$$

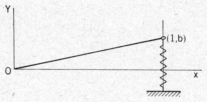

Fig. 100.

$$Y(0, t) = Y(1, t) = Y_t(x, 0) = 0, \qquad Y(x, 0) = F(x) \quad (0 < x < 1).$$
Derive the formula

$$Y(x, t) = \sum_{1}^{\infty} c_n\phi_n(x) \cos \beta_n t,$$

where $\beta_n = n\pi e/(e - 1)$ and

$$\phi_n(x) = \sqrt{\beta_2/\pi} \sin \beta_n(1 - e^{-x}), \qquad c_n = \int_0^1 F(x)e^{-x}\phi_n(x) \, dx.$$

10. The electrostatic potential $V(r, z)$ in the space bounded by the cylinders $r = a$ and $r = b$ above the plane $z = 0$ satisfies Laplace's equation $(rV_r)_r + rV_{zz} = 0$ and the boundary conditions

$$V(a, z) = V(b, z) = 0 \quad (z > 0), \qquad V(r, 0) = F(r) \quad (a < r < b);$$

also $V(r, z)$ is bounded as $z \to \infty$. Derive the formula

$$V(r, z) = \sum_{1}^{\infty} A_n e^{-\alpha_n z}\psi(\alpha_n r),$$

where $\psi(\alpha r) = J_0(\alpha r)Y_0(\alpha a) - J_0(\alpha a)Y_0(\alpha r)$, J_0 and Y_0 being Bessel functions of the first and second kind; the numbers α_n are the roots of the equation $\psi(b\alpha) = 0$, and

$$A_n = \frac{\int_a^b rF(r)\psi(\alpha_n r) \, dr}{\int_a^b r[\psi(\alpha_n r)]^2 \, dr}.$$

CHAPTER X

FOURIER TRANSFORMS

There are other integral transformations having operational properties similar to those of the Laplace transformation. Their uses in solving boundary value problems are limited to much narrower classes of problems; still these transformations serve as a useful supplement to the Laplace transformation and to the method of combining particular solutions. The finite Fourier sine and cosine transformations are particularly useful as additional devices for solving boundary value problems.

94. Finite Fourier Sine Transforms. Let $F(x)$ denote a function that is sectionally continuous over some finite interval of the variable x. By a proper choice of the origin and the unit of length, the end points of the interval become $x = 0$ and $x = \pi$. The Fourier sine transformation of $F(x)$ on that interval is the operation

$$\int_0^\pi F(x) \sin nx \, dx \qquad (n = 1, 2, \cdots),$$

denoted here by $S\{F(x)\}$. This operation produces a function $f_s(n)$ called the *finite sine transform* of $F(x)$; that is,

$$(1) \qquad S\{F(x)\} = \int_0^\pi F(x) \sin nx \, dx = f_s(n) \quad (n = 1, 2, \cdots).$$

The transformation sets up a correspondence between functions $F(x)$ on the interval $0 < x < \pi$ and sequences of numbers $f_s(n)$ $(n = 1, 2, \cdots)$. For example, the function $F(x) = 1$ has the transform

$$f_s(n) = \int_0^\pi \sin nx \, dx = \frac{1 - (-1)^n}{n} \quad (n = 1, 2, \cdots).$$

For the function $F(x) = x(0 < x < \pi)$, we have

$$S\{x\} = \int_0^\pi x \sin nx \, dx = \pi \frac{(-1)^{n+1}}{n} \quad (n = 1, 2, \cdots).$$

Let the first derivative of $F(x)$ also be a sectionally continuous function on the interval; moreover let $F(x)$ be defined at each point x_0 of discontinuity as follows:

$$(2) \qquad F(x_0) = \tfrac{1}{2}[F(x_0 + 0) + F(x_0 - 0)] \quad (0 < x_0 < \pi).$$

Then the Fourier sine series corresponding to the function $F(x)$ converges to the function

$$F(x) = \frac{2}{\pi} \sum_{1}^{\infty} \sin nx \int_{0}^{\pi} F(\xi) \sin n\pi\xi \, d\xi \quad (0 < x < \pi).$$

In view of the definition (1) of the sine transform, it follows that

$$(3) \qquad F(x) = \frac{2}{\pi} \sum_{1}^{\infty} f_s(n) \sin nx \qquad (0 < x < \pi).$$

This is the inversion formula for the transformation, giving the function in terms of the transform; that is, it is an explicit formula for $S^{-1}\{f_s(n)\}$, the function whose sine transform is $f_s(n)$. It follows that the inverse transformation is unique.

The sine transformation is clearly linear; that is,

$$S\{AF(x) + BG(x)\} = AS\{F(x)\} + BS\{G(x)\},$$

where A and B are constants. The inverse transformation is also linear.

The transform of a function defined over an interval $0 < x < l$ can be written easily in terms of a transform on our standard interval. For, by substituting $\xi = \pi x/l$, we can write the former transform as follows:

$$\int_{0}^{l} F(x) \sin \frac{n\pi x}{l} \, dx = \frac{l}{\pi} \int_{0}^{\pi} F\left(\frac{l}{\pi}\,\xi\right) \sin n\xi \, d\xi = \frac{l}{\pi} S\left\{F\left(\frac{lx}{\pi}\right)\right\}.$$

As an example, the function $F(x) = x$ on the interval $(0, l)$ has the sine transform

$$\frac{l}{\pi} S\left\{\frac{l}{\pi}\,x\right\} = \frac{l^2}{\pi^2} S\{x\} = \frac{l^2}{\pi} \frac{(-1)^{n+1}}{n} \quad (n = 1, 2, \cdots).$$

95. Operational Properties of the Transformation. For the derivatives of even order, differentiation of $F(x)$ corresponds to a simple algebraic operation on the transform $f_s(n)$. Let $F'(x)$ be continuous and $F''(x)$ sectionally continuous; then, integrating by parts, we have

$$\int_0^\pi F''(x) \sin nx\, dx = F'(x) \sin nx \Big]_0^\pi - n \int_0^\pi F'(x) \cos nx\, dx$$

$$= -n \cos nx F(x) \Big]_0^\pi - n^2 \int_0^\pi F(x) \sin nx\, dx.$$

Thus

(1) $S\{F''(x)\} = -n^2 S\{F(x)\} + n[F(0) - (-1)^n F(\pi)].$

Replacing $F(x)$ here by $F''(x)$ and assuming $F''''(x)$ continuous and the fourth derivative sectionally continuous, we see that

(2) $S\{F^{(4)}(x)\} = n^4 S\{F(x)\} - n^3[F(0) - (-1)^n F(\pi)]$
$$+ n[F''(0) - (-1)^n F''(\pi)].$$

Continuing in this manner we obtain the following theorem:

Theorem 1. *Let $F(x)$ have a sectionally continuous derivative of order $2\nu(\nu = 1, 2, \cdots)$ and a continuous derivative of order $2\nu - 1$, where $0 \leqq x \leqq \pi$. If $f_s(n)$ denotes the sine transform of $F(x)$, then*

(3) $S\{F^{(2\nu)}(x)\} = (-n^2)^\nu f_s(n) - (-1)^n n^{2\nu-1}[F(0) - (-1)^n F(\pi)]$
$$- (-1)^{\nu-1} n^{2\nu-3}[F''(0) - (-1)^n F''(\pi)] - \cdots$$
$$+ n[F^{(2\nu-2)}(0) - (-1)^n F^{(2\nu-2)}(\pi)].$$

This is the basic operational property for the solution of differential equations. Note that the coefficients of the polynomial in n, following the term $(-n^2)^\nu f_s(n)$, are determined by the values of $F(x)$ and its derivatives of even orders at the end points of the interval.

This property is also useful in obtaining transforms. For example, let $F(x) = x^2$. Then $F''(x) = 2$, and according to formula (1),

$$S\{2\} = -n^2 S\{x^2\} - n(-1)^n \pi^2.$$

Since $S\{2\} = 2S\{1\} = 2[1 - (-1)^n]/n$, it follows that

$$S\{x^2\} = \frac{\pi^2}{n}(-1)^{n-1} - \frac{2}{n^3}[1 - (-1)^n].$$

Let $F_1(x)$ denote the odd periodic extension of $F(x)$, with period 2π; that is,

$$F_1(-x) = -F_1(x), \qquad F_1(x + 2\pi) = F_1(x),$$

for all real x, and

$$F_1(x) = F(x) \qquad \text{when } 0 < x < \pi.$$

Then if k is any constant, we can write

$$f_s(n) \cos nk = \int_0^\pi F_1(x) \sin nx \cos nk \, dx.$$

Since the integrand is an even function of x, the integral here is one half the integral from $-\pi$ to π; thus the integral can be written

$$\tfrac{1}{4} \int_{-\pi}^\pi F_1(x)[\sin n(x - k) + \sin n(x + k)] \, dx =$$

$$\tfrac{1}{4} \int_{-\pi-k}^{\pi-k} F_1(\xi + k) \sin n\xi \, d\xi + \tfrac{1}{4} \int_{-\pi+k}^{\pi+k} F_1(\xi - k) \sin n\xi \, d\xi.$$

The integrands here are periodic functions of ξ with period 2π, so that the limits of both integrals can be replaced by the limits $-\pi$ to π. Moreover

$$\int_{-\pi}^0 F_1(\xi + k) \sin n\xi \, d\xi = - \int_0^\pi F_1(-\lambda + k) \sin n\lambda \, d\lambda,$$

and $F_1(-\lambda + k) = -F_1(\lambda - k)$. Making a corresponding change in the last integral of the preceding equation, we obtain the formula

$$f_s(n) \cos nk = \tfrac{1}{2} \int_0^\pi [F_1(x - k) + F_1(x + k)] \sin nx \, dx;$$

that is, if $f_s(n)$ is the transform of $F(x)$, then

$$(4) \qquad f_s(n) \cos nk = S\left\{\frac{F_1(x - k) + F_1(x + k)}{2}\right\}.$$

Let $k = \pi$. Since $F_1(x + \pi) = F_1(x - \pi) = -F_1(\pi - x)$, and since $F_1(\pi - x) = F(\pi - x)$ when $0 < x < \pi$, it follows that $f_s(n) \cos n\pi$ is the transform of $-F(\pi - x)$; *that is,*

$$(5) \qquad f_s(n)(-1)^{n+1} = S\{F(\pi - x)\}.$$

As an example, we can conclude from the transformation

$$S\{x\} = \frac{\pi(-1)^{n+1}}{n}$$

that

$$S\{\pi - x\} = \frac{\pi}{n} \qquad (n = 1, 2, \cdots).$$

PROBLEMS

1. With the aid of Theorem 1, obtain the following transformations, in which c is any real constant and k is a constant that is not an integer:

(a) $S\{e^{cx}\} = \dfrac{n}{n^2 + c^2}\,[1 - (-1)^n e^{\pi c}];$

(b) $S\{\sin kx\} = \dfrac{n(-1)^{n+1}}{n^2 - k^2}\,\sin \pi k;$

(c) $S\{\cos kx\} = \dfrac{n}{n^2 - k^2}\,[1 - (-1)^n \cos \pi k];$

(d) $S\{x^3\} = \pi(-1)^n \left(\dfrac{6}{n^3} - \dfrac{\pi^2}{n}\right).$

2. If $F(0) = F(\pi) = 0$, then

$$\frac{1}{n^2}\,S\{F''(x)\} = -S\{F(x)\};$$

hence obtain the inverse transformations

(a) $S^{-1}\left\{\dfrac{1 - (-1)^n}{n^3}\right\} = \dfrac{1}{2}\,x(\pi - x),$

(b) $S^{-1}\left\{\dfrac{(-1)^{n+1}}{n^3}\right\} = \dfrac{x(\pi^2 - x^2)}{6\pi}.$

3. If $F(\pi - x) = F(x)(0 < x < \pi)$, show that $f_s(n) = 0$ for even values of n.

4. Show that, when $|r| < 1$,

$$\log (1 + re^{i\theta}) = -\sum_{1}^{\infty}\frac{1}{n}\,(-r)^n e^{in\theta}.$$

Also, if $R^2 = (1 + r \cos \theta)^2 + r^2 \sin^2 \theta$ and $\tan \Theta = r \sin \theta/(1 + r \cos \theta)$, then

$$\log (1 + re^{i\theta}) = \log (Re^{i\Theta}) = \log R + i\Theta.$$

Thus by equating imaginary parts of the members of the first equation, show that

$$\arctan \frac{r \sin \theta}{1 + r \cos \theta} = -\sum_{1}^{\infty}\frac{1}{n}\,(-r)^n \sin n\theta.$$

When $|r| \leqq 1$, this can be shown to be a Fourier sine series. Show that it follows that

$$S \left\{ \arctan \frac{k \sin x}{1 + k \cos x} \right\} = \frac{\pi}{2} \frac{(-1)^{n+1}}{n} k^n \qquad (|k| \leqq 1)$$

5. Write a series for $\log (1 + re^{i\theta}) - \log (1 - re^{i\theta})$, and proceed as in Prob. 4 to obtain the transformation

$$S \left\{ \arctan \frac{2k \sin x}{1 - k^2} \right\} = \frac{\pi}{2} \frac{1 - (-1)^n}{n} k^n \qquad (|k| \leqq 1).$$

As a consequence, show that

$$S \left\{ \arctan \frac{\sin x}{\sinh y} \right\} = \frac{\pi}{2} \frac{1 - (-1)^n}{n} e^{-ny} \qquad (y \geqq 0).$$

96. Cosine Transforms. The finite Fourier cosine transformation is the operation

$$(1) \qquad C\{F(x)\} = \int_0^\pi F(x) \cos nx \, dx \quad (n = 0, 1, 2, \cdots),$$

on a function $F(x)$ defined on the interval $0 < x < \pi$. The resulting function of n ($n = 0, 1, 2, \cdots$) is the *finite cosine transform* $f_c(n)$. For example, if $F(x) = 1$, then

$$f_c(n) = \pi \quad \text{when } n = 0,$$
$$= 0 \quad \text{when } n = 1, 2, \cdots$$

As another example, if $F(x) = x$, then

$$f_c(n) = \frac{\pi^2}{2} \qquad \text{when } n = 0,$$
$$= -\frac{1 - (-n)^n}{n^2} \quad \text{when } n = 1, 2, \cdots.$$

The inverse transformation can be written at once from the Fourier cosine series; that is,

$$(2) \qquad F(x) = \frac{1}{\pi} f_c(0) + \frac{2}{\pi} \sum_1^\infty f_c(n) \cos nx$$
$$= C^{-1}\{f_c(n)\} \qquad (0 < x < \pi),$$

if $F(x)$ and $F'(x)$ are sectionally continuous functions.

Upon integrating by parts, we find that

(3) $C\{F'(x)\} = nS\{F(x)\} - F(0) + (-1)^n F(\pi)$
$$(n = 0, 1, 2, \cdots),$$

when $F(x)$ is continuous and $F'(x)$ is sectionally continuous. Likewise,

(4) $S\{F'(x)\} = -nC\{F(x)\}$ $(n = 1, 2, \cdots)$.

Integrating by parts successively, we find that

(5) $C\{F''(x)\} = -n^2 C\{F(x)\} - F'(0) + (-1)^n F'(\pi);$

likewise we can establish the following theorem:

Theorem 2.   *Let the derivative of order $2\nu(\nu = 1, 2, \cdots)$ of a function $F(x)$ be sectionally continuous and the derivative of order $2\nu - 1$ be continuous, when $0 \leqq x \leqq \pi$. Then the cosine transforms of the even-ordered derivatives of $F(x)$ are algebraic functions of n and $f_c(n)$, namely,*

(6) $C\{F^{(2\nu)}(x)\} = (-n^2)^\nu f_c(n) - (-1)^{\nu-1} n^{2\nu-2}[F'(0)$
$- (-1)^n F'(\pi)] - (-1)^{\nu-2} n^{2\nu-4}[F'''(0) - (-1)^n F'''(\pi)] - \cdots$
$$- [F^{(2\nu-1)}(0) - (-1)^n F^{(2\nu-1)}(\pi)].$$

Note that the values of only the odd-ordered derivatives of the function at the end points of the interval appear here.

Let $F_2(x)$ be the even periodic extension of $F(x)$; that is,

$$F_2(-x) = F_2(x), \qquad F_2(x + 2\pi) = F_2(x),$$

for all x, and

$$F_2(x) = F(x) \qquad \text{when } 0 < x < \pi.$$

By the method used to derive formula (4) of the last section, we find that *when $f_c(n)$ is the cosine transform of $F(x)$, then*

(7) $f_c(n) \cos nk = C\left\{\dfrac{F_2(x - k) + F_2(x + k)}{2}\right\}$
$$(n = 0, 1, 2, \cdots),$$

where k is any constant.   Setting $k = \pi$, *it follows that*

(8) $(-1)^n f_c(n) = C\{F(\pi - x)\}.$

PROBLEMS

1. Obtain the following transformations, assuming that the constant k is not an integer:

(a) $C\{\sin kx\} = k\dfrac{(-1)^n \cos \pi k - 1}{n^2 - k^2}$;

(b) $C\{\cos kx\} = k\dfrac{(-1)^{n+1} \sin \pi k}{n^2 - k^2}$;

(c) $C\{\pi - x\} = \frac{1}{2}\pi^2$ when $n = 0$,

$$= \dfrac{1 - (-1)^n}{n^2} \text{ when } n = 1, 2, \cdots .$$

2. Derive the transformations

(a) $C\{x^2\} = \dfrac{\pi^3}{3}$ when $n = 0$,

$$= 2\pi\dfrac{(-1)^n}{n^2} \text{ when } n = 1, 2, \cdots ;$$

(b) $C\left\{\dfrac{x^2}{2\pi} - \dfrac{\pi}{6}\right\} = 0$ when $n = 0$,

$$= \dfrac{(-1)^n}{n^2} \text{ when } n = 1, 2, \cdots .$$

97. Convolution. Let $P(x)$ be a function defined on the interval $-2\pi < x < 2\pi$, and let $Q(x)$ be defined on the interval $-\pi < x < \pi$. Then the function

$$(1) \qquad P(x) * Q(x) = \int_{-\pi}^{\pi} P(x - \xi)Q(\xi)\, d\xi$$

is called the *convolution* of P and Q on the interval $-\pi < x < \pi$. The reader can show that this function of x is even if the functions P and Q are both even or both odd and that it is odd if one of those functions is even and the other odd.

If $F(x)$ and $G(x)$ are two functions defined on the interval $0 < x < \pi$, we can show that the product of their sine or cosine transforms is a transform of a function defined by the convolution.

To prove this in the case of the product $f_s(n)g_c(n)$, we let $F_1(x)$ denote the odd periodic extension of $F(x)$, with period 2π, and let $G_2(x)$ denote the even extension of $G(x)$; thus $G_2(x)$ is defined on the interval $-\pi < x < \pi$. Then

$$f_s(n)g_c(n) = \int_0^\pi F_1(\lambda) \sin n\lambda \, d\lambda \int_0^\pi G_2(\mu) \cos n\mu \, d\mu$$

$$= \tfrac{1}{4}\int_{-\pi}^{\pi} F_1(\lambda) \sin n\lambda \, d\lambda \int_{-\pi}^{\pi} G_2(\mu) \cos n\mu \, d\mu$$

$$= \tfrac{1}{4}\int_{-\pi}^{\pi}\int_{-\pi}^{\pi} F_1(\lambda)G_2(\mu) \sin n\lambda \cos n\mu \, d\lambda \, d\mu.$$

Thus if A denotes the square bounded by the lines $\lambda = \pm\pi$ and $\mu = \pm\pi$, the product $f_s(n)g_c(n)$ can be written as

$$(2) \quad \tfrac{1}{8} \iint\limits_A F_1(\lambda)G_2(\mu) \sin n(\lambda + \mu) \, d\lambda \, d\mu$$

$$+ \tfrac{1}{8} \iint\limits_A F_1(\lambda)G_2(\mu) \sin n(\lambda - \mu) \, d\lambda \, d\mu.$$

In the first integral, let $\lambda + \mu = x$ and $\mu = \xi$. Then the lines $\lambda = \pm\pi$ in the $\lambda\mu$-plane become the lines $x - \xi = \pm\pi$ in the $x\xi$-plane. The square A becomes the parallelogram B shown in Fig. 101. Since the Jacobian of λ and μ with respect to x and

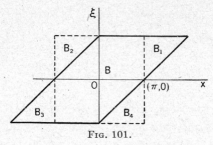

Fig. 101.

ξ is unity, the area element $d\lambda \, d\mu$ becomes $dx \, d\xi$, and the first of the integrals (2) becomes

$$\iint\limits_B F_1(x - \xi)G_2(\xi) \sin nx \, dx \, d\xi.$$

Since $F_1(x - \xi)$ is a periodic function of ξ for each fixed x, the integral over the triangle B_1 can be replaced by that over the triangle B_2, and the integral over B_3 by that over B_4. The resulting integral over the square can be written

$$\int_{-\pi}^{\pi} \sin nx \int_{-\pi}^{\pi} F_1(x - \xi)G_2(\xi) \, d\xi \, dx =$$
$$2 \int_0^{\pi} \sin nx \, [F_1(x) * G_2(x)] \, dx,$$

where we have used the fact that $F_1 * G_2$ is an odd function.

In like manner, the second integral can be transformed into the integral above; hence

$$f_s(n)g_c(n) = \tfrac{1}{2} \int_0^{\pi} [F_1(x) * G_2(x)] \sin nx \, dx.$$

That is, this product is a sine transform of a convolution,
$$f_s(n)g_c(n) = S\{\tfrac{1}{2}F_1(x) * G_2(x)\}.$$

The convolution integral can be written in terms of the original functions F and G. By making use of the descriptions of the extended functions F_1 and G_2 in terms of those functions, it can be seen that

$$(3) \quad F_1 * G_2 = \int_0^x F(x - \xi)G(\xi) \, d\xi - \int_x^\pi F(\xi - x)G(\xi) \, d\xi$$
$$+ \int_0^{\pi-x} F(x + \xi)G(\xi) \, d\xi - \int_{\pi-x}^\pi F(2\pi - x - \xi)G(\xi) \, d\xi.$$

The other cases included in the following theorem can be established by the above method.

Theorem 3. *Let $F(x)$ and $G(x)$ be two functions sectionally continuous on the interval $0 \leqq x \leqq \pi$; let $F_1(x)$ and $F_2(x)$ denote the odd and even periodic extensions of F, respectively, and $G_1(x)$ and $G_2(x)$ the odd and even extensions of G. Then the products of the transforms of F and G can be written as follows:*

$$(4) \qquad f_s(n)g_c(n) = S\{\tfrac{1}{2}F_1 * G_2\},$$
$$(5) \qquad f_s(n)g_s(n) = C\{-\tfrac{1}{2}F_1 * G_1\},$$
$$(6) \qquad f_c(n)g_c(n) = C\{\tfrac{1}{2}F_2 * G_2\},$$
$$(7) \qquad f_c(n)g_s(n) = S\{\tfrac{1}{2}F_2 * G_1\}.$$

If I_1, I_2, I_3, and I_4 represent the four integrals in the right-hand member of equation (3), it can be shown that the other three convolution integrals have the following expressions in terms of those integrals involving the original functions:

$$(8) \qquad F_1 * G_1 = -I_1 + I_2 + I_3 - I_4,$$
$$(9) \qquad F_2 * G_2 = I_1 + I_2 + I_3 + I_4,$$
$$(10) \qquad F_2 * G_1 = I_1 + I_2 - I_3 - I_4.$$

To obtain, for example, the inverse cosine transform of $(n^2 - k^2)^{-1}$, where k is not an integer, we can write

$$\frac{1}{n^2 - k^2} = \frac{n(-1)^{n+1}}{n^2 - k^2} \frac{(-1)^{n+1}}{n} = S\left\{\frac{\sin kx}{\sin k\pi}\right\} S\left\{\frac{x}{\pi}\right\}.$$

According to formula (5), this product is the cosine transform of the function $-\tfrac{1}{2}F_1 * G_1$, where F_1 is the periodic extension of the odd function $\sin kx/\sin k\pi$, with period 2π, and $G_1 = x/\pi$. Thus

$$C^{-1}\left\{\frac{1}{n^2 - k^2}\right\} = -\frac{1}{2\pi} \int_{-\pi}^\pi F_1(x - \xi)\xi \, d\xi,$$

TABLE 2.—FINITE SINE TRANSFORMS

	$f_s(n)$	$F(x)$
1	$f_s(n) = \displaystyle\int_0^\pi F(x) \sin nx \, dx \; (n = 1, 2, \cdots)$	$F(x)$
2	$(-1)^{n+1} f_s(n)$	$F(\pi - x)$
3	$\dfrac{1}{n}$	$\dfrac{\pi - x}{\pi}$
4	$\dfrac{(-1)^{n+1}}{n}$	$\dfrac{x}{\pi}$
5	$\dfrac{1 - (-1)^n}{n}$	1
6	$\dfrac{2}{n^2} \sin \dfrac{n\pi}{2}$	$\begin{cases} x & \text{when } 0 < x < \pi/2 \\ \pi - x & \text{when } \pi/2 < x < \pi \end{cases}$
7	$\dfrac{(-1)^{n+1}}{n^3}$	$\dfrac{x(\pi^2 - x^2)}{6\pi}$
8	$\dfrac{1 - (-1)^n}{n^3}$	$\dfrac{x(\pi - x)}{2}$
9	$\dfrac{\pi^2(-1)^{n-1}}{n} - \dfrac{2[1 - (-1)^n]}{n^3}$	x^2
10	$\pi(-1)^n \left(\dfrac{6}{n^3} - \dfrac{\pi^2}{n} \right)$	x^3
11	$\dfrac{n}{n^2 + c^2} [1 - (-1)^n e^{c\pi}]$	e^{cx}
12	$\dfrac{n}{n^2 + c^2}$	$\dfrac{\sinh c(\pi - x)}{\sinh c\pi}$
13	$\dfrac{n}{n^2 - k^2} \; (k \neq 0, 1, 2, \cdots)$	$\dfrac{\sin k(\pi - x)}{\sin k\pi}$
14	$\begin{cases} \dfrac{\pi}{2} \text{ when } n = m \\ 0 \text{ when } n \neq m \end{cases} (m = 1, 2, \cdots)$	$\sin mx$
15	$\dfrac{n}{n^2 - k^2} [1 - (-1)^n \cos k\pi]$ $(k \neq 1, 2, \cdots)$	$\cos kx$
16	$\begin{cases} \dfrac{n}{n^2 - m^2} [1 - (-1)^{n+m}] \\ \qquad \text{when } n \neq m = 1, 2, \cdots \\ 0 \qquad \text{when } n = m \end{cases}$	$\cos mx$
17	$\dfrac{n}{(n^2 - k^2)^2} \; (k \neq 0, 1, 2, \cdots)$	$\dfrac{\pi \sin kx}{2k \sin^2 k\pi} - \dfrac{x \cos k(\pi - x)}{2k \sin k\pi}$
18	$\dfrac{b^n}{n} \; (|b| \leqq 1)$	$\dfrac{2}{\pi} \arctan \dfrac{b \sin x}{1 - b \cos x}$
19	$\dfrac{1 - (-1)^n}{n} b^n \; (|b| \leqq 1)$	$\dfrac{2}{\pi} \arctan \dfrac{2b \sin x}{1 - b^2}$

TABLE 3.—FINITE COSINE TRANSFORMS

	$f_c(n)$	$F(x)$
1	$f_c(n) = \displaystyle\int_0^\pi F(x) \cos nx\, dx \ (n = 0, 1, 2, \cdots)$	$F(x)$
2	$(-1)^n f_c(n)$	$F(\pi - x)$
3	0 when $n = 1, 2, \cdots$; $f_c(0) = \pi$	1
4	$\dfrac{2}{n} \sin \dfrac{n\pi}{2}$; $f_c(0) = 0$	$\begin{cases} 1 \text{ when } 0 < x < \pi/2 \\ -1 \text{ when } \pi/2 < x < \pi \end{cases}$
5	$-\dfrac{1 - (-1)^n}{n^2}$; $f_c(0) = \dfrac{\pi^2}{2}$	x
6	$\dfrac{(-1)^n}{n^2}$; $f_c(0) = \dfrac{\pi^2}{6}$	$\dfrac{x^2}{2\pi}$
7	$\dfrac{1}{n^2}$; $f_c(0) = 0$	$\dfrac{(\pi - x)^2}{2\pi} - \dfrac{\pi}{6}$
8	$3\pi^2 \dfrac{(-1)^n}{n^2} - 6\dfrac{1 - (-1)^n}{n^4}$; $f_c(0) = \dfrac{\pi^4}{4}$	x^3
9	$\dfrac{(-1)^n e^{c\pi} - 1}{n^2 + c^2}$	$\dfrac{1}{c} e^{cx}$
10	$\dfrac{1}{n^2 + c^2}$	$\dfrac{\cosh c(\pi - x)}{c \sinh c\pi}$
11	$\dfrac{k}{n^2 - k^2} [(-1)^n \cos \pi k - 1]$ $ (k \neq 0, 1, 2, \cdots)$	$\sin kx$
12	$\dfrac{(-1)^{n+m} - 1}{n^2 - m^2}$; $f_c(m) = 0 \ (m = 1, 2, \cdots)$	$\dfrac{1}{m} \sin mx$
13	$\dfrac{1}{n^2 - k^2} \ (k \neq 0, 1, 2, \cdots)$	$-\dfrac{\cos k(\pi - x)}{k \sin k\pi}$
14	0 when $n = 1, 2, \cdots$; $ f_c(m) = \dfrac{\pi}{2} \ (m = 1, 2, \cdots)$	$\cos mx$

an integral which can readily be evaluated by breaking up the interval or by using formula (8). The inverse transform is found to be $-\cos k(\pi - x)/(k \sin \pi k)$.

Short tables of sine and cosine transforms are presented here, for convenience in the applications to follow.

98. Vibrations of a Horizontal String with Fixed Ends. Let us first illustrate the use of a finite Fourier transformation in determining the displacements $Y(x, t)$ in a horizontal string stretched from the origin to the point $(\pi, 0)$, when the motion is due to the weight of the string. If the string is released from rest in the position $Y = 0$, then

$$(1) \qquad\qquad Y_{tt}(x, t) = a^2 Y_{xx}(x, t) + g \quad (0 < x < \pi, t > 0),$$

(2) $Y(x, 0) = Y_t(x, 0) = 0,$ $Y(0, t) = Y(\pi, t) = 0,$

where g is the acceleration of gravity and the Y-axis is positive downward.

Since the value of $Y(x, t)$ is given at $x = 0$ and $x = \pi$, we use the sine transform with respect to x,

$$S\{Y(x, t)\} = y_s(n, t).$$

Then $S\{Y_{tt}(x, t)\} = \dfrac{d^2}{dt^2} y_s(n, t)$ and the transformation of both members of equation (1) leads to the ordinary differential equation

(3) $$\frac{d^2}{dt^2} y_s(n, t) = -a^2 n^2 y_s(n, t) + gS\{1\}.$$

We have used the last two of conditions (2) here in writing the transform of $Y_{xx}(x, t)$. Transforming the first two of those conditions, we have

(4) $$y_s(n, 0) = 0, \qquad \frac{d}{dt} y_s(n, t) = 0 \quad \text{when } t = 0.$$

The solution of equation (3) that satisfies conditions (4) is

(5) $$y_s(n, t) = \frac{g}{a^2} \left(\frac{1}{n^2} S\{1\} - \frac{1}{n^2} S\{1\} \cos nat \right),$$

where $S\{1\} = [1 - (-1)^n]/n$. If we make the inverse transformation with the aid of the Fourier sine series, our formal result takes the form

(6) $$Y(x, t) = \frac{2}{\pi} \sum_{1}^{\infty} y_s(n, t) \sin nx$$

$$= \frac{2g}{\pi a^2} \sum_{1}^{\infty} \frac{1 - (-1)^n}{n^3} (1 - \cos nat) \sin nx.$$

But we can write the solution in a more convenient form by first noting that (Table 2, No. 8)

$$\frac{1}{n^2} S\{1\} = S \left\{ \frac{1}{2} x(\pi - x) \right\}.$$

Then if $Q(x)$ is the odd periodic extension of the function $\frac{1}{2}x(\pi - x)$, it follows from formula (4), Sec. 95, that

$$\frac{1}{n^2} S\{1\} \cos nat = \frac{1}{2} S\{Q(x - at) + Q(x + at)\}.$$

Consequently the inverse transforms of the terms in formula (5) can be written in closed form, that is, without using infinite series. The solution becomes

$$(7) \qquad Y(x, t) = \frac{g}{2a^2} [x(\pi - x) - Q(x - at) - Q(x + at)],$$

where $Q(x) = \frac{1}{2}x(\pi - x)$ when $0 < x < \pi$, $Q(-x) = -Q(x)$ and $Q(x + 2\pi) = Q(x)$ for all x.

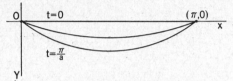

Fig. 102.

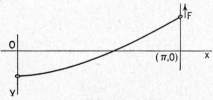

Fig. 103.

Formula (7) is easily verified as the solution of the problem. A study of the function by composition of ordinates, for fixed values of t, shows that the string vibrates between the extreme positions $Y = 0$ and $Y = (\pi x - x^2)g/a^2$, as indicated in Fig. 102. The motion of each point is periodic with the period $2\pi/a$.

99. A Horizontal String with Sliding Ends. Let the ends of a stretched string be looped about vertical supports along the lines $x = 0$ and $x = \pi$ (Fig. 103). The mass of the loops and the friction on the supports are assumed to be negligible. If a constant upward force acts on the right-hand loop, the displacements $Y(x, t)$, as the string falls from rest from the position $Y = 0$, satisfy the conditions

$$Y_{tt}(x, t) = a^2 Y_{xx}(x, t) + g \quad (0 < x < \pi, t > 0),$$
$$Y(x, 0) = 0, \qquad Y_t(x, 0) = 0,$$
$$Y_x(0, t) = 0, \qquad Y_x(\pi, t) = -b,$$

where b is the magnitude of the force divided by the tension.

Since the values of Y_x at the ends are prescribed here, we use the cosine transformation of $Y(x, t)$ with respect to x. Now

$$C\{Y_{xx}(x, t)\} = -n^2 y_c(n, t) - (-1)^n b;$$

hence the above problem transforms into the new problem

$$\frac{d^2}{dt^2} y_c(n, t) + a^2 n^2 y_c(n, t) = -a^2 b (-1)^n + g C\{1\},$$

$$y_c(n, t) = \frac{d}{dt} y_c(n, t) = 0 \qquad \text{when } t = 0.$$

When $n = 0$, $C\{1\} = \pi$ and the solution of this problem is

(1) $$y_c(0, t) = \tfrac{1}{2}(\pi g - a^2 b)t^2.$$

When $n = 1, 2, \cdots$, $C\{1\} = 0$ and the solution is

(2) $$y_c(n, t) = b \left[\frac{(-1)^n}{n^2} \cos nat - \frac{(-1)^n}{n^2} \right].$$

It will be convenient to consider the transform described by equations (1) and (2) as the sum of three transforms $u_c(n, t)$, $-p_c(n)$, and $p_c(n) \cos nat$, where

$$u_c(n, t) = 0 \quad \text{when } n = 1, 2, \cdots, \qquad u_c(0, t) = \tfrac{1}{2}(\pi g - a^2 b)t^2,$$
$$p_c(n) = b \frac{(-1)^n}{n^2} \quad \text{when } n = 1, 2, \cdots, \qquad p_c(0) = b \frac{\pi^2}{6}.$$

The inverse transform of $u_c(n, t)$ is

$$U(t) = \frac{\pi g - a^2 b}{2\pi} t^2;$$

that of $p_c(n)$ is

(3) $$P(x) = \frac{b}{2\pi} x^2 \qquad (0 < x < \pi).$$

When the argument of $P(x)$ is outside the range $0 < x < \pi$, let $P(x)$ denote the even periodic extension of the quadratic function defined by equation (3). Then according to formula (7), Sec. 96,

$$C^{-1}\{p_c(n) \cos nat\} = \tfrac{1}{2}[P(x - at) + P(x + at)].$$

The formula for the displacements can then be written

$$(4) \quad Y(x, t) = \frac{\pi g - a^2 b}{2\pi} t^2 + \frac{1}{2} [P(x - at) + P(x + at)] - P(x),$$

where $P(x + 2\pi) = P(x)$ for all real x and

$$P(x) = \frac{b}{2\pi} x^2 \qquad (-\pi < x < \pi).$$

The verification of this solution is easy if we note that $P'(x)$ is an odd periodic function and that any function of $x \pm at$ satisfies the homogeneous equation $Y_{tt} - a^2 Y_{xx} = 0$. The discussion of the vibration can also be left to the reader. In particular, when $a^2 b = \pi g$, the force on the right-hand end is equal to the weight of the string and the left-hand end executes the periodic motion

$$Y(0, t) = P(at).$$

Thus the extreme positions of the end are $Y = 0$ and $Y = \pi b/2$, and the velocity changes suddenly from ab to $-ab$ as the end reaches the latter position.

Using the inversion formula, the solution of the problem can also be written

$$(5) \qquad Y(x, t) = \frac{1}{\pi} y_c(0, t) + \frac{2}{\pi} \sum_1^\infty y_c(n, t) \cos nx,$$

where $y_c(0, t)$ and $y_c(n, t)$ are given by formulas (1) and (2).

100. Potential in a Slot. The two illustrative problems treated above could have been solved also by means of the Laplace transformation. We now consider some problems that are not so well adapted to methods treated earlier in this book. The first is a problem of a type that arises in the subject of electronics.

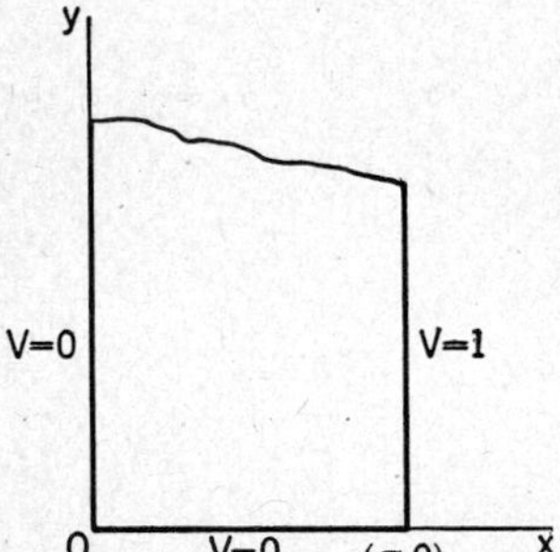

FIG. 104.

Let $V(x, y)$ denote the electrostatic potential in a space bounded by the planes $x = 0$, $x = \pi$, and $y = 0$ in which there is a uniform distribution of space charge of density $h/(4\pi)$. Then the function $V(x, y)$ satisfies Poisson's equation

$$(1) \qquad V_{xx}(x, y) + V_{yy}(x, y) = -h \quad (0 < x < \pi, y > 0).$$

Let the planes $x = 0$ and $y = 0$ be kept at potential zero and the plane $x = \pi$ at another fixed potential $V = 1$ (Fig. 104); also let $V(x, y)$ be finite as y tends to infinity.   Then

(2) $V(0, y) = 0,$ $V(\pi, y) = 1,$ $(y > 0),$
(3) $V(x, 0) = 0$ $(0 < x < \pi),$ $|V(x, y)| < M$
$$(0 \leqq x \leqq \pi, y \geqq 0),$$

where M is some constant.   Let us determine the function $V(x, y)$.

This is also the problem of finding the steady-state temperatures in a semi-infinite strip with a uniform source of heat, of strength proportional to h, in every element of the strip.

The problem in the sine transform of $V(x, y)$ becomes

$$\frac{d^2}{dy^2} v_s(n, y) - n^2 v_s(n, y) = n(-1)^n - hS\{1\},$$
$$v_s(n, 0) = 0, \qquad |v_s(n, y)| < M\pi.$$

The solution of this problem is

(4) $$v_s(n, y) = \frac{hS\{1\} - n(-1)^n}{n^2} (1 - e^{-ny})$$

$$= \left[h \frac{1 - (-1)^n}{n^3} + \frac{(-1)^{n+1}}{n} \right] (1 - e^{-ny}).$$

The formula for the potential can therefore be written

(5) $$V(x, y) = \frac{2}{\pi} \sum_{1}^{\infty} v_s(n, y) \sin nx.$$

In addition to this solution in terms of an infinite series we can derive a closed form of the solution.   Referring to Table 2 we find that

$$S^{-1} \left\{ \frac{1 - (-1)^n}{n^3} \right\} = \frac{x}{2} (\pi - x), \qquad S^{-1} \left\{ \frac{(-1)^{n+1}}{n} \right\} = \frac{x}{\pi},$$

and

$$S^{-1} \left\{ (-1)^{n+1} \frac{e^{-ny}}{n} \right\} = \frac{2}{\pi} \arctan \frac{e^{-y} \sin x}{1 + e^{-y} \cos x} = \frac{2}{\pi} \arctan \frac{\sin x}{e^y + \cos x};$$

also,

$$-\frac{S\{1\}}{n^2} e^{-ny} = -\frac{e^{-ny}}{n} \frac{S\{1\}}{n} = S \left\{ \frac{2}{\pi} \arctan \frac{\sin x}{e^y - \cos x} \right\} C\{x\}.$$

The even extension of the function $G(x) = x$ is $G_2(x) = |x|$. The inverse tangent function here is odd and periodic. Therefore, according to formula (4) of Theorem 3,

$$S^{-1}\left\{ -\frac{S\{1\}}{n^2} e^{-ny} \right\} = \frac{1}{\pi}\left(\arctan \frac{\sin x}{e^y - \cos x} \right) * |x|.$$

The convolution here can be written in the form

$$-\int_{-\pi}^{0} \xi \arctan \frac{\sin (x - \xi)}{e^y - \cos (x - \xi)}\, d\xi$$

$$+ \int_{0}^{\pi} \xi \arctan \frac{\sin (x - \xi)}{e^y - \cos (x - \xi)}\, d\xi,$$

and we can substitute λ for $-\xi$ in the first integral to gain a little simplification of the form.

The inverse transformation of the terms in formula (4), therefore, leads to the formula

$$(6) \quad V(x, y) = \frac{h}{2} x(\pi - x) + \frac{x}{\pi} - \frac{2}{\pi} \arctan \frac{\sin x}{e^y + \cos x}$$

$$+ \frac{h}{\pi} \int_{0}^{\pi} \lambda \left[\arctan \frac{\sin (x + \lambda)}{e^y - \cos (x + \lambda)} + \arctan \frac{\sin (x - \lambda)}{e^y - \cos (x - \lambda)} \right] d\lambda.$$

It can be seen that this function $V(x, y)$ does satisfy the conditions (1), (2), and (3) of our boundary value problem.

101. Temperatures When Thermal Coefficients Vary with Time. First let us note that if $\Psi(x, t)$ is the temperature in a slab $0 < x < \pi$, initially at temperature $\Psi = 1$, with its faces kept at temperature zero then, taking $k = 1$,

$$\Psi_t(x, t) = \Psi_{xx}(x, t) \quad (0 < x < \pi, t > 0),$$
$$\Psi(x, 0) = 1 \quad (0 < x < \pi), \qquad \Psi(0, t) = \Psi(\pi, t) = 0.$$

If $\psi_s(n, t)$ denotes the transform of this temperature function, then

$$\frac{d}{dt} \psi_s(n, t) = -n^2 \psi_s(n, t), \qquad \psi_s(n, 0) = S\{1\};$$

hence

$$(1) \qquad \psi_s(n, t) = S\{1\}e^{-n^2 t} = \frac{1 - (-1)^n}{n} e^{-n^2 t}$$

and

$$(2) \qquad \Psi(x, t) = \frac{2}{\pi} \sum_{1}^{\infty} \frac{1 - (-1)^n}{n} e^{-n^2 t} \sin nx.$$

We can express more complex temperature functions in terms of such basic temperature functions.*

Now let us find the solution of the problem

$$(3) \qquad U_t(x,\, t) = f(t)U_{xx}(x,\, t) + g(t) \quad (0 < x < \pi,\, t > 0),$$
$$(4) \qquad U(x,\, 0) = 0, \qquad U(0,\, t) = U(\pi,\, t) = 0.$$

Here $U(x, t)$ may represent the temperatures in a slender rod with thermal coefficients and heat sources or sinks that vary with time. The initial temperature is zero, and the ends are kept at temperature zero.

Let $u_s(n, t)$ denote the sine transform of $U(x, t)$. Then

$$(5) \qquad \frac{d}{dt}\, u_s(n,\, t) + n^2 f(t) u_s(n,\, t) = g(t)S\{1\},$$

$$(6) \qquad u_s(n,\, 0) = 0.$$

In terms of the function

$$F(a,\, t) = \int_a^t f(\tau)\, d\tau,$$

an integrating factor of the linear differential equation (5) is $e^{n^2 F(0,\, t)}$ and the solution satisfying condition (6) is

$$u_s(n,\, t)e^{n^2 F(0,\, t)} = S\{1\} \int_0^t g(\tau)e^{n^2 F(0,\, \tau)}\, d\tau.$$

Since $F(0,\, t) - F(0,\, \tau) = F(\tau,\, t)$, we can write

$$(7) \qquad u_s(n,\, t) = \int_0^t g(\tau)S\{1\}e^{-n^2 F(\tau,\, t)}\, d\tau;$$

thus one form of the solution is the following:

$$(8) \qquad U(x,\, t) = \frac{2}{\pi} \sum_1^\infty \frac{1 - (-1)^n}{n} \sin nx \int_0^t g(\tau)e^{-n^2 F(\tau,\, t)}\, d\tau.$$

To obtain another form we may apply the inverse transformation to both members of equation (7) and formally interchange the order of the operator S^{-1} and the integration with respect to τ. According to formula (1)

$$S^{-1}\{S\{1\}e^{-n^2 F(\tau,\, t)}\} = \Psi[x,\, F(\tau,\, t)],$$

* The function $\Psi(x,\, t)$ here is a simple combination of derivatives of the theta functions described, for instance, in Doetsch, "Theorie und Anwendung der Laplace-Transformation," p. 306, 1937.

where $\Psi(x, t)$ is the basic temperature function (2). Consequently

$$(9) \qquad U(x, t) = \int_0^t g(\tau)\Psi[x, F(\tau, t)] \, d\tau,$$

where

$$F(\tau, t) = \int_\tau^t f(\lambda) \, d\lambda.$$

The solution of many other boundary value problems whose coefficients vary with time can be expressed in terms of solutions of simpler problems with constant coefficients.*

102. Transverse Vibrations of a Beam. Let us find the transverse displacements $Y(x, t)$ in a beam with the ends $x = 0$ and

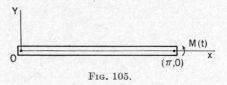

FIG. 105.

$x = \pi$ hinged, when a simple periodic torque is applied at the latter end (Fig. 105). The initial displacement and velocity are zero. Then the function $Y(x, t)$ satisfies the conditions

$$\frac{\partial^2 Y}{\partial t^2} + a^2 \frac{\partial^4 Y}{\partial x^4} = 0, \qquad Y(x, 0) = Y_t(x, 0) = 0,$$

$$Y(0, t) = Y_{xx}(0, t) = 0, \qquad Y(\pi, t) = 0, \qquad Y_{xx}(\pi, t) = b \sin \omega t,$$

where a, b, and ω are constants.

The sine transform of $Y(x, t)$ thus satisfies the conditions

$$\frac{d^2}{dt^2} y_s(n, t) + a^2 n^4 y_s(n, t) = n(-1)^n a^2 b \sin \omega t,$$

$$y_s = \frac{dy_s}{dt} = 0 \qquad \text{when } t = 0.$$

* A general study of such reductions for problems in heat conduction and vibrations was made by H. K. Brown, "The Resolution of Boundary Value Problems by Means of the Finite Fourier Transformation," a thesis written at the University of Michigan in 1941, part of which appeared in the *Journal of Applied Physics*, Vol. 14, pp. 609–618, 1943.

The solution of this problem in ordinary differential equations is

$$(1) \qquad y_s(n, t) = b \frac{n(-1)^n}{n^4 - \left(\dfrac{\omega}{a}\right)^2} \left(\sin \omega t - \frac{\omega}{an^2} \sin n^2 a t \right).$$

Instead of writing the inverse transform at once with the aid of the sine series, let us put $\omega/a = k^2$ and note that

$$\frac{n(-1)^n}{n^4 - k^4} = \frac{1}{2k^2} \left[\frac{n(-1)^{n+1}}{n^2 + k^2} - \frac{n(-1)^{n+1}}{n^2 - k^2} \right]$$

$$= S \left\{ \frac{1}{2k^2} \left(\frac{\sinh kx}{\sinh k\pi} - \frac{\sin kx}{\sin k\pi} \right) \right\}.$$

The inverse transform of the function (1) can then be written

$$(2) \quad Y(x, t) = \frac{ab}{2\omega} \left(\frac{\sinh x \sqrt{\dfrac{\omega}{a}}}{\sinh \pi \sqrt{\dfrac{\omega}{a}}} - \frac{\sin x \sqrt{\dfrac{\omega}{a}}}{\sin \pi \sqrt{\dfrac{\omega}{a}}} \right) \sin \omega t$$

$$+ \frac{2b\omega}{\pi a} \sum_1^\infty \frac{n(-1)^{n+1}}{n^4 - \left(\dfrac{\omega}{a}\right)^2} \sin n^2 a t \sin n x.$$

We have assumed here that the value of $\sqrt{\omega/a}$ is not an integer. When that value is close to some integer n_0, the component of $Y(x, t)$ with frequency ω has a large amplitude; that is, the resonance frequencies are

$$\omega = an_0^2 \qquad\qquad (n_0 = 1, 2, \cdots).$$

The solution of the problem here can also be found by means of the Laplace transformation.

PROBLEMS

1. When m is an integer, show that if the system

$$Y''(x) + m^2 Y(x) = F(x), \qquad Y(0) = Y(\pi) = 0,$$

is to have a solution then $F(x)$ must be such that

$$\int_0^\pi F(x) \sin mx \, dx = 0.$$

2. A constant transverse force acts at each point of a string with ends $x = 0$ and $x = \pi$ fixed; thus

$$Y_{tt} = a^2 Y_{xx} + F(x), \qquad Y(0, t) = Y(\pi, t) = 0.$$

If $Y(x, 0) = Y_t(x, 0) = 0$, derive the formula

$$Y(x, t) = \frac{1}{2a^2}[G(x - at) + G(x + at)] - \frac{1}{a^2}G(x),$$

where $G''(x) = F(x)$ when $0 < x < \pi$, $G(0) = G(\pi) = 0$ and, for all x, $G(-x) = -G(x)$ and $G(x + 2\pi) = G(x)$.

3. If a constant transverse force acts at each point of a beam, the transverse displacements $Y(x, t)$ satisfy an equation

$$\frac{\partial^2 Y}{\partial t^2} = -a^2 \frac{\partial^4 Y}{\partial x^4} + F(x).$$

If the ends $x = 0$ and $x = \pi$ are hinged so that Y and Y_{xx} vanish there, and if the initial displacement and velocity are zero, derive the formula

$$Y(x, t) = \frac{1}{a^2}G(x) - \frac{2}{\pi a^2}\sum_1^\infty \frac{f_s(n)}{n^4}\cos n^2 at \sin nx,$$

where $G^{(4)}(x) = F(x)$ and $G(x) = G''(x) = 0$ at $x = 0$ and at $x = \pi$.

4. Let $V(x, y)$ be a steady temperature or potential satisfying the conditions

$$V_{xx}(x, y) + V_{yy}(x, y) = 0 \quad (0 < x < \pi, y > 0),$$
$$V(0, y) = 0, \qquad V(\pi, y) = A \quad (y < 0); \qquad V(x, 0) = B \quad (0 < x < \pi);$$

also $V(x, y)$ is bounded.   Derive the formula

$$V(x, y) = \frac{A}{\pi}x - \frac{2A}{\pi}\arctan\frac{\sin x}{e^y + \cos x} + \frac{2B}{\pi}\arctan\frac{\sin x}{\sinh y}.$$

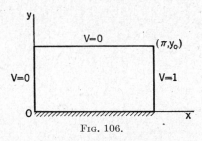

Fig. 106.

5. Let $V(x, y)$ satisfy the conditions (Fig. 106)

$$V_{xx} + V_{yy} = 0 \quad (0 < x < \pi, 0 < y < y_0),$$
$$V(0, y) = 0, \qquad V(\pi, y) = 1, \qquad V_y(x, 0) = V(x, y_0) = 0.$$

Derive the formulas

$$V(x, y) = \frac{x}{\pi} + \frac{2}{\pi} \sum_{1}^{\infty} \frac{(-1)^n}{n} \frac{\cosh ny}{\cosh ny_0} \sin nx$$

$$= \frac{x}{\pi} - \frac{2}{\pi} \sum_{\nu=0}^{\infty} (-1)^{\nu} \{\alpha[x, (2\nu + 1)y_0 + y]$$

$$+ \alpha\,]x, (2\nu + 1)y_0 - y]\},$$

where

$$\alpha(x, z) = \arctan \frac{\sin x}{e^z + \cos x}.$$

6. Solve the problem

$$V_{xx}(x, y) + V_{yy}(x, y) = F(x) \quad (0 < x < \pi, y > 0),$$
$$V(0, y) = V(\pi, y) = V(x, 0) = 0,$$

where $V(x, y)$ is bounded.   Obtain the solution in the forms

$$V(x, y) = G(x) + \frac{2}{\pi} \sum_{1}^{\infty} \frac{1}{n^2} f_s(n) e^{-ny} \sin nx$$

$$= G(x) - \frac{1}{\pi} \int_{-\pi}^{\pi} F_1(x - \xi)\beta(\xi, y)\, d\xi,$$

where $G''(x) = F(x)$, $G(0) = G(\pi) = 0$, $F_1(x)$ is the odd periodic extension of $F(x)$, and

$$\beta(x, y) = \int_{0}^{x} \arctan \frac{\sin \lambda}{e^y - \cos \lambda}\, d\lambda.$$

7. Obtain the temperature function $U(x, t)$ when

$$U_t(x, t) = U_{xx}(x, t) - h(t)U(x, t) + A \quad (0 < x < \pi, t > 0),$$
$$U(0, t) = U(\pi, t) \quad U(\pi, 0) = 0.$$

Show that the formula can be written

$$U(x, t) = Ae^{-H(t)} \int_{0}^{t} e^{H(\tau)}\Psi(x, t - \tau)\, d\tau,$$

where $H(t) = \int_{0}^{t} h(\tau)d\tau$ and $\Psi(x, t)$ is the basic temperature function described in Sec. 101.

8. Let $\Theta(x, t)$ be the temperature function that satisfies the conditions

$$\Theta_t = \Theta_{xx} \quad (0 < x < \pi, t > 0), \qquad \Theta(0, t) = \Theta(\pi, t) = 0,$$

$$\Theta(x, 0) = 1 - \frac{x}{\pi}.$$

Show that $\theta_s(n, t) = n^{-1}e^{-n^2t}$ and

$$\Theta(x, t) = \frac{2}{\pi} \sum_{1}^{\infty} \frac{1}{n} e^{-n^2t} \sin nx.$$

Then if $U(x, t)$ satisfies the conditions

$$U_t = U_{xx} \quad (0 < x < \pi, t > 0), \qquad U(0, t) = U(\pi, t) = 0,$$
$$U(x, 0) = F(x),$$

obtain the function $U(x, t)$ in terms of $\Theta(x, t)$. If $F(x)$ is continuous and $F(0) = F(\pi) = 0$, one form of the result is

$$U(x, t) = \tfrac{1}{2} \int_0^\pi F'(\lambda)[\Theta(x + \lambda, t) + \Theta(x - \lambda, t)] \, d\lambda.$$

103. Other Transforms. Other transformations can be devised for special types of boundary value problems. Consider the modification of the finite sine transformation,

$$S_0\{F(x)\} = \int_0^\pi F(x) \sin \lambda_n x \, dx \quad \left(\lambda_n = \frac{2n-1}{2}, n = 1, 2, \cdots\right).$$

It can be seen after the usual integration by parts that

$$S_0\{F''(x)\} = \lambda_n F(0) - (-1)^n F'(\pi) - \lambda_n^2 S_0\{F(x)\}.$$

Hence certain problems in which the unknown function itself is prescribed at $x = 0$ while its first derivative is prescribed at $x = \pi$ can be simplified in the usual manner by applying this transformation. If $f_0(n)$ denotes the transform of $F(x)$, it can be shown that

$$F(x) = \frac{2}{\pi} \sum_{n=1}^{\infty} f_0(n) \sin \lambda_n x \qquad (0 < x < \pi).$$

The Fourier sine transformation of a function $F(x)$ defined for all positive x is usually written

$$S\{F(x)\} = \sqrt{\frac{2}{\pi}} \int_0^\infty F(x) \sin \alpha x \, dx = f_s(\alpha).$$

Assuming that the integral

$$\int_0^\infty |F(x)| \, dx$$

converges and that $F(x)$ satisfies certain conditions of continuity, it follows from the Fourier integral theorem that

$$F(x) = \sqrt{\frac{2}{\pi}} \int_0^\infty f_s(\alpha) \sin \alpha x \, d\alpha = S\{f_s(\alpha)\}. \quad \cdot$$

That is, the inverse transformation is the same as the direct one. The second derivative transforms as follows:

$$S\{F''(x)\} = -\alpha^2 S\{F(x)\} + \alpha F(0) \sqrt{\frac{2}{\pi}}.$$

Thus the transformation is useful in certain problems in which the unknown function itself, but not its derivative, is prescribed at $x = 0$.

For the Fourier cosine transformation, on the other hand, $F'(0)$ is involved in the transform of the second derivative.

The common Fourier transformation is usually written in exponential form:

$$E\{F(x)\} = \frac{1}{\sqrt{2\pi}} \int_{-\infty}^\infty F(x)e^{i\alpha x} \, dx = f(\alpha).$$

Then, according to the Fourier integral formula,

$$F(x) = \frac{1}{\sqrt{2\pi}} \int_{-\infty}^\infty f(\alpha)e^{-i\alpha x} \, d\alpha.$$

The transformation of derivatives can be seen from the formula

$$E\{F'(x)\} = -i\alpha E\{F(x)\} = -i\alpha f(\alpha).$$

The condition that $F(x)$ be absolutely integrable over the infinite range is a severe one. Other features combine with this one to limit the type of boundary value problems to which these infinite Fourier transformations can be applied to advantage.*

---

* For other applications, see R. H. Cameron, Some Introductory Exercises in the Manipulation of Fourier Transforms, *National Mathematics Magazine*, Vol. 15, pp. 1–26, 1941. A few applications to partial differential equations are included in Titchmarsh, E. C., "Theory of Fourier Integrals," Chap. 10, 1937.

APPENDIX I

BIBLIOGRAPHY—LAPLACE TRANSFORMATION

Applications and Theory:

*Doetsch, G.: "Theorie und Anwendung der Laplace-Transformation," Springer, Berlin, 1937.

Carslaw, H. S., and J. C. Jaeger: "Operational Methods in Applied Mathematics," Oxford University Press, New York, 1941.

*Gardner, M. F., and J. L. Barnes: "Transients in Linear Systems," Vol. 1, John Wiley & Sons, Inc., New York, 1942.

McLachlan, N. W.: "Complex Variable and Operational Calculus with Technical Applications," Cambridge University Press, London, 1942.

Carson, J. R.: "Electric Circuit Theory and the Operational Calculus," McGraw-Hill Book Company, Inc., New York, 1926.

Courant, R., and D. Hilbert: "Methoden der mathematischen Physik," Vol. 2, Verlag Julius Springer, Berlin, 1937.

Theory:

Widder, D. V.: "The Laplace Transform," Princeton University Press, Princeton, N. J., 1941.

Titchmarsh, E. C.: "Theory of Fourier Integrals," Oxford University Press, New York, 1937.

* This book contains an extensive bibliography and a historical sketch of the transformation. However, H. Bateman has recently pointed out (*Bulletin of the American Mathematical Society*, Vol. 48, p. 510, 1942) that the method of the Laplace transform was initiated in 1815 by Poisson.

APPENDIX II

	$F(t)$	$f(s)$	Section
1	$F(t)$	$\int_0^\infty e^{-st}F(t)\,dt$	2
2	$AF(t) + BG(t)$	$Af(s) + Bg(s)$	2
3	$F'(t)$	$sf(s) - F(+0)$	4
4	$F^{(n)}(t)$	$s^n f(s) - s^{n-1}F(+0)$ $- s^{n-2}F'(+0) - \cdots$ $- F^{(n-1)}(+0)$	4
5	$\int_0^t F(\tau)\,d\tau$	$\dfrac{1}{s}f(s)$	14
6	$\int_0^t \int_0^\tau F(\lambda)\,d\lambda\,d\tau$	$\dfrac{1}{s^2}f(s)$	14
7	$\int_0^t F_1(t-\tau)F_2(\tau)\,d\tau = F_1 * F_2$	$f_1(s)f_2(s)$	14
8	$tF(t)$	$-f'(s)$	12
9	$t^n F(t)$	$(-1)^n f^{(n)}(s)$	12
10	$\dfrac{1}{t}F(t)$	$\int_s^\infty f(x)\,dx$	18
11	$e^{at}F(t)$	$f(s-a)$	7
12	$F(t-b)$, where $F(t) = 0$ when $t < 0$	$e^{-bs}f(s)$	10
13	$\dfrac{1}{c}F\left(\dfrac{t}{c}\right)$	$f(cs)$	10
14	$\dfrac{1}{c}e^{\frac{bt}{c}}F\left(\dfrac{t}{c}\right)$	$f(cs - b)$	10
15	$F(t + a) = F(t)$	$\dfrac{\int_0^a e^{-st}F(t)\,dt}{1 - e^{-as}}$	19
16	$F(t + a) = -F(t)$	$\dfrac{\int_0^a e^{-st}F(t)\,dt}{1 + e^{-as}}$	19
17	$F_1(t)$, the half-wave rectification of $F(t)$ in No. 16	$\dfrac{f(s)}{1 - e^{-as}}$	19
18	$F_2(t)$, the full-wave rectification of $F(t)$ in No. 16	$f(s)\coth\dfrac{as}{2}$	19
19	$\displaystyle\sum_1^m \dfrac{p(a_n)}{q'(a_n)}e^{a_n t}$	$\dfrac{p(s)}{q(s)}$, $q(s) = (s - a_1)(s - a_2)$ $\cdots (s - a_m)$	16
20	$e^{at}\displaystyle\sum_{n=1}^r \dfrac{\phi^{(r-n)}(a)}{(r-n)!}\dfrac{t^{n-1}}{(n-1)!} + \cdots$	$\dfrac{p(s)}{q(s)} = \dfrac{\phi(s)}{(s-a)^r}$	17

APPENDIX III

Table of Laplace Transforms

	$f(s)$	$F(t)$
1	$\dfrac{1}{s}$	1
2	$\dfrac{1}{s^2}$	t
3	$\dfrac{1}{s^n}\ (n = 1, 2, \cdots)$	$\dfrac{t^{n-1}}{(n-1)!}$
4	$\dfrac{1}{\sqrt{s}}$	$\dfrac{1}{\sqrt{\pi t}}$
5	$s^{-\frac{3}{2}}$	$2\sqrt{\dfrac{t}{\pi}}$
6	$s^{-(n+\frac{1}{2})}\ (n = 1, 2, \cdots)$	$\dfrac{2^n t^{n-\frac{1}{2}}}{1 \cdot 3 \cdot 5 \cdots (2n-1)\sqrt{\pi}}$
7	$\dfrac{\Gamma(k)}{s^k}\ (k > 0)$	t^{k-1}
8	$\dfrac{1}{s - a}$	e^{at}
9	$\dfrac{1}{(s - a)^2}$	te^{at}
10	$\dfrac{1}{(s - a)^n}\ (n = 1, 2, \cdots)$	$\dfrac{1}{(n-1)!}\,t^{n-1}e^{at}$
11	$\dfrac{\Gamma(k)}{(s - a)^k}\ (k > 0)$	$t^{k-1}e^{at}$
12*	$\dfrac{1}{(s - a)(s - b)}$	$\dfrac{1}{a - b}\,(e^{at} - e^{bt})$
13*	$\dfrac{s}{(s - a)(s - b)}$	$\dfrac{1}{a - b}\,(ae^{at} - be^{bt})$
14*	$\dfrac{1}{(s - a)(s - b)(s - c)}$	$-\dfrac{(b-c)e^{at} + (c-a)e^{bt} + (a-b)e^{ct}}{(a-b)(b-c)(c-a)}$
15	$\dfrac{1}{s^2 + a^2}$	$\dfrac{1}{a}\sin at$
16	$\dfrac{s}{s^2 + a^2}$	$\cos at$

* Here a, b, and (in 14) c represent distinct constants.

TABLE OF TRANSFORMS.—(Continued)

	$f(s)$	$F(t)$
17	$\dfrac{1}{s^2 - a^2}$	$\dfrac{1}{a} \sinh at$
18	$\dfrac{s}{s^2 - a^2}$	$\cosh at$
19	$\dfrac{1}{s(s^2 + a^2)}$	$\dfrac{1}{a^2}(1 - \cos at)$
20	$\dfrac{1}{s^2(s^2 + a^2)}$	$\dfrac{1}{a^3}(at - \sin at)$
21	$\dfrac{1}{(s^2 + a^2)^2}$	$\dfrac{1}{2a^3}(\sin at - at \cos at)$
22	$\dfrac{s}{(s^2 + a^2)^2}$	$\dfrac{t}{2a} \sin at$
23	$\dfrac{s^2}{(s^2 + a^2)^2}$	$\dfrac{1}{2a}(\sin at + at \cos at)$
24	$\dfrac{s^2 - a^2}{(s^2 + a^2)^2}$	$t \cos at$
25	$\dfrac{s}{(s^2 + a^2)(s^2 + b^2)} \ (a^2 \neq b^2)$	$\dfrac{\cos at - \cos bt}{b^2 - a^2}$
26	$\dfrac{1}{(s - a)^2 + b^2}$	$\dfrac{1}{b} e^{at} \sin bt$
27	$\dfrac{s - a}{(s - a)^2 + b^2}$	$e^{at} \cos bt$
28	$\dfrac{3a^2}{s^3 + a^3}$	$e^{-at} - e^{\frac{at}{2}}\left(\cos \dfrac{at\sqrt{3}}{2} - \sqrt{3} \sin \dfrac{at\sqrt{3}}{2}\right)$
29	$\dfrac{4a^3}{s^4 + 4a^4}$	$\sin at \cosh at - \cos at \sinh at$
30	$\dfrac{s}{s^4 + 4a^4}$	$\dfrac{1}{2a^2} \sin at \sinh at$
31	$\dfrac{1}{s^4 - a^4}$	$\dfrac{1}{2a^3}(\sinh at - \sin at)$
32	$\dfrac{s}{s^4 - a^4}$	$\dfrac{1}{2a^2}(\cosh at - \cos at)$
33	$\dfrac{s^n}{(s^2 + a^2)^{n+1}}$	$\dfrac{t^n \sin at}{2^n a n!}$
34*	$\dfrac{1}{s}\left(\dfrac{s - 1}{s}\right)^n$	$L_n(t) = \dfrac{e^t}{n!} \dfrac{d^n}{dt^n}(t^n e^{-t})$
35	$\dfrac{s}{(s - a)^{\frac{3}{2}}}$	$\dfrac{1}{\sqrt{\pi t}} e^{at}(1 + 2at)$
36	$\sqrt{s - a} - \sqrt{s - b}$	$\dfrac{1}{2\sqrt{\pi t^3}}(e^{bt} - e^{at})$

* $L_n(t)$ is the Laguerre polynomial of degree n.

TABLE OF TRANSFORMS.—(*Continued*)

	$f(s)$	$F(t)$
37	$\dfrac{1}{\sqrt{s} + a}$	$\dfrac{1}{\sqrt{\pi t}} - ae^{a^2 t} \operatorname{erfc}\,(a\sqrt{t})$
38	$\dfrac{\sqrt{s}}{s - a^2}$	$\dfrac{1}{\sqrt{\pi t}} + ae^{a^2 t} \operatorname{erf}\,(a\sqrt{t})$
39	$\dfrac{\sqrt{s}}{s + a^2}$	$\dfrac{1}{\sqrt{\pi t}} - \dfrac{2a}{\sqrt{\pi}} e^{-a^2 t} \displaystyle\int_0^{a\sqrt{t}} e^{\lambda^2}\,d\lambda$
40	$\dfrac{1}{\sqrt{s}\,(s - a^2)}$	$\dfrac{1}{a} e^{a^2 t} \operatorname{erf}\,(a\sqrt{t})$
41	$\dfrac{1}{\sqrt{s}\,(s + a^2)}$	$\dfrac{2}{a\sqrt{\pi}} e^{-a^2 t} \displaystyle\int_0^{a\sqrt{t}} e^{\lambda^2}\,d\lambda$
42	$\dfrac{b^2 - a^2}{(s - a^2)(b + \sqrt{s})}$	$e^{a^2 t}[b - a\operatorname{erf}\,(a\sqrt{t})]$ $- be^{b^2 t}\operatorname{erfc}\,(b\sqrt{t})$
43	$\dfrac{1}{\sqrt{s}\,(\sqrt{s} + a)}$	$e^{a^2 t}\operatorname{erfc}\,(a\sqrt{t})$
44	$\dfrac{1}{(s + a)\sqrt{s + b}}$	$\dfrac{1}{\sqrt{b - a}} e^{-at}\operatorname{erf}\,(\sqrt{b - a}\,\sqrt{t})$
45	$\dfrac{b^2 - a^2}{\sqrt{s}\,(s - a^2)(\sqrt{s} + b)}$	$e^{a^2 t}\left[\dfrac{b}{a}\operatorname{erf}\,(a\sqrt{t}) - 1\right]$ $+ e^{b^2 t}\operatorname{erfc}\,(b\sqrt{t})$
46*	$\dfrac{(1 - s)^n}{s^{n + \frac{1}{2}}}$	$\dfrac{n!}{(2n)!\,\sqrt{\pi t}} H_{2n}(\sqrt{t})$
47	$\dfrac{(1 - s)^n}{s^{n + \frac{3}{2}}}$	$- \dfrac{n!}{\sqrt{\pi}\,(2n + 1)!} H_{2n+1}(\sqrt{t})$
48†	$\dfrac{\sqrt{s + 2a}}{\sqrt{s}} - 1$	$ae^{-at}[I_1(at) + I_0(at)]$
49	$\dfrac{1}{\sqrt{s + a}\,\sqrt{s + b}}$	$e^{-\frac{1}{2}(a+b)t}I_0\left(\dfrac{a - b}{2}\,t\right)$
50	$\dfrac{\Gamma(\hbar)}{(s + a)^k(s + b)^k}\ (k > 0)$	$\sqrt{\pi}\left(\dfrac{t}{a - b}\right)^{k - \frac{1}{2}} e^{-\frac{1}{2}(a+b)t}$ $I_{k - \frac{1}{2}}\left(\dfrac{a - b}{2}\,t\right)$
51	$\dfrac{1}{(s + a)^{\frac{1}{2}}(s + b)^{\frac{3}{2}}}$	$te^{-\frac{1}{2}(a+b)t}\left[I_0\left(\dfrac{a - b}{2}\,t\right)\right.$ $\left. + I_1\left(\dfrac{a - b}{2}\,t\right)\right]$
52	$\dfrac{\sqrt{s + 2a} - \sqrt{s}}{\sqrt{s + 2a} + \sqrt{s}}$	$\dfrac{1}{t} e^{-at}I_1(at)$

* $H_n(x)$ is the Hermite polynomial, $H_n(x) = e^{x^2} \dfrac{d^n}{dx^n}\,(e^{-x^2})$.

† $I_n(x) = i^{-n}J_n(ix)$, where J_n is Bessel's function of the first kind.

	$f(s)$	$F(t)$
53	$\dfrac{(a-b)^k}{(\sqrt{s+a}+\sqrt{s+b})^{2k}}\ (k>0)$	$\dfrac{k}{t}\,e^{-\frac{1}{2}(a+b)t}I_k\left(\dfrac{a-b}{2}\,t\right)$
54	$\dfrac{(\sqrt{s+a}+\sqrt{s})^{-2\nu}}{\sqrt{s}\,\sqrt{s+a}}\ (\nu>-1)$	$\dfrac{1}{a^\nu}\,e^{-\frac{1}{2}at}I_\nu\left(\dfrac{1}{2}\,at\right)$
55	$\dfrac{1}{\sqrt{s^2+a^2}}$	$J_0(at)$
56	$\dfrac{(\sqrt{s^2+a^2}-s)^\nu}{\sqrt{s^2+a^2}}\ (\nu>-1)$	$a^\nu J_\nu(at)$
57	$\dfrac{1}{(s^2+a^2)^k}\ (k>0)$	$\dfrac{\sqrt{\pi}}{\Gamma(k)}\left(\dfrac{t}{2a}\right)^{k-\frac{1}{2}}J_{k-\frac{1}{2}}(at)$
58	$(\sqrt{s^2+a^2}-s)^k\ (k>0)$	$\dfrac{ka^k}{t}\,J_k(at)$
59	$\dfrac{(s-\sqrt{s^2-a^2})^\nu}{\sqrt{s^2-a^2}}\ (\nu>-1)$	$a^\nu I_\nu(at)$
60	$\dfrac{1}{(s^2-a^2)^k}\ (k>0)$	$\dfrac{\sqrt{\pi}}{\Gamma(k)}\left(\dfrac{t}{2a}\right)^{k-\frac{1}{2}}I_{k-\frac{1}{2}}(at)$
61	$\dfrac{e^{-ks}}{s}$	$S_k(t)=\begin{cases}0 \text{ when } 0<t<k\\ 1 \text{ when } t>k\end{cases}$
62	$\dfrac{e^{-ks}}{s^2}$	$\begin{cases}0 \qquad \text{ when } 0<t<k\\ t-k \text{ when } t>k\end{cases}$
63	$\dfrac{e^{-ks}}{s^\mu}\ (\mu>0)$	$\begin{cases}0 \qquad\quad \text{ when } 0<t<k\\ \dfrac{(t-k)^{\mu-1}}{\Gamma(\mu)} \text{ when } t>k\end{cases}$
64	$\dfrac{1-e^{-ks}}{s}$	$\begin{cases}1 \text{ when } 0<t<k\\ 0 \text{ when } t>k\end{cases}$
65	$\dfrac{1}{s(1-e^{-ks})}=\dfrac{1+\coth\frac{1}{2}ks}{2s}$	$S(k,t)=n \text{ when } (n-1)k$ $\quad<t<nk(n=1,2,\cdots)$ $\qquad\qquad\qquad\qquad\text{(Fig. 5)}$
66	$\dfrac{1}{s(e^{ks}-a)}$	$\begin{cases}0 \text{ when } 0<t<k\\ 1+a+a^2+\cdots+a^{n-1}\\ \quad \text{ when } nk<t<(n+1)k\\ \qquad\qquad (n=1,2,\cdots)\end{cases}$
67	$\dfrac{1}{s}\tanh ks$	$M(2k,t)=(-1)^{n-1}$ $\quad \text{ when } 2k(n-1)<t<2kn$ $\quad\quad (n=1,2,\cdots)\text{ (Fig. 9)}$
68	$\dfrac{1}{s(1+e^{-ks})}$	$\dfrac{1}{2}M(k,t)+\dfrac{1}{2}=\dfrac{1-(-1)^n}{2}$ $\quad \text{ when } (n-1)k<t<nk$
69	$\dfrac{1}{s^2}\tanh ks$	$H(2k,t)\text{ (Fig. 10)}$

TABLE OF TRANSFORMS.—(*Continued*)

	$f(s)$	$F(t)$
70	$\dfrac{1}{s \sinh ks}$	$2S(2k, t + k) - 2 = 2(n - 1)$ when $(2n - 3)k < t < (2n - 1)k$ $(t > 0)$
71	$\dfrac{1}{s \cosh ks}$	$M(2k, t + k) + 1 = 1 + (-1)^n$ when $(2n - 3)k < t < (2n - 1)k$ $(t > 0)$
72	$\dfrac{1}{s} \coth ks$	$2S(2k, t) - 1 = 2n - 1$ when $2k(n - 1) < t < 2kn$
73	$\dfrac{k}{s^2 + k^2} \coth \dfrac{\pi s}{2k}$	$\|\sin kt\|$
74	$\dfrac{1}{(s^2 + 1)(1 - e^{-\pi s})}$	$\begin{cases} \sin t \text{ when } (2n - 2)\pi \\ \qquad\qquad < t < (2n - 1)\pi \\ 0 \quad \text{when } (2n - 1)\pi \\ \qquad\qquad < t < 2n\pi \end{cases}$
75	$\dfrac{1}{s} e^{-\frac{k}{s}}$	$J_0(2\sqrt{kt})$
76	$\dfrac{1}{\sqrt{s}} e^{-\frac{k}{s}}$	$\dfrac{1}{\sqrt{\pi t}} \cos 2\sqrt{kt}$
77	$\dfrac{1}{\sqrt{s}} e^{\frac{k}{s}}$	$\dfrac{1}{\sqrt{\pi t}} \cosh 2\sqrt{kt}$
78	$\dfrac{1}{s^{\frac{3}{2}}} e^{-\frac{k}{s}}$	$\dfrac{1}{\sqrt{\pi k}} \sin 2\sqrt{kt}$
79	$\dfrac{1}{s^{\frac{3}{2}}} e^{\frac{k}{s}}$	$\dfrac{1}{\sqrt{\pi k}} \sinh 2\sqrt{kt}$
80	$\dfrac{1}{s^{\mu}} e^{-\frac{k}{s}} \ (\mu > 0)$	$\left(\dfrac{t}{k}\right)^{\frac{\mu-1}{2}} J_{\mu-1}(2\sqrt{kt})$
81	$\dfrac{1}{s^{\mu}} e^{\frac{k}{s}} \ (\mu > 0)$	$\left(\dfrac{t}{k}\right)^{\frac{\mu-1}{2}} I_{\mu-1}(2\sqrt{kt})$
82	$e^{-k\sqrt{s}} \ (k > 0)$	$\dfrac{k}{2\sqrt{\pi t^3}} \exp\left(-\dfrac{k^2}{4t}\right)$
83	$\dfrac{1}{s} e^{-k\sqrt{s}} \ (k \geqq 0)$	$\operatorname{erfc}\left(\dfrac{k}{2\sqrt{t}}\right)$
84	$\dfrac{1}{\sqrt{s}} e^{-k\sqrt{s}} \ (k \geqq 0)$	$\dfrac{1}{\sqrt{\pi t}} \exp\left(-\dfrac{k^2}{4t}\right)$
85	$s^{-\frac{3}{2}} e^{-k\sqrt{s}} \ (k \geqq 0)$	$2\sqrt{\dfrac{t}{\pi}} \exp\left(-\dfrac{k^2}{4t}\right)$ $- k \operatorname{erfc}\left(\dfrac{k}{2\sqrt{t}}\right)$

TABLE OF TRANSFORMS.—(*Continued*)

	$f(s)$	$F(t)$
86	$\dfrac{ae^{-k\sqrt{s}}}{s(a + \sqrt{s})}\ (k \geqq 0)$	$-e^{ak}e^{a^2t}\operatorname{erfc}\left(a\sqrt{t} + \dfrac{k}{2\sqrt{t}}\right) + \operatorname{erfc}\left(\dfrac{k}{2\sqrt{t}}\right)$
87	$\dfrac{e^{-k\sqrt{s}}}{\sqrt{s}\,(a + \sqrt{s})}\ (k \geqq 0)$	$e^{ak}e^{a^2t}\operatorname{erfc}\left(a\sqrt{t} + \dfrac{k}{2\sqrt{t}}\right)$
88	$\dfrac{e^{-k\sqrt{s(s+a)}}}{\sqrt{s(s + a)}}$	$\begin{cases} 0 & \text{when } 0 < t < k \\ e^{-\frac{1}{2}at}I_0(\tfrac{1}{2}a\sqrt{t^2 - k^2}) \\ & \text{when } t > k \end{cases}$
89	$\dfrac{e^{-k\sqrt{s^2+a^2}}}{\sqrt{s^2 + a^2}}$	$\begin{cases} 0 & \text{when } 0 < t < k \\ J_0(a\sqrt{t^2 - k^2}) & \text{when } t > k \end{cases}$
90	$\dfrac{e^{-k\sqrt{s^2-a^2}}}{\sqrt{s^2 - a^2}}$	$\begin{cases} 0 & \text{when } 0 < t < k \\ I_0(a\sqrt{t^2 - k^2}) & \text{when } t > k \end{cases}$
91	$\dfrac{e^{-k(\sqrt{s^2+a^2}-s)}}{\sqrt{s^2 + a^2}}\ (k \geqq 0)$	$J_0(a\sqrt{t^2 + 2kt})$
92	$e^{-ks} - e^{-k\sqrt{s^2+a^2}}$	$\begin{cases} 0 & \text{when } 0 < t < k \\ \dfrac{ak}{\sqrt{t^2 - k^2}}J_1(a\sqrt{t^2 - k^2}) \\ & \text{when } t > k \end{cases}$
93	$e^{-k\sqrt{s^2-a^2}} - e^{-ks}$	$\begin{cases} 0 & \text{when } 0 < t < k \\ \dfrac{ak}{\sqrt{t^2 - k^2}}I_1(a\sqrt{t^2 - k^2}) \\ & \text{when } t > k \end{cases}$
94	$\dfrac{a^{\nu}e^{-k\sqrt{s^2+a^2}}}{\sqrt{s^2 + a^2}\,(\sqrt{s^2 + a^2} + s)^{\nu}}$ $(\nu > -1)$	$\begin{cases} 0 & \text{when } 0 < t < k \\ \left(\dfrac{t - k}{t + k}\right)^{\frac{1}{2}\nu}J_{\nu}(a\sqrt{t^2 - k^2}) \\ & \text{when } t > k \end{cases}$
95	$\dfrac{1}{s}\log s$	$\Gamma'(1) - \log t \quad [\Gamma'(1) = -0.5772]$
96	$\dfrac{1}{s^k}\log s\ (k > 0)$	$t^{k-1}\left\{\dfrac{\Gamma'(k)}{[\Gamma(k)]^2} - \dfrac{\log t}{\Gamma(k)}\right\}$
97*	$\dfrac{\log s}{s - a}\ (a > 0)$	$e^{at}[\log a - \operatorname{Ei}(-at)]$
98†	$\dfrac{\log s}{s^2 + 1}$	$\cos t\,\operatorname{Si}(t) - \sin t\,\operatorname{Ci}(t)$

* The exponential integral function $\operatorname{Ei}(-t) = -\displaystyle\int_t^{\infty}\dfrac{e^{-x}}{x}\,dx\ (t > 0)$ is a tabulated function.   For tables of this function and other integral functions, see, for instance, Jahnke and Emde, "Tables of Functions."

† The cosine integral function is defined as $\operatorname{Ci}(t) = -\displaystyle\int_t^{\infty}\dfrac{\cos x}{x}\,dx$. $\operatorname{Si}(t)$ is defined in Sec. 18.

TABLE OF TRANSFORMS.—*(Continued)*

	$f(s)$	$F(t)$
99	$\dfrac{s \log s}{s^2 + 1}$	$- \sin t \, \mathrm{Si}(t) - \cos t \, \mathrm{Ci}(t)$
100	$\dfrac{1}{s} \log (1 + ks) \; (k > 0)$	$-\mathrm{Ei}\left(-\dfrac{t}{k}\right)$
101	$\log \dfrac{s - a}{s - b}$	$\dfrac{1}{t}\left(e^{bt} - e^{at}\right)$
102	$\dfrac{1}{s} \log (1 + k^2 s^2)$	$-2\mathrm{Ci}\left(\dfrac{t}{k}\right)$
103	$\dfrac{1}{s} \log (s^2 + a^2) \; (a > 0)$	$2 \log a - 2\mathrm{Ci}(at)$
104	$\dfrac{1}{s^2} \log (s^2 + a^2) \; (a > 0)$	$\dfrac{2}{a}\left[at \log a + \sin at - at \, \mathrm{Ci}(at)\right]$
105	$\log \dfrac{s^2 + a^2}{s^2}$	$\dfrac{2}{t}\left(1 - \cos at\right)$
106	$\log \dfrac{s^2 - a^2}{s^2}$	$\dfrac{2}{t}\left(1 - \cosh at\right)$
107	$\arctan \dfrac{k}{s}$	$\dfrac{1}{t} \sin kt$
108	$\dfrac{1}{s} \arctan \dfrac{k}{s}$	$\mathrm{Si}(kt)$
109	$e^{k^2 s^2} \, \mathrm{erfc} \, (ks) \; (k > 0)$	$\dfrac{1}{k \sqrt{\pi}} \exp\left(-\dfrac{t^2}{4k^2}\right)$
110	$\dfrac{1}{s} e^{k^2 s^2} \, \mathrm{erfc} \, (ks) \; (k > 0)$	$\mathrm{erf}\left(\dfrac{t}{2k}\right)$
111	$e^{ks} \, \mathrm{erfc} \, \sqrt{ks} \; (k > 0)$	$\dfrac{\sqrt{k}}{\pi \sqrt{t} \, (t + k)}$
112	$\dfrac{1}{\sqrt{s}} \, \mathrm{erfc} \, (\sqrt{ks})$	$\begin{cases} 0 & \text{when } 0 < t < k \\ (\pi t)^{-\frac{1}{2}} & \text{when } t > k \end{cases}$
·113	$\dfrac{1}{\sqrt{s}} e^{ks} \, \mathrm{erfc} \, (\sqrt{ks}) \; (k > 0)$	$\dfrac{1}{\sqrt{\pi(t + k)}}$
114	$\mathrm{erf}\left(\dfrac{k}{\sqrt{s}}\right)$	$\dfrac{1}{\pi t} \sin (2k \sqrt{t})$
115	$\dfrac{1}{\sqrt{s}} e^{\frac{k^2}{s}} \, \mathrm{erfc}\left(\dfrac{k}{\sqrt{s}}\right)$	$\dfrac{1}{\sqrt{\pi t}} e^{-2k\sqrt{t}}$
116*	$K_0(ks)$	$\begin{cases} 0 & \text{when } 0 < t < k \\ (t^2 - k^2)^{-\frac{1}{2}} & \text{when } t > k \end{cases}$
117	$K_0(k \sqrt{s})$	$\dfrac{1}{2t} \exp\left(-\dfrac{k^2}{4t}\right)$

* $K_n(x)$ is Bessel's function of the second kind for the imaginary argument.

TABLE OF TRANSFORMS.—*(Continued)*

	$f(s)$	$F(t)$
118	$\dfrac{1}{s} e^{ks} K_1(ks)$	$\dfrac{1}{k} \sqrt{t(t + 2k)}$
119	$\dfrac{1}{\sqrt{s}} K_1(k \sqrt{s})$	$\dfrac{1}{k} \exp\left(-\dfrac{k^2}{4t}\right)$
120	$\dfrac{1}{\sqrt{s}} e^{\frac{k}{s}} K_0\left(\dfrac{k}{s}\right)$	$\dfrac{2}{\sqrt{\pi t}} K_0(2 \sqrt{2kt})$
121	$\pi e^{-ks} I_0(ks)$	$\begin{cases} [t(2k - t)]^{-\frac{1}{2}} & \text{when } 0 < t < 2k \\ 0 & \text{when } t > 2k \end{cases}$
122*	$e^{-ks} I_1(ks)$	$\begin{cases} \dfrac{k - t}{\pi k \sqrt{t(2k - t)}} & \text{when } 0 < t < 2k \\ 0 & \text{when } t > 2k \end{cases}$

* Several additional transforms, especially those involving other Bessel functions, can be found in the tables by G. A. Campbell and R. M. Foster, "Fourier Integrals for Practical Applications," or N. W. McLachlan and P. Humbert, "Formulaire pour le calcul symbolique." In the tables by Campbell and Foster, only those entries containing the condition $0 < g$ or $k < g$, where g is our t, are Laplace transforms.

INDEX